ADOLESCENT PSYCHIATRY

VOLUME II

*DEVELOPMENTAL AND
CLINICAL STUDIES*

Annals of the American Society for Adolescent Psychiatry

ADOLESCENT PSYCHIATRY

VOLUME II

DEVELOPMENTAL AND CLINICAL STUDIES

EDITED BY

SHERMAN C. FEINSTEIN
PETER L. GIOVACCHINI

BASIC BOOKS, INC., PUBLISHERS

NEW YORK

IN MEMORIAM

ARTHUR A. MILLER, M. D.

This volume is dedicated to the memory of Arthur A. Miller, our dear friend, colleague, and comanaging editor who died at the age of forty-nine on February 15, 1971.

Born in Detroit, Michigan, he graduated from Wayne University School of Medicine and served his internship and psychiatric residency at Michael Reese Hospital, Chicago. He was also a graduate of the Chicago Institute for Psychoanalysis and served on the faculty as a training and supervising analyst. He was Attending Psychiatrist at the Psychosomatic and Psychiatric Institute of Michael Reese Hospital and Professor of Psychiatry at the University of Illinois Medical School.

In 1969, moving to Ann Arbor with his wife and three daughters, he became Professor of Psychiatry, University of Michigan School of Medicine, and Training Analyst, Detroit Institute for Psychoanalysis. He was active in many societies including the American Psychoanalytic Association and the Group for the Advancement of Psychiatry. He was a past president of the Chicago Society for Adolescent Psychiatry and co-founder and managing editor of this publication.

Arthur was interested in the process of identification and had worked for many years on research in this area. He published numerous papers on his studies of this phenomenon which had led him into a deep understanding of adolescence. His last essay, which he was working on at the time of his death, is published in this volume.

We will miss his sense of humor, his insight, and the loyalty of his friendship which he so generously gave us for many years.

SHERMAN C. FEINSTEIN
PETER L. GIOVACCHINI

THE AUTHORS

ARMINDA ABERASTURY was a Faculty Member, Argentine Institute for Psychoanalysis, and Director of the Child Psychoanalytic Program.

PETER BARGLOW is Director, Residency Training and Assistant Professor, Department of Psychiatry, Northwestern University Medical School. He is also Associate Attending Physician, Departments of Psychiatry and Gynecology, Michael Reese Hospital and Medical Center, Chicago, Illinois.

JULIAN I. BARISH was formerly Director of the Psychiatric Treatment Center and Chief, Four Winds Hospital Adolescent Service, New York.

JEAN E. BEDGER is Research Director, Welfare Council of Metropolitan Chicago.

ROBERT S. BERNS is Associate Psychiatrist, Student Health Service, Consultant in Psychiatry, The Counseling Center, and Clinical Associate Professor, School of Psychology, University of California at Los Angeles.

GENE H. BOROWITZ is Professor of Psychiatry and Director of Psychiatric Residency Training at the University of Illinois School of Medicine, Chicago, Illinois.

DOYLE I. CARSON is Director of the Boys' Unit, Adolescent Service, Timberlawn Psychiatric Center, Dallas, Texas.

EMANUEL CHIGIER is Medical Director, Youth Aliyah Service, Tutor, Department of Family Medicine, Tel Aviv University School of Medicine, and National Secretary, Israel Society for Rehabilitation of the Disabled.

BERTRAM J. COHLER is Assistant Professor, Department of Education and Committee on Human Development, University of Chicago.

RUDOLF EKSTEIN is Director, Childhood Psychosis Program, Reiss-Davis Child Study Center, and Clinical Professor, University of California at Los Angeles. He is a Training Analyst, Los Angeles Psychoanalytic Society and Institute, and recipient of the 1971 William A. Schonfeld Distinguished Service Award of the American Society for Adolescent Psychiatry.

PHILIP J. ESCOLL is Senior Attending Psychiatrist, the Institute of the Pennsylvania Hospital and Assistant Professor of Clinical Psychiatry, University of Pennsylvania.

DANA L. FARNSWORTH is the Henry K. Oliver Professor of Hygiene Emeritus and Consultant on Psychiatry, School of Public Health, Harvard University. He received the William A. Schonfeld Distinguished Service Award of the American Society for Adolescent Psychiatry in 1971.

SHERMAN C. FEINSTEIN is Director, Child and Adolescent Psychiatry Training, Psychosomatic and Psychiatric Institute, Michael Reese Hospital, and Clinical Associate Professor, Pritzker School of Medicine, University of Chicago. He is Past President, American Society for Adolescent Psychiatry, and Managing Editor of this volume.

PETER L. GIOVACCHINI is Clinical Professor of Psychiatry at the University of Illinois College of Medicine and is in Private Practice of Psychoanalysis. He is Comanaging Editor of this volume.

ARNOLD GOLDBERG is a Faculty Member of the Chicago Institute for Psychoanalysis and Associate Attending Psychiatrist, Psychosomatic and Psychiatric Institute, Michael Reese Hospital and Medical Center.

JOHN T. GOSSETT is Clinical Psychologist, Adolescent Service, Timberlawn Psychiatric Center, and Research Psychologist, Timberlawn Foundation, Dallas, Texas.

LEON GRINBERG is Professor and Training Analyst at the Argentine Psychoanalytic Institute. He is Past President of the Argentine Psychoanalytic Society and Past Vice-President of the International Psychoanalytic Society.

ISIS ISTIPHAN is Director of Research and Evaluation, Florence Crittenton Association of America.

EDUARDO KALINA is Faculty Member, Argentine Psychoanalytic Institute, and Publishing Director of the *Journal of the Argentine Society of Psychiatry and Psychology of Children and Adolescents*.

JOE W. KING is Director, Adolescent Service, Timberlawn Psychiatric Center, Dallas, Texas.

MAURICIO KNOBEL is President of the Argentine Society for Psychiatry and Psychology of Childhood and Adolescence, Professor of Clinical Psychiatry, National University of Buenos Aires, and Faculty Member, Argentine Psychoanalytic Institute.

MALVINA W. KREMER is Chief, Adolescent Clinic, Metropolitan Hospital Center, Training Analyst, Division of Psychoanalysis, and Assistant Clinical Professor of Psychiatry, New York Medical College. She is Associate Clinical Professor of Psychiatry, New York University School of Medicine.

MOSES LAUFER is Director, Center for the Study of Adolescence, the Brent Consultation Center, and is a staff member of the Hampstead Child Therapy Clinic, London.

L. DAVID LEVI is an Associate, Professional Associates of Psychiatric Institute and Instructor, Psychiatric Institute Foundation, Washington, D.C.

JERRY M. LEWIS is Director of Professional Education and Clinical Programs, Timberlawn Psychiatric Center, and Director of Research and Training, Timberlawn Foundation, Dallas, Texas.

HAROLD I. LIEF is Professor of Psychiatry and Director, Division of Family Study, University of Pennsylvania School of Medicine. He is Director, Marriage Council of Philadelphia; and Director, Center for the Study of Sex Education in Medicine.

JAMES F. MASTERSON is Professor of Clinical Psychiatry, Cornell University Medical College, and Head, Adolescent Program, Payne Whitney Clinic, New York Hospital.

ARTHUR A. MILLER (1922–1971) was Professor of Psychiatry, University of Michigan School of Medicine, and Training Analyst, Michigan Psychoanalytic Institute and Society.

DEREK H. MILLER is Professor of Psychiatry and Chief, Adolescent Service, Neuropsychiatric Institute, University of Michigan School of Medicine.

HUMBERTO NAGERA is Director, Child Analytic Study Program and Professor of Psychiatry, University of Michigan School of Medicine. He is Director, Child Analysis Training Program, and Training Analyst, Michigan Psychoanalytic Institute and Society.

LAWRENCE E. NEWMAN is a staff member of the Gender Identity Research and Treatment Clinic, and Clinical Instructor, Department of Psychiatry, University of California at Los Angeles School of Medicine.

DANIEL OFFER is Associate Director of the Institute for Psychosomatic and Psychiatric Research and Training of Michael Reese Hospital and Medical Center and Associate Professor of Psychiatry at the Pritzker School of Medicine, University of Chicago. He is Past President of the American Society for Adolescent Psychiatry.

ROBERT J. SAVARD is Psychiatric Social Worker, Section on Social Work, National Institute of Mental Health.

WILLIAM A. SCHONFELD (1904–1970) was Assistant Clinical Professor of Child Psychiatry at the College of Physicians and Surgeons, Columbia University. He was on the attending staff of the New York State Psychiatric Institute and Columbia-Presbyterian Hospital and was formerly Chief of the Adolescent Research Unit in the Department of Psychiatry at Columbia Presbyterian Medical Center. He was Past President of the American Society for Adolescent Psychiatry and was recipient of the society's first Distinguished Service Award (1969).

ROBERT W. SHIELDS is a psychoanalyst and a member of the faculty, Institute of Education, University of London.

BERTRAM SLAFF is Coordinator of Training in Adolescent Psychiatry and Associate Clinical Professor, Mount Sinai School of Medicine, City University of New York. He is Past President, American Society for Adolescent Psychiatry.

ERWIN R. SMARR is Director, Professional Education, Haverford State Hospital, Haverford, Pennsylvania, and Clinical Assistant Professor, Thomas Jefferson University, Philadelphia.

HELM STIERLIN is Acting Chief, Adult Psychiatry Branch, National Institute of Mental Health, Washington, D.C.

CLAUDIA WELBOURNE is a Social Worker with the Florence Crittenton Association, Chicago, Illinois.

FRANK S. WILLIAMS is Assistant Chief, Department of Child Psychiatry, Cedars-Sinai Medical Center, Los Angeles.

D. W. WINNICOTT (1896–1971) practiced child psychoanalysis in England where he was a physician on the staff of Paddington Green Children's Hospital. He was Past President of the British Psychoanalytical

Society and was formerly Chairman of the Medical Section of the British Psychological Society and President of the Paediatric Section of the Royal Society of Medicine.

PREFACE

This volume is the second of a series which will extend the exploration of the integrative features of the adolescent processes as they continue their effects throughout the life span. The importance and implications of the intrapsychic changes occurring during adolescence are constantly emphasized as our clinical experience broadens. Consequently, the nature of these changes as well as their pathological vicissitudes become the focus of our interest and are reflected in this series.

Here we have chapters that encompass a broad range of topics. They vary from an almost exclusive preoccupation with how the mind of the adolescent works to broad areas such as the function of ideologies or the impact of culture in general. In some chapters, theory predominates both in terms of clinical issues and developmental factors and in others technical factors and management become the critical issues.

The vast emotional upheavals the adolescent undergoes require an approach that brings in many frames of reference if we wish to achieve thorough understanding. Still, our viewpoint is primarily clinical, and whatever we learn from areas that go beyond the clinical has to be assessed in terms of how it helps us deal with patients.

Reviewing the numerous chapters sent to us as editors, we are gradually coming to the conclusion that adolescence as a process cannot be chronologically fixed. Perhaps certain psychic mechanisms first occur at the time of sexual maturation, but the modalities the ego achieves at that time in some form or other persist throughout life. If this proves to be true, the study of the adolescent stage should not be considered a specialized area but an essential aspect of general clinical psychiatry. Psychoanalysis has taught us that adult psychopathology cannot be understood unless one knows about the early developmental stages of infancy. Adolescence seems to be of similar importance as the infantile period for the understanding of the adult, at least from a characterological viewpoint.

Today, adaptive modalities are receiving increasing interest in our clinical formulations. Thus, interactions with people and the external world in general are highlighted. Tracing the genesis of adaptive techniques, both healthy and pathological, often reveals that they were first constructed and used during adolescence. The investigation of the fate of such ego mechanisms and their modifications should be of wide interest and augment our understanding of the individual, but it can also help clarify some of the tumultuous social changes we are experiencing.

SHERMAN C. FEINSTEIN

1973   PETER L. GIOVACCHINI

CONTENTS

PART III
PSYCHOPATHOLOGICAL ASPECTS OF STAGES OF ADOLESCENT DEVELOPMENT

PART IV
PSYCHOTHERAPY OF ADOLESCENCE

Contents

PART V
THE ADOLESCENT IN THE WORLD

PART I

ADOLESCENCE: GENERAL CONSIDERATIONS

INTRODUCTION

The theme, adolescence: terminable and interminable, which was adopted for the 1971 scientific meeting of the American Society for Adolescent Psychiatry and is reflected in the title of Dana L. Farnsworth's chapter in this part, is of course an adaptation of Freud's "Analysis: Terminable and Interminable." In this famous paper, Freud discussed whether analytic therapy could ever reach a natural end and concluded that though a few patients reach this gratifying outcome, the great majority struggle throughout life with recurring difficulties. Rather than focusing on the technical aspects of treatment, Freud felt that the question of the obstacles that prevent a cure should be investigated.

Our interest in adolescence has a similar basis for questioning the reasons so many do not resolve adolescence in a comfortable, natural fashion but rather continue to struggle with the adolescent tasks either by prolonging the process (delayed adolescence) or forming pathological ego states (characterological defects).

Rudolf Ekstein, in discussing the schizophrenic adolescent, illuminates the vicissitudes of the ego struggling with the separation-individuation process of adolescence. He feels that schizophrenic illness forces a pathological solution and illustrates the effects of distortion in the sense of distance on adolescent resolution.

Frank S. Williams in discussing Rudolf Ekstein's chapter emphasizes the empathic approach to the schizophrenic adolescent and the vicissitudes in dealing with separation-individuation and countertransference aspects of the symbiosis. He suggests the use of concomitant family therapy to facilitate the individual therapy of the youngster.

Dana L. Farnsworth discusses the needs of the adolescent for affection, a feeling of belonging, freedom from excessive domination, consistency and guidance, stimulation and opportunity, and good role models. He believes that the vast social problems and adult confusion about values

3

in our society have deeply interfered with providing adolescents a proper framework for growth, and he hopes that we will somehow learn to engage the energies and idealism of the young in helping solve some of these problems.

Humberto Nagera discusses maladaptive adolescent ego techniques; these correlate with the three factors that Freud deemed decisive for the success of analysis: the influence of traumas, constitutional strength of the instincts, and alterations of the ego. In modern terms Nagera deals with developmental psychopathology from infancy, intrapsychic and developmental conflicts of adolescence, special environmental pressures —both familial and social—intrapsychic elements, group psychological pressures from peers, and a "collective" traumatic neuroses. Moses Laufer describes his research studies on adolescence as a developmental stage, and his work on mental breakdown in adolescence. He is interested in the decision to kill oneself in adolescence and the meanings of the fantasy that endangers the person's life in reality; like Freud, he believes that understanding the mutually opposing action of the two primal instincts will help explain the rich multiplicity of adolescent development.

Derek H. Miller considers drug dependency in adolescence from the ego viewpoint and makes an important contribution by considering how the adolescent integrates the experience at different stages of development. Arnold Goldberg traces the capacity to tell the truth through its developmental stages, and concludes that it is not necessarily a higher order of behavior or an ethical good.

Erwin R. Smarr and Philip J. Escoll discuss the effects of technological change and the resulting ethical modifications in our society, emphasizing the deep impacts on character development. They discuss the tasks of adolescence and conclude that young people must still master them, though they note some interesting modifications that might shock the adult generation.

1] THE SCHIZOPHRENIC ADOLESCENT'S STRUGGLE TOWARD AND AGAINST SEPARATION AND INDIVIDUATION

RUDOLF EKSTEIN

> For what is time? Who can readily and briefly explain this? Who can even in thought comprehend it, so as to utter a word about it? But what in discourse do we mention more familiarly and knowingly, than time? And, we understand, when we speak of it; we understand also, when we hear it spoken of by another. What then is time? If no one asks me, I know: if I wish to explain it to one that asketh, I know not: yet I say boldly, that I know, that if nothing passed away, time past were not; and if nothing were coming, a time to come were not; and if nothing were, time present were not.
> *Confessions of St. Augustine* (ca. 397 A.D.)

I wish to paraphrase St. Augustine and say that if no one asks me, then I know about the nature of schizophrenia, about the nature of adolescence, and also about the nature of identity, but if I wish to explain it to one that asks, I do not know. The saintly philosopher, of course, tells us that the question about the nature of time is but a question about the nature of process and of change. We are able to measure time, but St. Augustine wondered with us: "Do I then measure, oh my God, and know not what I measure?"

The 1971 conference theme of the American Society for Adolescent Psychiatry, "Adolescence: Terminable and Interminable," hints at the difficulties we face if we are to define the changes that must take place in the adolescent's personality so that we may then speak about adult personality. The problem becomes more complex if we move from the normal or neurotic adolescent to those young persons whom we con-

William A. Schonfeld Distinguished Service Award Address presented at the 1971 Annual Meeting of the American Society for Adolescent Psychiatry in Washington, D. C., May 2, 1971.

5

sider schizophrenic or borderline and who are confronted with seemingly insurmountable problems as they try to solve the developmental task of adolescence as defined within the epigenetic scheme: the resolution of the identity crisis and the successful achievement of the second individuation.

The treatment of schizophrenic adolescents seems to bring out in us a magnified version of Freud's (1937) concern with "Analysis: Terminable and Interminable." We seem to face interminable processes, unbelievably slow changes toward growth, and repeated and powerful regressions; we try to enter the schizophrenic experience in which time in our sense seems to have no place, where the primary process—dreamlike as it is—wipes out our customary notions of time as expressed in measurable change.

It becomes clear that schizophrenic illness, even if incurable, does not obviate the need to meet life's tasks, to move through crises to a form of identity. The illness merely changes the forms of the identity crisis and the identity struggle, the setting of life goals and their achievement, and the use or misuse of the identity moratorium. Just as different cultural climates will influence the adolescent's psychosocial tasks, it seems clear to me that different forms of emotional or mental illness create differing psychic climates within which differing solutions, albeit of a pathological nature, are attempted.

I am fond of an epigram of Kant's that says, "Experience without theory is blind, and theory without experience is empty." Nevertheless, I will set out to meet my own task today, that is, to throw some light on the separation and individuation struggles of schizophrenic adolescents during treatment by staying on a clinical level as far as possible. I wish to make our patients' experience vivid, so that we can somehow identify with it and them, empathically understand it, and live up to an important requirement for a psychotherapist who works with schizophrenic youngsters, as expressed by S. T. Coleridge in his famous phrase "willing suspension of disbelief for the moment." We need the capacity to suspend disbelief in the psychotic experience, the seeming denial of reality, the fusion of past and present, the order of schizophrenic thought (usually referred to as "thought disorder"), the inability to maintain object self-representations, the fluctuating abilities and disabilities to love and to work, and the impulse-ridden flights from and assaults on their environment. To strengthen our capacity, it seems useful to me to use Coleridge's notion in a different way, and to require of the psychotherapist a "willing suspension of belief for the moment" in his assumptions and theories, his customary clinical responses or formulations. Through my years of experience with childhood and adolescent

6

psychosis I have become accustomed to believe dogmatically that much of what one learns from case to case is better learned if accompanied by the certainty that each case requires new formulations and cannot be completely grasped unless one is ready to suspend one's belief in what one has learned before and the way one has thought until now. I do not propose, as Descartes, that one has to give up all one has learned in order to arrive at a newer and truer theoretical construction, but I suggest that the willing suspension of belief, postponing one's return to one's notion of psychic organization and theory of technique, will help us find new sideways and byways into and in the wonderland of schizophrenic illness.

In a previous publication (Ekstein, 1968) I discussed one issue related to today's topic, namely, the strange ways that these psychotic adolescents pursue goals, their particular substitute for the healthy adolescent's growing commitment toward life goals. Their goals were small and short term, comparable to the first steps that somebody might attempt after a long bedridden illness. They represented a magnified and slow-motion version of the adolescent's crisis which has been so beautifully described by Anna Freud (1946). In this classic statement she described adolescents as:

excessively egoistic, regarding themselves as the center of the universe and the sole object of interest, and yet at no time in later life are they capable of so much self-sacrifice and devotion. They form the most passionate love relations, only to break them off as abruptly as they began them. On the one hand they throw themselves enthusiastically into the life of the community and, on the other, they have an overpowering longing for *solitude* (italics added). They oscillate between blind submission to some self-chosen leader and defiant rebellion against any and every authority. They are selfish and materially-minded and at the same time full of lofty idealism. They are aesthetic but will suddenly plunge into instinctual indulgence of the most primitive character. At times their behavior to other people is rough and inconsiderate, yet they themselves are extremely touchy. Their moods veer between light-hearted optimism and the blackest pessimism. Sometimes they will work with indefatigable enthusiasm and, at other times, they are sluggish and apathetic.

This struggle hides the conflicts between impulse and delay functions, instinctual gratification and establishment of moral and social values, the process of individuation and the separation from the parental home, and the establishment of their own place in society.

Erikson (1956) tried to characterize this struggle by the concept of identity, a psychosocial term, and instead of aiming at a concise definition, he felt he could make the subject matter of identity more explicit by:

. . . approaching it from a variety of angles—biographic, pathographic, and theoretical; and by letting the term identity speak for itself in a number of connotations. At one time, then, it will appear to refer to a conscious *sense of individual identity;* at another to an unconscious striving for a *continuity of personal* character; at a third, as a criterion for the silent doings of *ego synthesis;* and, finally, as a maintenance of an inner *solidarity* with a group's ideals and identity. In some respects the term will appear to be colloquial and naïve; in another, vaguely related to existing concepts in psychoanalysis and sociology. If, after an attempt at clarifying this relation, the term itself will retain some ambiguity, it will, so I hope, nevertheless have helped to delineate a significant problem and a necessary point of view.

These two statements encourage the synthesis I spoke about earlier, the combination of willing suspension of disbelief and belief, and the Freudian requirement of suspended attention in order to follow the struggle of our patients. I reported (Ekstein, 1968) a research patient, Donald, a schizophrenic adolescent (see also Caruth and Ekstein, 1964, 1965) who was then described as being occupied in establishing goals for the next few months by making plans, such as eating lunch with the other children in the private school he then attended. It took him months to master his anxiety and fears so that he could accomplish this. Other actions concerned his fear of using the public bathroom, of joining children in a baseball game, and of eating and talking together with his parents. He was impelled to discuss these problems for hours and weeks with obsessive rigidity, and one gained the impression that a powerful and merciless struggle developed around seemingly trivial issues.

During psychotherapy it became clear that an enormous struggle between two kinds of self-representations was going on within him. He saw himself as an enormous genius, a famous musician ready for Carnegie Hall, a political world leader ready for a rich and powerful life and great success. But behind these megalomanic expectations and the concomitant powerful notion of omni-impotence there was a self-image of utter helplessness, weakness, and constant loss of self. The goal of utopian success was entirely unrealistic; in reality, he was seeking a minimum adjustment, a kind of token integration into reality.

Before Donald came for treatment it had been impossible to keep him within any school system. He stayed at home during puberty, while his mother worked. He spent hours alone in a dark closet, with a dummy, "Mr. Punishment," that he fashioned out of pillows and his own clothing. Sexual fantasies of Mr. Punishment threatening and torturing him were the foreplay to compulsive masturbatory acts. A few years later, when treatment had helped him to return to a private school, and to work successfully toward a high school diploma, we observed a new version of the sexual game. He now fantasied that he was part of a community in which the nightly routine consisted of a meeting at which he was the chairman. He had a variety of people from reality, movies, and cartoons meet him in order to discuss whether he should masturbate or not. He tried to remain the impartial and arbitrating leader of the group, but slowly became its passive victim because the inevitable end result, after some three or four hours of obsessional struggle, disguised as a democratic group discussion, consisted of his being given either the permission or the order to masturbate. But changes have taken place between impulse and delay, between self-representations and object representations. In later games the psychotherapist became a part of that inner struggle, at times countering Mr. Punishment and at other times taking his place and being experienced then as "Mr. Prudence."

What is the current situation? Our research psychiatric social worker [1] helped him separate from the family. He is now living in a boarding home where there are other young people who cannot be maintained at home. A careful attempt was made to bring about a slow separation from the parental home so that it would be experienced—as much as this is possible under the circumstances—not as a rejection, but as necessary growth. Actually, this was introduced at a time when Donald was ready to struggle for this kind of partial independence. At first, he worked as a telephone solicitor for newspaper subscriptions, and earned his first few dollars. Telephoning is a good illustration of the kinds of human contact he was capable of establishing at the time. He lost jobs once or twice and got into dangerous crisis situations a few times, each time associated with interruption of therapy because of the therapist's vacations. Usually these crisis situations were involvements with unreliable people, substitutes for Mr. Punishment, which actually got him into serious danger. During the absence of the psychotherapist it was easy for Donald to regress from the notion of Mr. Prudence to the notion of Mr. Punishment, almost as if he were saying that he could maintain the relationship with the therapist during absence only by projecting onto him all the destructive impulses.

But these regressions, as they became material for the therapeutic process, actually led to consolidation that showed a new self emerging, a new identity. I want to illustrate this with the therapist's notes from a recent hour (669th treatment hour, January 1971). The patient, still resembling a very young adolescent, is presently employed with a team of laborers in a factory, loading and unloading heavy material. He has

9

been able to maintain this full-time job for a year and has made himself eligible for union membership. He has lost only a few days of work because of smaller inner crises. The hour reads as follows:

Don starts the hour telling me that he has almost $1,300 in savings and is entrenched in the work situation, in maintaining his plan for regular savings, and in sustaining a compulsive structure of living. The social worker had told me that when she saw him last, he seemed shaky; she felt we might be moving toward a new crisis. But he gives a picture contrary to hers; he says he wants to test his strength to see whether he could withstand temptation. He bought beer and wonders whether he will drink too much. I wonder with him how it is that I never need to put something in front of myself in order to be tempted, such as money in order to see whether I would steal, and I wonder why he feels at this moment that he should play with temptation. We then go through the usual gamut of temptations that he enumerates, such as that the beer might make him into an alcoholic, and that if he carries out his idea to stop work and to run to a gambling center he might lose his money, as he did once before. He knows now that these temptations are created by himself. I wonder whether he really needs these temptations, and what purpose they serve. He now identifies with the constructive side of the argument and starts to speak about the new nature of Mr. Punishment. He tries to influence Mr. Punishment and make him into something constructive.

I will now try to describe how he uses this basic fantasy about Mr. Punishment constructively and ties it to reality, while at the same time continuing his psychotic thinking.

He speaks about the enormous trucks the company uses, some forty feet or so in length, and how these trucks are twice the length of my office. He has to unload them. He meets the task by imagining the truck is an enormous red monster, and he uses his great strength to attack and defeat the monster. The attack also has a sexual connotation. The original sexual encounter with Mr. Punishment in the dark closet is now viewed constructively. As he unloads the trucks, he is proud of his strength and ability to work a full day, and he is aware of his erect and strong penis. He literally describes a sexual assault on a truck, emphasizing how he overwhelms it. Thus, he gets immense joy out of his job. Rather than being self-destructive, losing against Mr. Punishment, or losing money to a swindler in a gambling center, he uses psychotic fantasy in the service of work and in adaptation. If he succeeds in overwhelming the big red monster during his work day, he will get a big salary check, which he will put into a savings account, and this will allow him a summer trip. He also suffers from a destructive fantasy stimulated by some ants he sees around a garbage can. He imagines they will turn into giants, frightening and driving him away from work—causing him to lose the job. I try to use these examples to point out the struggle going on within him between the commitment to work and the fear of work, between being a powerful working man or a helpless baby.

While all this goes on, he has maintained this job for many months, and will be taking off in midsummer for two weeks to travel to Europe to see a relative. He has worked himself into a stable position, getting paid now more than $3.00 per hour.

What a long way this is from those days, now five or six years ago, when the almost insurmountable task was to be able to eat lunch in the same room with other people.

During these years he maintained some peripheral and superficial social contact with youngsters his own age. Although full of fear and worry, he feels relatively safe because he has now learned to block impulsive acting out and to find reality substitutes for Mr. Punishment and Mr. Prudence.

Wordsworth's "the child is father of the man" could be paraphrased to suggest that psychosis is father of a more neurotic adjustment, but it never ceases to exert some pressure and continues to remain a part of the total adjustment. The quality of more adaptive self-representations is constantly being undermined by primitive self-representations of earlier phases, and Donald needs constant help.

Though there was much growth, so to speak, in Mr. Punishment, we see in him an early forerunner of the reality principle and the notion of the external object as auxiliary ego. He moves from the talion principle to the reality principle, from the persecutory object to the auxiliary ego. While on the one hand Donald struggles for independence, and soon wants to move into a private apartment, he maintains some contact with his parents, social worker, and therapist, through which his precarious self-representation is bolstered in the struggle against feared, as well as beloved, earlier psychotic identities.

During the last hour preceding my putting these thoughts on paper, he spoke about his wish to move away from playing with homosexual identifications to bisexual ones. He wants to live in a world where he could love both men and women. These relationships sound like phantom relationships in the service of instant gratification rather than permanent object relations. There is presently an autistic quality to both his notions of self and others. Still, he is no longer an autistic person in the dreadful world he once occupied within that dark closet. His objects are now ego objects.

This feat was possible only because of the constant environmental support which is so essential in the treatment of such patients (Cooper, 1969; Ekstein et al., 1969). I have lost other patients who seemed less sick than this young man, but whom I could not help because of the lack of a realistic psychosocial situation to support my work. If we are to define adulthood in terms of achieved identity, the capacity to love and to work, what are we to say about Donald? To some degree he has achieved schizophrenic versions of all these requirements for adulthood.

He knows who he is, what he is, and, to a large degree, his limitations and goals. He may even become a self-supporting individual, a somewhat bizarre young man, not without some primitive joys and satisfactions, not without appeal, and, of course, never beyond crises. Is he a terminable case? Will he perhaps be a cured schizophrenic?

Adolescent identity struggles assume many forms in different individuals and different social realities. This indeed holds true for schizophrenics as well. I turn now to another case that has occupied our research group at the Reiss-Davis Child Study Center for many years. Friedman and I gave illustrations from the treatment of Robby as early as 1959 (Ekstein and Friedman, 1959). Robby was nearly five when he was brought for treatment because of disciplinary problems, incomprehensible behavior, wild emotional outbursts, and severe temper tantrums. His fragmentary play was interrupted constantly and impulsively, and slowly developed into a compulsive ritual.

When Robby arrived for his therapy hour, he quickly dashed to the therapist's drawer where his favorite screwdriver lay waiting for him. Following his familiar pattern, he quickly went to the playroom and removed the doorknobs and the plates from the two doors in the playroom. The therapist had been interpreting to Robby his need for doorknobs as his need for "mama," who left him with the therapist, whom Robby called "Friend." For many weeks Robby had gone through a ritual of demanding many kisses from his mother when she left him, where with reassurance that she would return, he would immediately dash to the doors with the therapist's screwdriver to dismantle the doorknobs. This would leave Robby with a smile of satisfaction, mischievous cunning, and an almost ecstatic pleasure in which the therapist could feel Robby's great relief from his anxiety over the mother's leaving; the therapist told him that he knew that Robby needed the knobs in order not to be afraid that mama would leave him, and sometimes he needed the knobs so that he would not be afraid of mama. But Friend wanted to help him so that he would not have to be afraid, and he would feel big and strong even without Friend's knobs. Although Robby listened and betrayed a fleeting, satisfied smile, he maintained his insistence that he must have the knobs and could not put them back, repeatedly asking why the doors needed the knobs. When it became clear to him that he could not take the knobs with him but would have to replace them on the door and leave them with Friend, his anxiety mounted to panic proportions as he looked at Friend and in a terrified whisper confessed, "Don't want to be a girl."

We were at that time interested in this strange, repetitive play, a compulsivity characterized by uncontrollable passion. He struggled to avoid isolation, to keep access to the protecting and nourishing mother, and to achieve symbiotic fusion. We saw his use of play material as related to influencing machines classically described by Tausk (1933). We

considered the doorknobs as narcissistic fetish objects. Recently Greenacre (1970) made a similar point.

Originally, Robby was suspected of suffering from an organic condition, one characterized by autistic withdrawal and wild impulsivity. He
received many years of psychotherapy at the Reiss-Davis Child Study
Center and then in another city. During puberty he could not be kept at
home or in private schools for emotionally disturbed children, and was
placed in a university hospital followed by a state hospital. He had
many different forms of treatment such as drugs and behavior therapy
based on reinforcement methods. Through all these years the parents
and the patient maintained some loose contact with Dr. Friedman. The
patient continued referring to him as "Friend." There were occasional
telephone calls and an increasing insistence by the boy to resume treatment with Friedman in spite of all the other contacts that he had with
other therapists. During the last few years he had been home again and
had some private treatment with a psychiatrist who believed in educational therapy, a treatment experience which ended in battle fatigue.

Because of our interest more than a decade earlier, we decided to accept this adolescent for a new phase of treatment in which there would
be a combination of individual psychotherapy and a controlled use of
the therapeutic environment (Ekstein *et al.,* 1969) as far as this might
be possible with our treatment facilities. Friedman would now resume
work with Robby while a social worker would work with him and his
parents. The idea was to accept him for treatment only if it were acceptable that he live away from the parents and accept programs of rehabilitation that would create a new kind of social structure. The family
and the patient accepted this to the degree that they could, and it was
possible to place the boy in a "halfway" house and to try various rehabilitation programs. Though these have failed so far, he is still in a halfway house, the second we have tried. He manages by moving between
halfway house and clinic, and between visits with his parents or telephone calls. In a frantic search for independence and individuation, he
constantly and impulsively asks anyone he can: "Do you have faith that
I will make it?" He waits for a reassuring answer, then drops the subject as well as the person whom he had asked. We wonder what kind of
identity he wishes to establish, and what he means by "make it,"
whether his goal is reunification with an object or the establishment of a
stable self. The frantic search then continues. He may address another
person, borrow a dime from a third person, run to the telephone and
call a fourth person. He may then aimlessly and frantically wander
through the streets toward the next "goal" that he has to reach and then

give us token resolutions (Schlesinger, 1964) concerning his intention to work some day. With the social worker he builds magnificent plans for the return to the parental home, the resumption of his studies, and earning a living—only to avoid anxiously the responsibility for the here and now.

Several times I was momentarily selected as the person from whom he sought to find out whether I had faith that he would make it. Still, what at first seemed an enormous demand ended as disinterest. I soon realized that he was in search of an object, but really disinterested in finding one.

This frantic search for an object could reach distressing proportions. In the corridor he might suddenly threaten to bang his head against the wall. I once had to interrupt my work to stop him since he actually did so. Nevertheless, he could be easily stopped and led to the office by hand as though he were a small, lost child instead of a tall, enraged young man.

I wish to demonstrate the quality of his struggle for and against individuation and for and against separation, by utilizing a recent incident described by his psychotherapist.

The fifteenth hour of the new psychotherapeutic program took place shortly after Christmas and a few months after the incident described above. The therapist records the prologue to this hour as follows:

When I entered the ground floor of the clinic, just about the time for the hour, I saw Robby engaged with a taxi driver in a moderately intense discussion which I quickly gathered had to do with the taxi driver's fare. Robby was arguing that it wasn't fair for him to have to pay the fare, that the director of the halfway house should have paid it, and that the taxi driver should not expect to be paid by him. At this point, I intervened and, for a moment, wondered whether I should pay the fare and relieve the taxi driver. But thinking that I should not step out of my therapeutic role, I discussed the situation with Robby and ascertained that he had awakened late, was afraid he would miss the hour, and ordered a cab. He then asked me to pay the fare. I told him that he had done a big thing—knowing that he would have been late for the hour and then finding an immediate solution. I thought he would want to complete the solution of the problem by also paying the fare and commented that he should feel very good about such an achievement. He said he did not have enough money and, furthermore, he did not want to use his money for this purpose. I replied that money—his money—would be a very good thing to use for the big and grownup thing that he had done. Besides, was it not worth the money to get here and for us to have our time? Slowly, he began to take the money out of his wallet, but he then slowly put it back. I continued talking with him for a few more minutes. Finally he took the money out of his wallet, and smilingly paid the taxi driver. As the driver started to leave, Robby quickly asked him if he had a Christmas present for him. The taxi driver was momentarily nonplussed. He replied that he did not give Christmas presents. Robby thought this was unfair because, after all, he had given him money and what did the cab driver give him? I told Robby that the cab driver had already given him his present. He had come when he had called and he had made it possible for him to come to our hour on time. The cab driver smiled, and Robby relinquished his demand for a present. Then I asked Robby to wait for me in the lobby, because I had some things I needed to deposit before we could go to our therapy office.

Robby was very serious about his treatment. He kept his appointments and he felt it was important to be on time. Nevertheless, he had difficulty waking up, and on that very morning he overslept. By ordering a taxi he succeeded in not being late. He had met his immediate goal; he had lived up to the promise that he had given himself; he had taken the responsibility for this hour; and had even found a solution instead of panicking as he would have in the past, or of relying on mother or whomever took care of him. He had met some of the conditions for independence that he wanted to live up to.

His behavior in relation to paying the driver can be considered a dramatic example of psychotic acting out, an example that constitutes not only experimental recollection, as we have defined acting out (Ekstein and Friedman, 1951), but is also indicative of what form future acting out will take. This behavior is in the service of schizophrenic adaptation and contains seeds of experimental adaptation, the search for adult commitments. His version of trying to fulfill the task is implied in the question: "Do you have faith that I will make it?" He met the task of being on time with the quasi-mature decision to take a taxi. But then, he does not wish to keep his end of the bargain. Why should he pay? The director of the halfway house should be the one to pay for him. Is it not the mother's or the caretaker's task to pay for his transportation? Should not the psychotherapist pay for him? Why should the taxi driver charge him at all when he, the patient, tried so hard to be on time?

He discounts the obligation to pay and tries to turn the taxi driver into another person. He appeals to him the way a child appeals to his parents. In spite of being eighteen he forgets what he had known just a few moments ago, and the promise to pay is meant to be fulfilled simply by the promise (Schlesinger, 1964), rather than by the act of living up to the promise. He then turns the taxi driver into a person who should reward him for being on time, and he asks him for a Christmas present.

These first few weeks of psychotherapy were constant negotiations regarding gifts he needed from his father or psychotherapist. Many of the therapeutic interviews consisted of endless demands for Christmas gifts which we understood as an attempt to establish an anaclitic relationship. He yearns for an external object, which he views realistically as long as he searches for it. The very moment he finds the object, he cannot maintain the requirements for contemporary object relationships, the requirements for age-appropriate love. He either loses the object, or must, in turn, change its nature, that is, convert it into an object of the infantile past, one which will recapitulate the maternal symbiosis. Thus, he cannot maintain the self he had been striving for, the age-appropriate identity leading toward independence, learning, and working. He can maintain the object in his mind only as long as he searches for it, only as long as he longs for it, as long as he is without fulfillment.

His problem reminds us of a beautiful discussion published by Deutsch (1969) in which she discussed two variants of the son-mother relationship by the study of the myth of Dionysus and Apollo. She refers to two types of object relationships of Zeus to Hero and Leto. Hero is always present at the side of Zeus and he is passively exposed to her aggressions. In order to safeguard his masculinity, he deeply loves and needs the passive femininity of Leto who always remains the object of his longing.

As long as Robby longs for the object, he must search for the object, and he will promise to live up to the requirements of such a relationship. Thus, his question about having faith in his making it really refers to his need for our implied promise that we will always be available. As soon as he reaches the object, the object becomes a demanding one.

His chaotic life history reflects the internal struggle between impulsive passivity that ceaselessly demands, and the compulsive attempt to meet the demands which will restore the love of those who are to take care of him, those who have faith he will make it and not have to return to a state hospital lost forever in illness. This is his double bind.

This, of course, is not merely an interpersonal battle; it is also a reflection of an immense intrapsychic struggle. When he hits his head against the wall, he is obeying hostile introjects, and he appeals to the outside world to save him from chaotic, self-destructive independence. As the social worker grasps his hands, reassures him, and accepts him again as the little, helpless boy, he restores the positive object who is to have faith that he will make it, and who does not make demands, but is there instead to meet his demands; thus, he achieves temporary and short-lived inner peace, the symbiotic paradise.

However, his demands cannot be met. For example, he wanted a radio from his father, even though he had numerous radios. He could not stop asking. No collection of doorknobs, no collection of radios, would convince him the object had faith in him, that such a person existed. He struggles with object representations which result in frantic

16

searching, desperate longing, unbelievable threats and anxiety; they are beyond fulfillment.

The fortieth session characterizes the problem well. The therapist states:

When we got into the office, he immediately launched into his need to have more time. He was not satisfied with my explanations. Now that he was better because of our sessions he was able to use more time. He lamented that God was not perfect. I tried to find out what he thought God really was like. He immediately picked up the cue to protest further about God, whom he felt was mean, imperfect, and selfish. I helped him elaborate feelings that God was not loving or caring enough for him. He felt that his mother loved him, but he began to worry that his father did not.

We were able to see that he meant that loving was not the same as caring, and he really wanted caring and sympathy more than loving. He felt that I was not caring for him, that I was mean, and not nice as Dr. L. had been. I had taken money from his parents when he was in treatment with me as a little boy, and too young to talk. What was worse, when he could talk, I did not make him talk, and I wasted his parents' money. I tried to convey to him that he was really telling me that he counted on me to help him do what had to be done even though he could not do it himself, such as talking. Besides feeling helpless and a little boy, he also believed that his thoughts had the power to make everybody act the way he wanted them to. No wonder he was always agitated and confused when he was torn between being so helpless and so all-powerful.

I tried to focus on how we could help make his thoughts, fears, and wishes work for him and serve him rather than threaten him with being sent away, destroyed, or abandoned. I then attempted to focus on his omnipotent thinking, but he constantly turned to other subjects that he regarded as more important, in fear of finding out that the more he talked about God being imperfect and mean, the more he would find he did not believe in Him, and then he would be afraid that God would send him to hell. I was aware that we could not, or need not, deal simply with his irrationality, but rather tried to get him to see that his thoughts were in constant conflict with one another and with him. I interpreted that his thinking of me as bad and mean made him feel triumphant, but induced in him fear that he would lose me or make me disappear.

The hour ended with his trying to extract more time and more answers to questions that he introduced by telling me he had only one more question, and then he would promise to leave. I insisted that we restrict ourselves to only one more question, but he was unable to keep his promise as evidenced by a disruptive flow of questions: I interpreted this reaction as an expression of his fear that I might disappear. He did not have faith that I would be with him even though he did not come and that I would see him the following hour just as we had agreed. I would be here even if he were not. This I could promise him.

His question then as to whether we have faith that he will make it really represents his internal question as to whether he has faith that we will stay with him, and whether he will be able to overcome his panic and to establish an identity of confidence—that when he searches for the object, he will find it: his criticism or hostility will neither destroy it nor him.

Freud once said that patients cure themselves by means of transferences. If they cure themselves by means of psychotic transferences we are dealing with a new countertransference problem. Psychotic transferences cannot sustain separation and individuation for very long. Primitive projections and introjections literally force the patients to create and re-create us in their own image. Whereas basically neurotic adolescents might create us in the image of significant adults in their life now and their life in childhood, the psychotic adolescent, who has never really learned to separate and to individuate, will re-create us within the context of his inner turmoil, in which primitive self- and object representations fuse with each other, murder each other, or isolate themselves from each other.

He can maintain therapeutic contact with us only if we do not permit him to re-create us in his image. At the same time, we cannot remain isolated dealing with the patient only on an interpretive level. To understand these patients we must identify with them and become part of their inner world, which has feeble bridges to what we call reality. I spoke earlier about the necessity to suspend disbelief in the schizophrenic's inner world and to suspend belief in our own usual assumptions so that we can become part of his world, his waking dreams, without being devoured by them, and by providing a basis that will make it clear that we are not only he, but also ourselves as well. If we are to maintain fusion and a separate identity at the same time, such a task requires that we fully understand his particular difficulties in achieving self- and object constancy.

Perhaps another vignette will help underline struggles between fusion and individuation and age-appropriate identity. I am referring to a sixteen-year-old borderline schizophrenic girl, a junior in high school, who is now in the second year of treatment with me. She has a history of wild acting out, experimentation with sex and drugs, a tie-up with some of the morbid aspects of current hippie culture, and self-destructive behavior with serious suicidal gestures. Ava had been in therapy before and tried once to test the trustworthiness of her psychotherapist, who promised her she could use the hour any way she wanted, by swallowing drugs in front of him. The therapist did not know what to do and waited too long; the child had to be brought to an emergency station to have her stomach pumped. In this way, the therapist succeeded in undermining the parents' trust.

18

She conscientiously kept her hours with me. The emergency situations abated though there was a suicide gesture at home and a variety of wild contacts with the Sunset Strip culture. In the beginning she gave wild reports about her sexual exploits. This clashed with the impression she gave me: that of a little poetic elf rather than of an acting-out, sexual delinquent. Ava constantly spoke of her contacts with the underworld, and of her commitment to activities reminiscent of the more primitive communes which make newspaper headlines. She had to be taken out of a private school because her work was unacceptable, though she was bright. It was questionable whether she would be able to make an adjustment in a public high school. The family did not know how to cope with her. Ava's parents seemed like distant objects, involved with obligations in the entertainment industry, which kept them frequently out of town and out of sight. The father often was aloof, but at times would get very angry with his daughter. The mother tried to be close, but she felt she had to accompany her husband in his travels. We considered separation from the family, but decided it would be unwise. Now she lives at home, does fairly well in high school, and the external emergencies have ceased to a large extent.

She insisted on every second of her time although she brought very little material into the sessions. She would sometimes bring knitting or other needlework, and would indulge in only conventional and banal conversation, or she would occasionally ask me to go with her to the drugstore for something she needed to buy. I inferred that she was anxiously hiding her thoughts.

Ava kept her distance from me while, at the same time, she tried to live up to the normal expectations of adolescence. She became more and more committed to high school, started to talk about college plans —in marked contrast to the beginning when she was rebellious, with compulsions to run away to a commune. She accepted conventional goals and even dressed conservatively. Her behavior at home also changed and the parents were relieved. The underlying thought disorder, the underlying conflicts with objects and self, and the fear of any true contact, were revealed in indirect ways and I could only respond in indirect ways.

I will give two examples which will describe the adaptations of therapeutic technique required for Ava's treatment.

She had found a quasi obstacle to treatment. She wanted me to start the hour ten minutes earlier so that she could get home in time to see a television program that dealt with vampires. I was able to get her to speak about the show and the nature of vampires. She said they all look like ordinary people, and she spoke particularly about one actor, who was her ideal vampire, a secret love. A vampire's kiss is designed to suck blood out of the victim and to either change him into a murderer or kill him.

Within this context interpretive work could be done. I referred to myself as a doctor who would have liked to treat these vampires and help them become normal and human, so that love would not have to be murderously destructive. I soon found out that sometimes vampires may even pose as doctors. Whenever the material became too intense, Ava would close the subject by suggesting that I was simply being foolish. I had no doubt that on some level we understood each other perfectly well.

Toward the end of the school term she was assigned a project. She decided to prepare a research study on the history of vampires, entitled, "All You Wanted to Know about Vampires and Could Not Ask." She brought books about vampires to some of our hours. She must have collected a great deal on this subject, gleaning material from all parts of Europe as well as other parts of the world. She had promised to let me read her essay but delayed endlessly. These hours seemed empty. Finally, she permitted me to read her essay after it had received a good grade. Much to my surprise, I found it was a competent study. Not one line betrayed how thin the wall was between delusional preoccupation and reality testing. She carefully phrased her sentences so that one would not know whether she believed in vampires, or whether she believed she was a vampire.

This is an interesting example, comparable to Donald's red truck incident, where the basic delusional fantasy is used adaptatively and leads to productive, acceptable work.

Recently, she told me that the television series, "Dark Shadows," had ended and she did not need to leave early any more. Again she insisted on using every second of her time with me. This was accompanied by a new activity. She brought drawings to our sessions which represented attempts to copy the faces of famous movie actors from magazine pictures and snapshots. This followed our discussions of how one determines whether a person is human or a vampire. She was particularly intrigued with Mr. Spock, one of the heroes of "Star Trek," a television show. I wondered whether she could draw my face. At first she refused, feeling it would be too difficult. Later on she agreed to do it, but stated that she would be unable to draw me directly in a real social situation. She could draw me only from a photograph which I supplied. As before, she had not told me about her studies of vampires and withheld the essay from me long after completion, now she did not speak of her attempts to draw me from the photograph I gave her. Nevertheless, she

20

carried Mr. Spock's picture and my photograph with her, even on her vacation. She finally revealed that Mr. Spock's eyebrows were hard to draw and that his father came from another planet, "Vulcan," and that his mother was from earth. He was a man from outer space with unbelievable gifts, a man who could not feel like human beings, but could understand them.

In a recent hour, Ava brought a number of books, among them *Star Trek One.* I wondered about the particular story she had been reading in the waiting room. She asked me to read the first few paragraphs, telling me that they would explain everything about an adolescent boy who was the hero of the story. As I started to read the material I had the uncanny feeling of déjà vu which one experiences often with patients who discuss a movie or book. The story could have been written by her, and as a matter of fact, could be considered equivalent to free association. It was as if she had borrowed from science fiction the free associations she had to keep repressed during the hour and substitute with "normal" adolescent behavior.

Enterprise, a magnificent spaceship, had met another smaller spaceship, *The Antares.* Enthusiastically, the crew of the latter spoke of a young adolescent, Charlie, whom they had found on a distant planet. His parents had been killed when he was three or four, and he was growing up alone, being brought up by memory banks on tapes. There must have been other creatures who brought him up on that distant planet but nobody knew. Mr. Spock was not certain whether it would be wise to take this adolescent, and he distrusted the enthusiasm of the other crew members. Nevertheless, Charlie was taken aboard and was eager to learn to adapt himself to this new world, to become a member of it, and to learn its rules. But soon trouble started. He fell in love with one of the female space personnel and made passes at her. She complained to the leader who tried to talk to the young man. He had immense powers and all attempts to stop him failed. Through his powerful mind and secret knowledge he was able to blow up the smaller spaceship from which he had come, and to make two of the crew who were in his way disappear. He threatened to use his power vis-à-vis the people of the *Enterprise* unless all of his immediate and impulsive demands were met. Mr. Spock, having a strong mind that could break through Charlie's power, found a way to disarm him, to make him powerless and helpless. As soon as he was powerless and helpless, he was forced to return to the planet from which he came. His megalomanic power was turned into helplessness; his beginning contacts with the human beings on *Star Trek* turned into desperate isolation and exile back to his home planet.

Here was an adolescent who tried to move into a new world, to learn the rules of this new society, and to cope with the awakening wishes for love, intimacy, and power, but he was overwhelmed by megalomanic impulses. Destruction, complete annihilation was the result, and even Mr. Spock could not help him. Mr. Spock, not a human but a Vulcan, was described by Ava as extremely clever, but without true understanding of human feelings. One might well wonder to what extent she equates me with Mr. Spock, clever, but without true feelings and understanding of patients. Her attempts to draw a picture of Mr. Spock and her promise to draw my picture are metaphoric indices of her attempt to maintain internal representations of the therapist and to make use of his insights. But she says that she cannot yet do it. She promises she will try to do so, but asks for time.

There is a connection between the vampire who kisses and kills women or turns them into monsters and the cool Mr. Spock who is without human feelings but understands. They both represent a struggle between murderous and sexual impulses. The synthesis of these qualities and the corresponding fantasy objects will form a new identity, one which Ava is capable of constructing.

Conclusions

These clinical vignettes emphasize the adolescent's struggle toward identity, the psychotic dilemma between individuation and fusion, between task fulfillment and empty promise, between self and object, and the inner civil war between different fragments of object and self-representations, have given the problem of distance a new qualitative dimension. As distance decreases, the object and the self frequently turn into opposites, or somehow change their respective nature in unpredictable qualitative ways. The simile of the Moebius strip (Caruth, 1968) suggests, through the notion that outside is inside, how shortening of distance may turn into even longer distance.

Therapeutic techniques that aim at optimum distance have to be developed. In some cases this will result in a new capacity for adaptation, with the development of self- and object constancy without any change in the inner schizophrenic core. These patients may benefit immensely from treatment, but their struggle with and against Mr. Punishment and Mr. Prudence, the longed-for object that turns into the destroying object, the vampire and the rational object who has no feelings and no empathy, all indicate subtle differences in our task with neurotics and the task that these patients set for themselves and for us.

The achievement of a new identity contains the need to be identified by others and to experience the sense of identity not only in relation to one's self, but in relation to the rest of the world, the object world. Therapists are part of this object world, and they too—in the counter-transference and in their relationships to the professional world—have an identity problem, the problem of professional identity. It is obviously difficult to maintain a professional identity when one copes with tasks that are considered by the patient, the family, the general public, and also the professional world, as unrealistic tasks.

The danger of role diffusion is a professional danger and I see only one basic and powerful protection of our identity as therapists. We must continue collecting data, testing and retesting our formulations, and prepare ourselves for an endless series of bewildering new obstacles.

Only by diligent research can we maintain a strong and flexible professional identity. This identity, although not defined, has been described by Freud (1937) as follows:

This in turn raises a host of other questions to which we can at present find no answer. We must be patient and await fresh methods and occasions of research. We must be ready, too, to abandon a path that we have followed for a time, if it seems to be leading to no good end. Only believers, who demand that science shall be a substitute for the catechism they have given up, will blame an investigator for developing or even transforming his views. We may take comfort, too, for the slow advances of our scientific knowledge in the words of the poet: "What we cannot reach flying, we must reach limping. . . . The Book tells us it is no sin to limp."

NOTE

1. I am grateful to Mrs. B. Cooper for the use of her material. She also is the social worker mentioned in all the clinical vignettes in this chapter.

REFERENCES

Caruth, E. (1968). The onion and the moebius strip: Rational and irrational models for the secondary and primary process. *Psychoanalytic Review,* 55:416.
———, and Ekstein, R. (1964). Certain phenomenological aspects of the countertransference in the treatment of schizophrenic children. *Reiss-Davis Clinic Bulletin,* 1:80.
———. (1965). To sleep but not to dream: On the use of electrical tape recording in clinical research. *Reiss-Davis Clinic Bulletin,* 2:87.

Cooper, B. (1969). Casework with psychotic children and their parents. *Reiss-Davis Clinic Bulletin*, 6:122.

Deutsch, H. (1969). *A Psychoanalytic Study of the Myth of Dionysus and Apollo—Two Variants of the Son-Mother Relationship*. New York: International Universities Press.

Ekstein, R. (1968). Psychotic adolescents and their quest for goals. In: *The Course of Human Life*, ed. C. Buhler and F. Massarik. New York: Springer.

———, and Caruth, E. (1965). The working alliance with the monster. *Bulletin of the Menninger Clinic*, 29:189.

Ekstein, R., and Friedman, S. (1951). The function of acting out, play action and play acting in the psychotherapeutic process. *Journal of the American Psychoanalytic Association*, 5:581.

———. (1959). On the meaning of play in childhood psychosis. In: *Dynamic Psychopathology in Childhood*, ed. L. Jessner and E. Pavenstedt. New York: Grune & Stratton.

Ekstein, R., Friedman, S., Caruth, E., and Cooper, B. (1969). Reflections on the need for a working alliance with environmental support systems. *Reiss-Davis Clinic Bulletin*, 6:111.

Erikson, E. H. (1956). The problem of ego identity. *Journal of the American Psychoanalytic Association*, 4:1.

Freud, A. (1946). *The Ego and the Mechanisms of Defense*. New York: International Universities Press.

Freud, S. (1920). Beyond the pleasure principle. Standard Edition, 18:7–64. London: Hogarth, 1955.

———. (1937). Analysis: Terminable and interminable. Standard Edition, 23:216–253. London: Hogarth, 1964.

Greenacre, P. (1970). The transitional object and the fetish with special reference to the role of illusion. *International Journal of Psychoanalysis*, 51:447.

Schlesinger, H. (1964). *A Contribution to a Theory of Promising: The Making of Promises: Primary and Secondary Promises*. Unpublished manuscript.

Tausk, V. (1933). On the origin of the "influencing machine" in schizophrenia. *Psychoanalytic Quarterly*, 2:519.

24

2] DISCUSSION OF RUDOLF EKSTEIN'S CHAPTER

There is a marked difference between therapeutic caring and diagnostic caring. Dr. Ekstein's poetic, poignant, and clear chapter reflects enormous therapeutic caring. The following two psychotherapists' notes about a seventeen-year-old boy—who reminds me very much of Donald and Robby (see Chapter 1)—reflect the worst and the best in diagnostic and therapeutic caring. The latter's notes are more representative of Dr. Ekstein's type of concern, commitment, and constructive wonderment regarding the schizophrenic and borderline schizophrenic adolescent.

The first therapist says about Steve: "chronic schizophrenic . . . will remain a schizophrenic all his life. Prognosis is very guarded. . . ."

The second therapist's notes about the same seventeen-year-old boy read: "It is pitiful about Steve. Maybe it would be better to be completely crazy. This boy is struggling and fighting to be sane, to be clear, to express, to relate, to be a normal teenager with normal sexual drives, but it is a grueling struggle for him and for the therapist. I would recommend an optimistic, long-term, but hopeful approach to help him learn how to interact and share communications."

Dr. Ekstein—in a similar manner to this second therapist—does not throw up his hands and become hopelessly pessimistic because of diagnostic labels. Instead, he demonstrates the essence of empathy, and the perplexities involved in a therapist's attempt to truly empathize with a psychotic or borderline psychotic adolescent. He stresses the need to "make the experience of our patient vivid so that we can somehow identify with it and then empathically understand it." I agree thoroughly that only through experiencing the schizophrenic adolescent's desperate attachments and terrors can we begin to understand the struggle he has in the direction of separation and individuation. Unfortu-

25

nately, empathy is most difficult with these troubled youngsters. Usually we empathize with a patient by identifying with him or his experiences just long enough to feel his plight or his joy, and then we "get out" in order to look and understand. With the borderline schizophrenic adolescent and the psychotic adolescent, there is no complete autonomous existing identity with which to identify. One must identify, instead, with a partially fused, symbiotic state. One becomes part of the symbiosis—a symbiosis from which it is difficult to extricate ourselves. With the neurotic adolescent, one can generally identify long enough even to get vicarious pleasure in his acting out, but we can, generally, quickly "get out" of this identification and reflect back and understand. That is empathy. With the psychotic adolescent one becomes more intensively enveloped in the symbiosis. Yet, should the psychotherapist resist entry into the symbiosis, very little therapy occurs, and both patient and doctor wind up with the "battle fatigue" Dr. Ekstein described when he referred to the psychiatrist who tried to employ "educational therapy" with Robby. The most perplexing questions, then, are: How much should the therapist get into the symbiosis? When should he avoid getting in? When should he get out, if possible?

Maintaining a symbiotic relationship reassures the patient that you will support and protect him from catastrophic ego dissolution. However, the therapist will soon want to "drop" the patient in order to save himself from a state of symbiotic identity-loss. Knowing this can help the therapist identify with the even greater desperateness experienced by the psychotic adolescent.

When the psychotherapist tells Robby that he fears the therapist will "disappear," this, in addition to representing the patient's anxieties, may also reflect the therapist's wish to disappear—to save himself from the fused state. The therapist, however, does not disappear and, in fact, tells Robby he is committed to be with him and even remain partially fused with him, though Robby may not come to sessions. He says, "I would be here even if he were not. . . . This I could promise him." He implies to the patient, You and I are somehow fused; "you" is not you, and "me" is not me. Do not worry, you are not quite ready to make it. But, Dr. Ekstein knows that should the therapist maintain this position too long with the patient, he will not, in the long run, be able to help him, since the therapist will be re-created in the image of the patient's fused object representations. How, Ekstein questions, can one fuse, identify, and yet separate without becoming isolated from these youngsters? How does one let the patient know that we are not only "he" but also our "self"? Ekstein recommends balance and goes on to demonstrate this balance in his exquisite clinical descriptions. One can

26

sense his identification, empathy, and return to separateness as he tells us about Donald, Robby, and Ava. An example of how clearly the therapist can separate himself from the patient at appropriate moments is seen in the session in which Donald describes how he handles temptation by buying beer and wondering whether he will drink too much. Dr. Ekstein says, "I wondered with him how it is that I never need to put something in front of myself in order to be tempted, such as money, in order to see whether I would steal and I wondered why he felt, at this moment, he should play with temptation." Such moments of separateness in the psychotic adolescent's therapy not only maintain the sanity of the therapist, but also help construct healthy object representations which are not fused and symbiotic. The therapist re-establishes himself and his boundaries frequently as a model for the eventual boundaries and inner self-constancy that one hopes the patient will establish.

Resistance to Separation-Individuation

These youngsters have a tenacious resistance against individuation, particularly at points of imminent psychological separation. The author describes this perplexing frustration as it is reflected in Robby in his incident with the taxi driver, and Ava, in her resistance to drawing Dr. Ekstein's face. In these accounts we see clearly how any beginning mutual transaction which even faintly resembles social reciprocity and separateness leads to regression, to a quest for a primitive symbiosis—a fusion with the object. Robby cannot maintain the taxi driver's separate identity just because the taxi driver treats Robby as separate. And for Ava, once she can draw Dr. Ekstein's face, he becomes separate; and so might she! This is dangerous. The part of the therapist that wants to help these patients become separate, becomes the enemy as well as the friend. When they begin to treat themselves as separate and when the therapist treats them as separate, they must fight to retrieve the symbiosis. At this point, we can only infer that they seem terrified of being separate. Dr. Ekstein suggests several reasons for this terror. The borderline adolescent fears he might have to "make it" right then and there; or, he suggests, he is terrified of the self-destructive elements of his independence—as one patient might have said, "See, I won't make it if I am alone and separate. I will bang my head!"

I should like to suggest an additional factor which blocks growth toward separation-individuation. The therapist often feels anxious about being trapped in the symbiosis. The patient is supersensitive to our wish to cut ourselves loose.

27

Family Therapy and the Schizophrenic Adolescent

At one time I believed that family therapy approaches with the schizophrenic-symbiotic adolescent were of secondary importance, having less impact than intensive long-term individual therapy, with the goal of expanding the adolescent's nonsymbiotic interpersonal relationships. More recently I have found great value in the use of intensive concomitant family interviewing techniques as a means of overcoming familial resistances to the psychosocial growth of these severely troubled young people.

When I speak of family interviewing techniques, I do not mean only the essential therapeutic environment which must be created and supported by the social worker and others working with the family and the community. Rather, I mean skilled observation of family dynamics—observation which helps the therapy team to understand those perpetuating factors which make it difficult for schizophrenic adolescents to achieve more adaptive intrapsychic self-concepts. When speaking of family interviewing techniques, I am not referring to short cuts to the arduous work that is needed for meaningful progress with youngsters like Robby, Donald, and Ava. In fact, the type of family therapy we advocate for such youngsters would most likely entail the assignment of an additional separate therapist. The family therapist would see the parents conjointly, usually with their disturbed child present. He would look for those familial communication patterns and interactions which make the already difficult individual therapeutic work even more difficult. Frequently, when a schizophrenic adolescent begins to achieve some adaptive self-representations, the quality of his growing intrapsychic self-concept is undermined not only by his primitive self-representations, but also by familial forces.

Some parents have a psychological need to project their repressed primitive self-representations on to their adolescent sons or daughters. They have often achieved a type of pseudoindividuation and pseudoseparation, which they can maintain only as long as they project their primitive unconscious sense of helplessness onto their schizophrenic youngsters. A seventeen-year-old patient tried to help his father in his workshop, and did well the first time. The father, more than ever, treated him as if he were a helpless weakling. He needed to create and maintain the myth of weakness in his son to keep himself strong. He made this myth a psychic reality for his son.

At points of growth in a psychotic adolescent's individual treatment we often observe in concomitant family therapy cueing mechanisms by one or both parents which foster regression back to primitive self-representations and primitive superego attitudes. A sixteen-year-old schizoid girl, in addition to anorexia nervosa, had obsessively withdrawn from all social contacts in spite of many fantasies about sex and dating. She finally reached a point in treatment where she could consider going to a party with a boy she had met at school. After she expressed the idea of dating, she began to withdraw once again. In a family meeting, the mother stated how happy she was that Marie was going to date and how important it was for girls to get out of their homes and meet boys. Then, apparently out of context, she added ". . . my father was a policeman you know, and I've learned about all the rapes and murders that go on, particularly with young girls. . . ." Mother clearly retriggers her daughter's primitive anxieties. This mother—behind her competence and flagrant flare for free sexual talk—was continually repressing a self-representation of physical and sexual helplessness, and bribing a merciless superego. Behind her "pseudo-Mr. Prudence" was a harsh "Mr. Punishment" which she projected onto her daughter.

Many parents struggle with primitive unconscious fears of object loss and separation. One often sees a revival of the parents fantasied object loss when their adolescents are about to make steps toward separation and individuation. Saul L. Brown [1] has indicated how the family transactional field is often used to reaffirm and preserve the internal infantile object constellation. The parents are usually not aware that they are protecting themselves from an inner sense of object loss by keeping their youngsters in a symbiotic attachment to them.

Family interviewing techniques involving the parents of the schizophrenic adolescent, as well as parents of nonpsychotic children, are also helpful in noting certain familial psychotic *communication styles*. It is a form of communication which implies that there is no such thing as separation or individuation; a form of communication which invalidates the separate existence of the other. For example, a sixteen-year-old girl who seems fairly integrated in individual consultation becomes more and more borderline schizophrenic when she sits with her parents. This is not surprising, because the therapist himself becomes more and more "borderline schizophrenic" as he sits there, if he does not intervene. Communication is chaotically confusing. There is massive invalidation of each other's existence. The mother says, "I am hurting." The father says, "You do not hurt." Then the father says, "I do not worry." And mother says, "You do worry." There is massive tangentiality and answering for each other. I, as a therapist, would like to put my fingers in my ears and pray for autism to befall me so that I can avoid all these confusing stimuli.

29

Conclusions

Let me conclude by returning to what I consider the major factor in total therapeutic progress, when progress occurs, with schizophrenic adolescents—the therapist's commitment. The willingness to stay with the patient is beautifully illustrated by Dr. Ekstein's willingness to enter his patient's inner world, to get out in time, and willingness to enter again. When Robby says, "Do you have faith that I will make it?" he is also saying, "I will fight your making me strong, but please stay attached and keep trying, won't you?" The therapist (Friend) "had faith" when Robby was five, when he said, "Friend wanted to help him so that he would not have to be afraid and he would feel big and strong, even without Friend's doorknobs." When Robby, as a teenager, compulsively asks, "Do you have faith?" it indicates progress, because less acting out is involved than in dismantling doorknobs. It is healthier, although more terrifying, to anticipate the horror of impending individuation and separation.

The author constantly emphasizes the long-term and intensive commitment needed for schizophrenic adolescents, especially because of their "limping" slow progress. I agree that limping is no sin. In fact, it is better to limp and stay with it and get some place, than to leap around and quickly give up.

I should like to thank Dr. Ekstein for a most meaningful and thoughtful description of high quality and devoted therapeutic caring.

NOTE

1. Chief, Department of Child Psychiatry, Divisions of Psychiatry, Cedars-Sinai Medical Center, Los Angeles, California.

3] ADOLESCENCE: TERMINABLE

AND INTERMINABLE

DANA L. FARNSWORTH

Never before in history have so many people and so many nations been acutely concerned about the attitudes and behavior of their young people. The current unrest among the young is worldwide; the countries without a youth problem are few. There appears to be some correlation between economic status and unrest, in that it is usually the more prosperous nations that seem to have the most disturbances among their students, particularly. In general, we can say with some assurance that only the adolescents of affluent nations have the time and the resources to experience a long period of uncertainty and discontent.

The needs of a young person during adolescence have probably changed very little over the centuries. These needs include affection from family and friends, a feeling of belonging and being needed as well as wanted, and recognition as a separate person rather than an extension of his parents. A favorable climate for growth and development includes freedom from excessive domination or interference in his affairs, but just as surely it includes firm discipline from persons he respects, in most cases his parents. Consistency is particularly important, because divided authority is extremely confusing to anyone, especially to the young. And a system of values to follow or to rebel against is essential. Ethical relativism is particularly destructive to the young person trying to determine limits and learn what he can get away with and what he cannot.

The adolescent has the intelligence, energy, and idealism of the adult, but he does not have the experience, patience, and judgment that he may, ideally, acquire later. To grow most effectively, he needs opportu-

Presented as the keynote address at the Annual Meeting of the American Society for Adolescent Psychiatry, Washington, D.C., May 2, 1971.

31

nity, stimuli, and guidance, particularly when he asks for them. If he does not have such opportunities, he tends to overcompensate by too much slavish adherence to customs or fads of his peers; rather than imitate the best of what he sees in older persons, he tends to imitate the worst, possibly because this brings him more attention. He needs to develop patience and the ability to tolerate ambiguity, and to assimilate a wide variety of experiences without feeling that he is trapped. He has to learn how to keep his options open and how to attain self-esteem and the esteem of others.

He needs good role models for imitation, or in some cases for contrast. By this latter term I mean that he can observe a person who is functioning well in a particular role, esteem that person and that role, but decide that this is not the life for him. Encouragement by receiving credit for tasks well done is more apt to influence his motivation in a favorable manner than is severe criticism for poor accomplishment. He needs provision for alternation of stimulation and relaxation, and for privacy. And he must have change, because adolescence is by its nature a time of change, even in relatively stable societies. But change should not be so rapid as to make it impossible for him to adapt or be able to relate the past and present to what he projects for the future.

Though these fundamental needs have not changed, the means of meeting them have changed drastically during the last few decades. In agrarian societies, adults and young people were in contact nearly all the time, sharing many facets of their lives. But as people began to accumulate more and more in villages, cities, and then suburbs, the life style caused members of the family to go their separate ways. The extended family has been cut down to the nuclear family, or in some cases not even that.

Duties and responsibilities of the young have changed. It is quite important, as I mentioned, for an adolescent to feel needed as well as wanted, and as relations between children and their parents have become more attenuated, being needed has become increasingly less likely. Economic changes have made it difficult for the child to contribute to the family's economic survival in any real way, and thus it is often not clear to him whether he is actually needed. The sharing of experiences between young people and their elders is not always possible, and frequently it is only accomplished during recreation. This creates a slanted view as compared to the older situation where young people shared in both work and recreation or actively participated in the duties necessary to keeping the family together.

Even parent substitutes, who can do much to inculcate values, have become unavailable in some communities. Youngsters living in the deteriorated central cities, especially, have experienced increasing difficulty in meeting their basic needs. The influence of the church and school has weakened, and the preponderant influences, in many instances, are now those derived from the peer group and from pressures generated through the mass media. In many communities, the influences from the family, church, and school are quite at variance with these others, especially those coming from the role models presented in movies, television, magazines, and popular music.

Our present group of young people have been accustomed to instant dissemination of immense volumes of knowledge through newspapers, radio, and television, permitting each person to have a range of information about events all over the world that was quite impossible only three or four decades ago. The knowledge that is presented, however, is often distorted in order to achieve a purpose—sometimes educational, sometimes propagandistic, sometimes exploitative. Violence is usually featured strongly. Attitudes are often changed while knowledge is being imparted. Some youngsters from rural areas may have too few stimuli, but most of those in the cities seem to have too many.

The vast range of knowledge concerning developments in so many fields makes it hard to achieve a sense of continuity. Many young people cannot arrive at a sense of order, of comprehension of the numerous factors in their environment. This tends to make many of them feel that the future is unwelcome. All these tendencies have united to prolong the period of adolescence, even as they have diluted the involvement of adults and young people with one another.

What does the late adolescent-young adult see about him as he views society? He sees a lowered status of belief, conviction, values, standards, restraint, and tradition, with a high emphasis on self-seeking and immediate impulse expression. Freedom of speech has become license. The press and the theater now often produce widespread feelings of repugnance; in fact, they have produced so much that their proponents have become defensive and moralistic themselves in the defense of their new freedom, which is not working too well. He sees increasing manipulation of recreational pursuits, with emphasis on vicarious rather than actual participation and with constant pressure to sell products.

He sees a world in which every person is greatly interdependent with many other persons, but in which there is a very high degree of suspicion. Wishing to trust others, he often finds his trust unjustified or abused. It is not at present in vogue to depend on such concepts as "a man's word," "a gentlemen's agreement," or other components of a gentle society, and agreement on a substitute for them in the form of rules and regulations is almost impossible to attain.

33

He sees his family members so overburdened with various activities that there is often little familial interaction in common pursuits. Schools, churches, service and social organizations seem to him to have little relationship to the rest of the world. He frequently sees adults who think the only way to communicate is to copy the external signs of the youth culture—mothers in bell bottoms and fathers letting their hair grow. The only unambiguous influence that emerges is that of his peer group.

He sees a world in which expression of feeling is obligatory but is hedged around with many unwritten rules about which feelings are to be expressed and how they are to manifest themselves. Helene Deutsch (1967, p. 100), speaking of sexual freedom for girls, states that, "The new morality not only assumes the right of girls to sexual freedom, but it makes the utilization of that freedom a kind of obligation." The same phenomenon appears to apply to preferences in grooming, dress, reading, music, political and social opinions, and to some extent drug abuse. Many young people feel most unsupported in doing what they prefer to do if it is not consistent with current fads.

The adolescent-young adult discovers that in a world where knowledge rapidly becomes out-of-date, education is still often based on obsolete concepts of what its goals and methods should be. He finds that instead of only a few pursuits, there are now many possible vocations and professions and ways of self-support, most of them requiring longer and longer periods of preparation. As Erikson (1959) has said, "To be firmly told by tradition who one is can be experienced as freedom; while the permission to make an original choice can feel like enslavement to some dark fate." Furthermore, when he begins preparation for one occupation or profession and then wishes to change to another, the penalties in lost time are increasingly great.

Erikson (1959) also noted that college education is one of the long apprenticeships of our time, is getting longer and more specialized, and constitutes a radical postponement of some emotional satisfactions and a replacement by others. It cultivates some forms of extended childishness even as it cultivates certain forms of one-sided precocity.

Since that time, the necessity of such postponement has been increasingly questioned (as expressed in the demand for relevance in education), and the one-sided precocity has taken the mass form of acute analysis of society's defects, but without a corresponding comprehension of what changes are necessary to correct them. Thus some young people have become so concerned about the failures of our social system that they have embarked on a life of mostly protest, which has prevented them from completing their own maturational tasks. For them, feelings

34

are dominant, and their strong actions often bring reactions from others that weaken their efforts. An important obligation of those of us interested both in the attainment of maturity by young people and in the correction of the regrettable features of our society is that we help them keep their critical spirit alive and constructive. We can probably do this best by constant interchange.

Many of the youngsters whose experiences have been too numerous, too confusing, and basically too discouraging are filled with anger, resentment, bitterness, and defiance. This is frequently, however, only a cover up or reaction to their confusion, their doubts, their depression or anxiety, their feelings of loneliness and futility. They tend to become what we now call "alienated." They begin to look for quick answers to complex situations. They tend to become rigid and dogmatic in their thinking, and pay more attention to what they hear from one another than what they hear from older persons. Their considerable energy tends to express itself in the form of violent, destructive protest rather than a more reasoned effort to work toward the changes they envisage.

In adolescence the individual has to live with heightened impulses and find a balance between desire and restraint. If his social idealism develops without this balance, it is all too often impulsive, explosive, demanding, and expressed in terms of confrontation rather than in terms of working toward goals of mutual understanding, cooperative living, devotion to quality, respect for all people, and commitment to the common good. Many of our young people (and some of the older ones too) are strong in opposition but weak in affirmation.

We are now hearing a prominent aspect of the counterculture described as following a "hang-loose" ethic (Suchman, 1968). This phrase was coined, I imagine, to contrast with "up tight," but it does not necessarily imply a lack of moral conviction. In fact, it usually includes opposition to the Vietnam War, the draft, and various governmental or social policies that are seen as being wrong. Other constituents are dissatisfaction with one's education and the general social system, approval of sexual freedom, an emotional reaction to the feeling of a gap between generations, participation in various sorts of mass demonstrations and festivals, interest in underground communications such as newspapers and films, and belief in circumventing (though not necessarily breaking) laws when possible. Most of the persons who adhere to this ethical system emphasize present rather than future enjoyment whenever possible, and anticipate more satisfaction from leisure than from work. They have a conviction that they need not worry about physical survival and so have the luxury of concentrating on either amusement or social involvement.

Among the many obstacles to the maturational process are confused teachers, rigidity in thought and action of other persons, moral flabbiness and ethical relativity, those who work out their hostilities by attacking others, those who do not realize how strong their examples are, and those who exploit the young for their own gain. I cannot recall any period in history during which young people have been so mercilessly exploited as during the last few years. The natural propensity of adolescents to want to be more like others than like themselves has been skillfully utilized in promoting products appealing to the temporary rather than the more durable needs of adolescents and young adults. Fortunately, many young persons (and adults too) are recognizing this phenomenon, at least in some of its more clearly exploitative forms. Extremely graphic and obscene movies, for example, are losing their drawing power.

One of the most widespread and, unfortunately, effective methods of postponing maturity is the use of drugs for nonmedicinal purposes. There have been epidemics of such drug use in the past, but never before on such a wide scale, nor have so many different kinds of drugs been involved at one time. Warnings about the danger of their indiscriminate use have gone unheeded. Whereas formerly the misuse of drugs was concentrated among people who were distressed, disappointed, or disillusioned and looking for escape from their woes, it is now practiced by a wide variety of persons who presumably have positive as well as negative reasons.

This pandemic of drug abuse has created wide uneasiness (not to say dismay) among parents, teachers, law enforcement officials, physicians, and all those interested in young people. The voice of the medical profession, which should be authoritative, is divided and confusing. Much of the literature in this field is couched in terms suitable for a debate over an esoteric subject in which cleverness in the turning of phrases, rather than accuracy of fact, determines the winner. All of us who are involved in this problem seem to agree that we do not have enough knowledge about the actions of some drugs, but we seem to be at odds over what to do with the knowledge we do have. Because of these and other reasons, young people tend to discount anything that a physician says on the subject.

Drug abuse as presently exhibited is not a mere fad, but a symptom of a very complex social malaise reflecting the uncertainty, insecurity, and frustration that so many young people feel. It has become one of the major vehicles for expressing anger at our present form of society, which, it is believed, is insensitive and ineffective in dealing with social injustice. Such drug usage is furthered by the easy availability of all types of drugs, accompanied by exhortations from members of peer groups, songwriters, entertainers, and some artists and clergymen, who believe that drugs have enhanced their creativity and their understanding of themselves and other people.

Despite the conspicuous lack of objective evidence that the nonmedicinal use of drugs has in fact increased creativity and self-insight (Farnsworth, 1970), many young people do believe in their value in this regard. They often feel that the experience of the new sensations produced by drugs will be instrumental in their intellectual development. Perhaps the best response to these assumptions is that of a student, a sophomore at the time he wrote it, who observed (Gerzon, 1969), "What is valuable is not experience in itself, but the ever-increasing capacity to gain insight from experience. To settle for experience alone is to sacrifice the human capacity to gain insight from it." This same student also observed, somewhat enigmatically, "Drugs cost in physical well-being and self-reliance what psychotherapy costs in money."

Drug abuse is a public health problem because it has many similarities with other forms of communicable disease. The infectious agent, that is, the drug itself and the desire to use it, is spread either directly from one host to another or through an intermediate agent, a vector or carrier. The use of drugs, or even their misuse, under medical supervision is not contagious, but "street" use certainly is. Spread of the latter is facilitated by the fervor with which most drug users urge others to follow their example, as well as by the pressure from those who are financially dependent on drug distribution. The tendency toward its spread is increased by a toxic environment, in this case the social conflicts and pressures that center around today's suspicion, alienation, and rejection of social and political institutions.

The young people whom society has failed most conspicuously are the "street people," mostly young, many feeling rejected by their parents and rejecting them, few having any idea of what they want to do. They have apparently repealed the past, rejected the future, and are thus faced with the difficult task of keeping the present permanent. Along with rejecting their parents and traditions, they have given up the basic principles of nutrition and avoidance of disease. By their disdain of those customs and habits that most people consider basic in regulating their behavior, the street people are faced with considerable disfavor and isolation.

Since they have no permanent base, no future for which to prepare, and no feeling of obligation to anyone's expectations, the use of drugs to achieve sensations not otherwise available becomes almost obligatory in their social system. But their inability to trust anyone outside their

37

circle, including most physicians, makes treatment difficult. Those who might be willing to go to established institutions for help all too often have no money to pay for it. Their methods of caring for their basic financial, emotional, and hygienic needs usually alienate them still further from the larger society. Institutions set up to provide free medical care and counseling are at best only a stopgap. They tend to perpetuate these young people's conviction that the usual institutions have nothing to offer them and that the society they have rejected will continue to take care of them with no obligation, financial or otherwise, on their part. For the moment, however, these free clinics and counseling centers offer one of the best means we have to keep in touch with the street people and to learn how to develop new forms of communication and institutions that will serve their needs as they move toward maturity.

Solving the drug problem depends to a considerable extent on helping young drug users, their parents, their potential friends, and their associates of the future to make peace with one another. Unless this problem is solved, we are faced with the possibility of a new kind of lost generation made up of the many young persons who have been unwilling or unable to solve the main problems of adolescence. We are already seeing this situation quite often in our colleges, where very bright young men and women who have a great accumulation of general knowledge and are quite capable of passing their courses with good grades find themselves at the end of several years of college unprepared for a major career and without the will to attempt to establish themselves in an occupation or profession.

May I mention again here that if we as professionals adopt the outer signs of the drug culture, thinking thereby to bridge the gap between ourselves and the young people with whom we are trying to work, we defeat the purpose completely. These young people are looking very hard for any kind of reinforcement of their goals, but they respect honesty and prefer people to be themselves. From my patients and student friends I have learned that when a professional adopts the outer appearance of those he is trying to help, he indicates his unsureness, his fear of the future, his fear or hidden envy of his patients. In so doing, he magnifies their confusion as well as his own.

Progress toward maturity may be hastened if the young person becomes involved in current social or political issues and finds a way of making himself effective. But if he can see no evidence that his concerns are being taken seriously, he may increase his efforts without regard to how they are being received, minimizing his effectiveness and delaying his growth in the ability to achieve results within a realistic framework. The task of the teacher or therapist is to help keep his dissatisfactions and idealism constructive, thus aiding both the maturation of the individual and the correction of society's shortcomings. René Dubos (1968, p. 5) has said, "as long as there are rebels in our midst, there is reason to hope that our societies can be saved," which he explains as meaning that their concern with increasing dehumanization may cause corrective action in time to reverse the trend.

Young people also avoid attaining maturity by not making up their minds about a career; by eschewing permanent emotional or sexual relationships; and by trying out various roles in a semiserious way, not yet motivated by any firm conviction of what they want to be. Take the opposite side of the coin first, the young man with moderate intelligence who graduates from high school and gets married at the age of eighteen. He gets a job in a local business establishment; his family begins to arrive; he becomes active in a church. He starts to get interested in the schools, the town government, and the local issues that are going to concern him and his family in the very near future. In effect, by the time he and his wife are twenty-five they have been adults for several years.

Another young man who graduates from high school at the same time goes to college and there encounters a much wider range of stimuli and activities. He hopes at first to be a teacher and gets interested in human behavior. Then he toys with medicine, theology, law, and similar professions. He becomes interested in psychology, economics, urban affairs, and business, possibly with receptive looks toward the sciences and the humanities. Meanwhile, he is discovering a number of different political and philosophical ideologies. He meets a great many young women who are interesting and attractive. In short, he finds so many possibilities, so many things to be done, that it is very difficult to know which one to pursue.

What gets him off dead center? First, pressure from home toward one goal or another is likely to be ineffective or even to have a negative effect. He may study books on vocational guidance or talk with counselors. He talks with friends. He is most often affected, however, by seeing someone in one of the fields which interest him whom he admires and whose life style is attractive to him. Sometimes he gets off dead center by trying out mini-careers of one kind or another. Very frequently a summer job gives him experiences that stimulate him to think constructively of the future.

While he is dealing with the uncertainties of career choice, he should be helped to realize that remaining comfortable in his temporary uncertainty is likely to make him more effective at a later period. Human beings with little ambition can mature quickly but do not grow very much after maturity. The person who is using his intellect most effectively requires many experiences to achieve the balance between action and restraint that is one of the characteristics of maturity.

Though my discussion of troubled adolescents might suggest that all adolescents are similar, this is fortunately not the case. Many people tend to judge the young by the behavior and attitudes shown by the more visible young people. The great majority, however, continue to work effectively, surpass what their elders did in the same age period, and go on to make new records of accomplishment in academic and extracurricular fields.

Knight (1970) investigated the positive motivational factors in 200 applicants to medical school, representing thirty-five states and ninety-nine colleges, most of whom had concentrated in the sciences during their premedical work. All were asked what they felt in their background had caused them to work directly toward their chosen field, rather than to become involved in modes of life that involve protest or withdrawal from ordinary society.

The majority of the students (70 percent) identified their family as the most important motivational factor in determining the direction of their lives. Ten percent of the others listed the family in second, third, or fourth place. Twenty-four percent identified their own personality make-up as the crucial factor and related it to a goal-directed orientation from within. Seventeen percent of the others put this factor in second or third place. Educational experiences in school were given first place by 3 percent, but second, third, or fourth place by 23 percent. Religious influences received first place in 2 percent, and second, third, or fourth place in 18 percent.

Prominent characteristics of family life that ranked high among these students were firmness, direction without dictation, rules that made sense, high expectations of all family members, and mutual trust and respect. They valued the fact that they had been taught how to make decisions, think on their own, and defend rationally their point of view. The family emphasized high standards of achievement within itself as well as responsibility to both oneself and to society. Hard work was portrayed as a supreme value, with the firm conviction that it is always rewarded in one way or another. The students appreciated the fact that their parents not only had their precepts but also set good examples.

The rebellion common among these young persons as well as others was generally verbal in character, and rarely took the form of acting out or destructive behavior, such as experimenting with drugs or quitting school. Their family life seemed to save them from severe identity crises, for they usually had a strong feeling of who they were and where they were going. Their parents were available when needed and gave generously of their time, a kind of giving that seemed to outweigh in importance every other. Values were very similar among parents in spite of vast differences in economic status. Nearly all the parents spent some time and resources in constructive service to the community. Most students felt that what they needed more than counselors were good role models to show them how men cope with the vast and impersonal chaos of existence.

My discussion thus far has been almost entirely within the context of experiences of the middle-class adolescent and young adult. For the less privileged groups, the needs for effective maturation are quite different. In some cases, there is the problem of too few rather than too many stimuli, but too few satisfying relationships. The child who has been brought up in a rural environment, with poor schools and limited contact with people and books, needs to receive the kind of encouragement that stimulates his intellectual curiosity without measuring his deficiencies in such a way as to stifle it. He needs time, and he needs to be urged on by those who concentrate on what he could be, rather than what he has been.

A similar difficulty faces the young black child who has lived his entire life in the ghetto, who may be extremely bright, but has had such poor schooling that he can express himself only in the dialect of the ghetto and is ill at ease in dealing with formal English. If he is held to the same standards as those youngsters of richer backgrounds, his development is likely to be stifled and he may be fatally discouraged. On the other hand, if his style of expression and writing is accepted as satisfactory, it is quite probable that he may never be able to make his way into activities that will give him real satisfaction or an adequate income.

Compromises will of necessity have to be made to encourage him for what he can do while simultaneously leading him to acquire those skills that make it possible for him to function effectively in school, business, industry, or whatever occupation he may enter. He may interpret the imposition of values from an alien culture in such a way that his ambition is destroyed. But if he comes in contact with young persons who have made the transition successfully, he may then develop the inner motivation to actually learn the new and (to other people) usual methods of communication.

Almost every field now has more than any one person can master. The emphasis must be on learning how to find one's way around in a field, learning how to learn, formulating the problem, and organizing the resources necessary to solve it. Education, rather than training, should be the goal. Sanford (1963, pp. 8–22) described education as revealing the potential in the individual, which if successful makes each individual different from any other, a liberating and differentiating influence. Training tends to process individuals so that they become more alike and do things in a prescribed way. He observed that training is in one sense the enemy of education and should be postponed as long as we can afford to do so.

One move that colleges might make to hasten maturation is to change the emphasis on attending for four years, starting right after high school and continuing without interruption. Students could instead be admitted to come any time within one or two years, as they wished, and to stay in college until they felt that they had exhausted the immediate possibilities. They would then be free to take time out for work, travel, or any activity that they felt desirable and to return to college when they thought they could do so with satisfaction. College could thus be a place for thought, meditation, a consideration of past and future, and it would offer opportunities for the person to make up his mind about the many questions that arise. Indeed, the most important questions are those he asks of himself.

Conclusions

In high schools and colleges we must find a way for involvement that serves to complete the basic tasks of adolescence. These include the development of independence to replace dependence; learning how to deal with authority; living with ambiguity; achieving a mature sexuality; developing inner security, prestige, and esteem; and forming standards and values to guide one's activities (Farnsworth, 1969).

As members of a society in distress, we will make little progress toward terminating adolescence at an appropriate point until we learn how (as one applicant to Harvard College said) to talk with our adolescents rather than at them. All too many parents and teachers still do not realize that contradiction, denial, moralizing, and prejudging are not effective ways of beginning conversations with their children or students. Somehow we in the homes, schools, and colleges must learn how to engage the energies and idealism of the young toward solving the vast social problems now so unsettling to all our people. When we learn how this can be done, our adolescents will once again set about their maturational tasks with zest, a sense of meaning and purpose, and a feeling that what they are doing is truly relevant to their own development and to society's problems.

REFERENCES

Deutsch, H. (1967). *Selected Problems of Adolescence.* New York: International Universities Press.

Dubos, R. (1968). *So Human an Animal.* New York: Scribner's.

Erikson, E. H. (1959). Late adolescence. In: *The Student and Mental Health: An International View,* ed. D. H. Funkenstein. New York: World Federation for Mental Health, pp. 66–106.

Farnsworth, D. L. (1969). *Psychiatry, Education, and the Young Adult.* Springfield, Ill.: Charles C Thomas.

————. (1970). Drugs: Do they produce open or closed minds? In: *What Everyone Needs to Know About Drugs.* Washington, D. C.: Books by U. S. News & World Report, pp. 214–229.

Gerzon, M. (1969). *The Whole World Is Watching: A Young Man Looks at Youth's Dissent.* New York: Viking Press.

Knight, J. A. (1970). Resisting the call of the cave. *Medical Insight,* 2(10):67–77.

Sanford, N. (1963). Factors related to the effectiveness of student interaction with the college social system. In: *Higher Education and Mental Health: Proceedings of a Conference,* ed. B. Barber and E. E. Hall. Gainesville: University of Florida Press.

Suchman, E. A. (1968). The "hang-loose" ethic and the spirit of drug use. *Journal of Health and Social Behavior,* 9(2):146–154.

4] ADOLESCENCE: SOME DIAGNOSTIC, PROGNOSTIC, AND DEVELOPMENTAL CONSIDERATIONS

HUMBERTO NAGERA

I think most observers of adolescents will probably agree that the usual and developmentally normal adolescent revolt has acquired, during recent times, forms of expression that are in many cases, to say the least, distressing and frequently totally maladaptive and destructive, both in the personal and the social sense. Naturally, the above does not apply to all adolescents. However, it seems to apply, in this country, to an ever-increasing number of them. Further, though some casualties have always resulted from the attempts at mastery of the developmental tasks of adolescence, it seems to me that the number of such casualties has been augmented significantly in our time. Even more, such failures as take place have a degree of malignancy that is alarming. Take, for example, drug addiction with its nefarious results, the many varieties of dropping out from college, society, and life, organized destruction and quasi warfare, and the increased numbers of suicide. Obviously, no sensible society can afford this waste of human talent and lives or tolerate the amount of individual suffering created by such maladaptive results. Furthermore, since the percentage of adolescents and children, in terms of our total population, has recently reached new heights and will continue to do so, there can be no question that we can ignore these problems much longer without concomitant disastrous results.

I consider it essential for the diagnosis of adolescent disturbances to differentiate five different types of phenomena that can lead to symptom formation and/or behavioral disorders.

First, there are those symptoms, character traits, or behavioral disorders that are leftovers of conflicts from earlier developmental phases

44

and that have led to psychopathology of various kinds, including the establishment of fixation points. As such, they have been manifested all the way through childhood and latency and continue to be apparent during the adolescent stage. Properly speaking, they are not derived from the adolescent revolt. Nevertheless, they will contaminate and to various degrees influence the form taken by it.

Second, symptoms derived from intrapsychic and typical developmental conflicts of the adolescent stage. These different types of manifestations have been widely described in the literature and we are well familiar with them. They are based on internal imbalances between different agencies of the mind, imbalances that are typical of this stage of development. As such they are, to some extent, independent of what is happening outside.

Third, symptoms and behavior derived from the impact that special environmental conditions have on the internal problems of the adolescent during this stage. They can be considered as developmental interferences, two types deserving consideration. The first can best be described as parental or familial developmental interferences, such as take place whenever either the parents or immediate family of the adolescent does or does not do something that is required for normal development. A sexually exhibitionistic or bodily seductive mother will, for example, strengthen the adolescent's incestuous fantasies, wishes, etc., and intensify concomitant guilt and defensive maneuvers required to cope with such heightened feelings. The second type can be described as social or environmental developmental interferences, by which is meant those social or environmental conditions that hinder the adolescent developmental processes. Since one set of factors, the environmental conditions, are constantly changing, the responses may change from generation to generation.

Fourth, some symptoms and behavior are derived not from individual intrapsychic conflicts, but from peer-group pressure. Here we are in the realm of group, not individual, psychology. There is no doubt that the impact of the peer group will be frequently modulated by the personality characteristics of the recipient. However, most of the phenomena observed here really belong and can only be explained in terms of group, not individual, psychology. It is probably on this basis that large numbers of adolescents are introduced to drugs. Among the young people exposed and introduced to the use of drugs in this manner, a certain number seem to become drug addicts, whereas a substantial number, after a few experiences, will stop taking them. It seems possible that those adolescents who are "hooked" after being exposed to drugs have reached this stage with significant personality weaknesses.

Such weak spots as important oral fixations acquired early in life may favor the establishment of a long-term and sometimes irreversible addiction.

Fifth, it seems to me that a substantial number of the behavior disorders and symptoms produced during this stage have a completely different mechanism. I believe that the conditions operating here are similar and somewhat akin to those observed and described for the traumatic neuroses. The conflict here is between opposite ego ideals and superego ideals. These contradictory ego and superego ideals may have been acquired simultaneously, or they may have been acquired during the course of many years: some in early infancy, some during the resolution of the oedipus complex, some in the latency period, and some during the adolescent stage. These conflicts, for some adolescents, seem insurmountable and lead to a kind of paralysis of the constructive and adaptive capacities of the ego. We are accustomed to thinking of traumatic neuroses in terms of the individual. What I have in mind now is a state of collective traumatic neuroses. Large numbers of adolescents are exposed simultaneously to the sudden realization that they carry within themselves contradictory and irreconcilable ego and superego ideals. This appears to overwhelm their egos, and, in some cases, since it has been acquired collectively, it leads to collective attempts at solution. I believe that such phenomena as dropping out from college and the organization of communities of hippies, flower children, and the like, may occasionally be the result of the mechanisms described. I believe too that this state of collective traumatic neuroses to which some adolescents succumb is a phenomenon that is on the increase and in good measure determined by present-day social conditions. I have in mind here, as well, the difficulties that many adolescents of the present generation find in maintaining certain forms of splits in their introjects, splits that seem to have been quite common for earlier generations. In the past, it was possible, for some reason, for these splits (in terms of introjects) to coexist without necessarily leading to conflict. Also, past generations were given ideals: Brotherhood among mankind, and equality among all men. They were told, too, that we were all children of God; they were told to behave well, not to abuse their neighbors or to exploit them; they were told not to discriminate; and so on. All such moral ideals have long been embodied in the teachings of religion, school, and furthermore, have long been an intrinsic part of the Constitution of this country. Nevertheless, though at a conscious level these were the explicit ego and superego ideals that were offered for assimilation, there was a second more subtle message concomitant with it that allowed many people to behave in any manner that suited their interests while consciously professing the just-mentioned high ideals. Such people are quite capable of discrimination and abuse without of necessity finding themselves in conflict. Thus, two sets of introjects were actually acquired, one, as it were, for external consumption and the other one for internal consumption. Yet, it seems as though adolescents today find it difficult to live with such a split. For some reason the second and most subtle message—"Do as you please as long as it suits your purposes"—becomes conflictive, and the clash between these two opposite introjects leads to unrest, shame, guilt, and anxiety. Not infrequently, it seems to reach such proportions that the ego becomes paralyzed and offers no constructive solutions. The final result is a maladaptive compromise for large numbers of adolescents.

The parallel drawn earlier with the traumatic neuroses is in need of some further elaboration. In a traumatic neurosis the ego becomes overwhelmed and is largely put out of action. It is not capable of producing an adaptive solution to the traumatic event. Further, it frequently remains incapable (to different degrees) of coping with ordinary events, owing to the intense amounts of unbound anxiety present. For as long as this is the case the ego remains disrupted. Two significant factors in the development of the ordinary traumatic neuroses are (1) the element of surprise, the lack of preparation on the ego side to cope with the suddenly overwhelming event, and (2) the dramatic, overwhelming nature of the event that becomes traumatic.

The mechanism that I have in mind for the adolescent is in some ways similar and in some ways different from the above factors. It lacks the sudden, dramatic nature of those traumatic neuroses that result from a car accident or natural catastrophe. The trauma is more subtle, continuous; it has retrospective elements, and its effect is cumulative, to use Masud Kahn's (1963) term. An example may clarify this. The present generations of adolescents have been exposed through the different communication media (press, radio, and especially television) to the effects of human aggression and destructiveness through war. Their exposure started many years ago with the Korean War. It continued afterward with exposure to the atrocities of the Vietnam War. It is likely that such prolonged exposure had some influence in the development of their ideals and in the process of identification. Anybody observing childrens' reactions to television news, showing cities being bombed and destroyed, mutilated bodies, wounded civilians (children and adults), and dead bodies, would have noticed their fear, horror, and simultaneous fascination. Not infrequently their sleep may be disrupted directly or through nightmares, or they become clinging. We have here the continuous exposition to frightening events, including the threat of nuclear war, and must wonder about the possible cumulative effects of it. Naturally, the younger the child the more confusing and frightening these observations are. Similarly, though the events are real and in some form or another assimilated, they have simultaneously, and for most children, an air of unreality, at least for some time. During later years, when better understanding and fuller awareness of what has been observed becomes possible, they have a retroactive traumatic effect, more especially so when such events become an actual narcissistic threat and are seen in reference to the self. The adolescent, more so the late adolescent, becomes suddenly aware that he is destined to be an actor in the tragedy. He knows he may be drafted, he may be asked to kill and destroy (without being motivated for it), and, furthermore, his own personal destruction becomes a serious consideration. The confluence of all these factors, the cumulative effects of the exposure, acquire now a retroactive traumatic effect that, for many, is of overwhelming proportions; hence the trauma. By the time this happens the adolescent belongs to a community of peers and much of his insight, awareness, and anxiety are brought about through group and peer interaction. Solutions to these basic anxieties are frequently brought about collectively too. Naturally, the solutions may be adaptive or maladaptive.

The diagnostician should always take the trouble to dissect from the symptomatic and behavioral picture offered by the adolescent those of the observed manifestations that correspond to one of the five groups outlined above. It is clear that they are not identical. It is clear, too, that there are significant diagnostic and prognostic differences and considerations to be taken into account. Similarly, from the therapeutic and corrective point of view, different measures will be required to deal with these different types of conflicts. Attempts at understanding what I can only describe as the adolescent revolution are, to say the least, daring and frequently bound to fail. Whatever approach one takes, whatever vantage point one decides to adopt, can only be a simplistic, pale, and partial reflection of what in reality is a multidimensional and extremely complex phenomenon. Nevertheless, I shall discuss a number of factors concerning changes in child-rearing practices, sociocultural changes and their possible influence in structure formation and development. Development is after all, to a good measure, a function of the interaction between internal and environmental forces.

In considering what factors may be influencing the clinical pictures presented by adolescents nowadays or what factors may have determined or influenced some of the present forms of the adolescent revolt, I think we can assume that the nature of the drives (instinctual impulses) has not changed nor have the tasks the adolescent must accomplish before reaching adulthood. Other factors must be held responsible for what we observe.

It may be that certain changes in present-day society and in child-rearing practices can account for some of the problems. Thus, for example, the role played by the family organization in development has been gradually undermined, distorted, and disrupted. Many factors are of influence here. Sometimes they act in isolation; at other times they are reinforced by a number of other variables. Consider, for example, the significant increases in the number of broken marriages and divorces. We are all familiar with the disruptive results that growing up under these conditions have for many children, as well as with the numerous complications introduced in the development of children under such circumstances. Naturally, the impact is variable according to the child's age and stage of development.

The affluence of present-day society may be a significant and subtle factor capable of influencing human development in negative directions. We seem to live more and more according to the pleasure principle. This is an attitude that seems to be influencing all sectors of our social organization, as such slogans as "Buy now, pay later" and "Enjoy your vacation today, worry about payments afterward" clearly illustrate. By a similar token we have become very tolerant about child rearing, perhaps excessively so. As a result, we not only encourage living according to the pleasure principle, but we may unintentionally interfere with the sound development of the reality principle, and as such with the ability to postpone gratification, the capacity to accept substitutes, the tolerance and handling of tension, the development of the capacity to establish controls, and so on. To give but one example, we need only think of the question of masturbation in children. We have turned around from earlier attitudes, taking a much more lenient and tolerant view of such practices in early childhood. Many people in the field, including child psychoanalysts, take the view that masturbation need not be discouraged. In fact, it is frequently encouraged (if only indirectly) as long as the child does it privately. We hear such things as "It is all right to play with yourself to get the nice feelings but we do not do that in front of other people, only when we are alone." It seems to me that we tend to forget that masturbation is a composite, consisting of the actual manipulation of the genitals (in different ways) and the fantasies that accompany it. It is the latter that are particularly troublesome in terms of psychopathological development. When we say to the child to go ahead and masturbate as long as he does it privately, we are obviously not taking into account the nature of the fantasies that accompany the masturbatory act. Since, for example, the masturbatory practices of the phal-

49

lic-oedipal child are frequently accompanied by highly conflictual incestuous fantasies one cannot but wonder how sound this attitude is.

Freud (1892–1899), as early as 1897, established a connection between addictions, of whatever type, including of course drug addiction and masturbation. He wrote to Fliess (letter 79): "It has dawned on me that masturbation is the one major habit, the 'primal addiction' and that it is only as a substitute and replacement for it that the other addictions —for alcohol, morphine, tobacco, etc.—come into existence." Years later, in a letter to Reik concerning "Dostoevsky and Parricide" (Freud, 1928), he established a connection between those neuroses accompanied by a severe sense of guilt and the struggles against masturbation. Further, he linked masturbation and addictions to gambling, such as that shown by Dostoevsky. In his view, excessive masturbation was damaging both biologically and psychologically (Freud, 1908). Thus he thought that excessive masturbation predisposes to various neuroses "which are conditional on an involution of sexual life to its infantile forms." He thought, too, that it vitiates the character in several ways through indulgence;

it teaches people to achieve important aims without taking trouble and by easy paths, instead of through an energetic exertion of force—that is, it follows the principle that *sexuality lays down the pattern* of behavior; secondly, in the fantasies that accompany satisfaction the sexual object is raised to a degree of excellence which is not easily found again in reality.

Later on in the same publication he stated that men given to masturbatory practices go into marriage with diminished sexual potency.

In his 1912 "Contributions to a Discussion of Masturbation," Freud objected to Stekel's position. The latter claimed that there was no real damage produced by masturbation, only prejudices associated with it. Freud argued: "We are therefore brought back once more from arguments to clinical observation, and we are warned by it not to strike out the heading 'Injurious Effects of Masturbation.' We are at all events confronted in the neuroses with cases in which masturbation has done damage."

Similarly, there has been a marked change in the attitude of many parents regarding the setting of limits and controls in respect to their children. Many parents have gone to extremes that seem to me highly questionable in their wisdom. Frequently, they have chosen to abandon many of their obligations and prerogatives as parents and, since they are hesitant in setting the necessary controls and limits, they finally pass much of the responsibility for this to the teenager. In my experience this happens frequently far too early and in areas where the young adolescent is neither capable nor ready to assume such responsibility. Such areas include the control of sexual and aggressive impulses. Teenagers are allowed to come and go freely without any supervision of hours or of individuals or groups with whom they mix. In so doing many are exposed to intolerable stresses and seductions of a sexual and aggressive character by the environment and peers. It is possible that those children reaching adolescence with important weak spots in their personality development—and given the further upset created by the typical adolescent developmental processes and revolt—are an easy prey to the negative influences of a sick environment and especially to their most disturbed peers. Some support, even some sheltering against such influences, seems to me essential. Furthermore, I consider it advisable for parents to continue to play the role of ego and superego auxiliaries when and where required. Naturally, such a parental stand may increase the clashes with the adolescent in revolt. Naturally, too, it should be done sensibly and with due awareness of legitimate adolescent developmental needs and rights. Briefly, in my view, parents should continue to fulfill their parental roles with the necessary modifications during their child's adolescent revolt; a total abandonment of the young adolescent to his internal and external struggles for the sake of peace is at best a disservice that may occasionally lead to undesirable consequences. Indifference is always worse than the legitimate concern that may be interpreted by the adolescent as an interference with his freedom and rights.

The parents' confusion regarding parental roles may be partly related to the fact that many of them were subjected to similar upbringings. One cannot avoid being concerned with the fate of the children of substantial numbers of the present adolescent generation. The capacity of this problem to become geometrically compounded seems to me a realistic risk and a serious consideration.

Other potential dangers concern the increasing demand, especially by activist feminists, for day-care services. Children are somewhat burdensome to some in the new generation of parents, perhaps especially to college and graduate students. Hence, there is a demand for day-care services. Unfortunately, many such services are bound to become dumping places for babies and toddlers with little consideration given to the best interests of the child and his future emotional health. Many young mothers are, of course, unaware of the potentially damaging effects of such practices to their childrens' emotional growth, but are led in that direction by the biased activist feminist who demands equal rights and opportunities for young student mothers on campus. Though I have no objection to equal opportunities and rights for men and women, I do have objections to the rights of the child being neglected, especially his right for the best chance to develop emotionally healthy. Such babies and toddlers as will grow up under inappropriate conditions in the new day-care services will in due time become adolescents. I fear that many of them will be damaged to the point of becoming irretrievable casualties during their own adolescent revolts. Clearly, serious thought and consideration will have to be given to the conflictual needs of different generations, parents and children, if we are to avoid major catastrophes in a few years.

It is important to refer also to the manipulative techniques our teenagers are exposed to. Because of this country's present-day affluence, adolescents have become an important billion-dollar market. They are bombarded by stimulation and seductive techniques of all kinds. Still worse, they have become an excellent target and market for drug peddlers. In a social sense we have an obligation to examine such problems and bring forth rational and desirable suggestions and solutions concerning some form of regulation of present-day assaults on the teenager. This situation is an example of collective, or social, developmental interferences. Forces in society have been organized to exploit this new market without any consideration as to the results that such techniques may produce in the child or the adolescent.

Our last example illustrates how a specific change in societal conditions may interfere with one of the fundamental developmental tasks of adolescence; that is, acquiring a final and definitive degree of independence from primary objects. Such a task is complicated by the revival and recathexis of oedipal figures during adolescence, a situation that is further hindered by the fact that at this point adolescents are under the impact of the full strength of their sexual drives because of their recently acquired sexual maturity. Yet, with the constantly increasing length of time required for education, we have extended significantly the adolescent dependence on parental support well into the years of young adulthood. It is common enough in a university setting to come across young men and women who not infrequently are married and have one or two children, own a car, and so on. But these young families and couples are supported by their parents. This naturally has many implications in terms of dependence-independence conflicts.

Consider, too, another fundamental task of adolescence, namely, the search for an identity, by which I mean not only a sexual identity but a professional identity as well, and even more important, a personal, individual identity.

All these developmental tasks and the inner turmoil that accompanies them are well known. To master such turmoil and such tasks has traditionally been, I believe, one of the developmental obligations of the adolescent. Since these are internal processes and are related to the instinctual nature of human beings there is no new factor here. Yet, these same tasks have to be accomplished against constantly changing environmental circumstances, changes that take place at such a rate of speed that adaptation to them is becoming extremely difficult. Since internal developmental processes take place in interaction with specific environmental circumstances and life experiences, it is conceivable that such constantly changing external conditions may at times favor and at times hinder emotional development.

In the sociocultural sense (up to relatively recently) superego development was for the most part and in the great majority of individuals based on the introjection of standards of behavior and ideals that were handed down from generation to generation with only slight modifications. These standards and ideals (imposed from the outside) were not so generally or widely questioned then as they are today. It thus seems to me that a fruitful line of inquiry and speculation may lie in asking: Why is there so much questioning today of our traditions, codes of behavior, moral standards, and ideals? Why was this not so to the same degree in earlier generations?

Developmentally and structurally, I think that there are two essential mechanisms involved in the process of developing superego structure and the ego and superego ideals. The first is based upon introjection of those standards, morals, behavior codes, and ideals that are passed down to children by their progenitors, teachers, and cultural environment. These are blind introjects, mostly accepted at face value and without questioning. In this way, part of our cultural heritage is passed on. I want to highlight that this was and still is a very efficient procedure leading to the acceptance and maintenance of the established order of values of any given society. I will add that, though efficient, it is a rather primitive mechanism since it does not involve much ego participation, questioning, or rational examination of what is being introjected. The rules are just accepted and adhered to because they come from the elders whose wisdom is not open to examination. On the contrary, whoever attempts to do so is, to say the least, discouraged, frequently reprimanded, and in extreme cases severely punished.

The second mechanism responsible for superego development and the establishment of ego ideals is totally different insofar as it is not based on introjection of standards imposed from outside or on identifications with special figures in the environment, but on introjects and ego ideals resulting from subjective introspection, inner awareness and convictions, knowledge, rational thinking processes, and empathy.

It seems feasible that especially during the last thirty years there has

53

been a substantial shift from the first type of ego and superego ideal formation to the second type. In my view several factors may have contributed to this change. Let us examine, for example, the area of education. Though higher education was the privilege of only a few (at least education beyond the elementary grades), in many countries it is nowadays available to all. Higher education obviously means that more individuals are in possession of more information, more knowledge, a better capacity to think, and enlightened understanding leading to a greater ability for many young human beings to judge for themselves the merits or lack of them of all types of problems and propositions. It certainly does not favor blind obedience to our traditions or to the opinions of our elders, but it rightly leads to examination and questioning of previously accepted premises. Further, this increased capacity for independent critical judgment, coupled with the fantastic developments in communication media, has created a situation where we are in possession of the facts (we not only hear about them but can indeed see the actual events) practically at the same time that the events are taking place. Naturally, the young are quite capable of drawing their own independent and frequently quite legitimate conclusions, thanks to their increased knowledge, information, and education. It is on this basis that many more people in the younger generations are constructing idiosyncratic ego and superego ideals.

Though all the above seems highly desirable and welcome, something is frequently missing as evidenced by occasionally undesirable results. They do not always lead, at least not initially, to constructive solutions, to more order and better relations among members of a community or among nations. On the contrary, they frequently misfire, leading to disruption, chaos, and destruction, as is attested to by the general unrest of this nation and especially the many instances of campus violence and destruction. Is this to be considered a transitory unbalance between the results of the earlier order and the new one, an unbalance that will correct itself at some point? Are we overlooking something fundamental to human nature in this new order of things? If so, what?

By the same token, the role played in the past by religion, the church, the police, and the courts as auxiliary external superegos is no longer so effective as it used to be and in many cases has totally broken down. Though some of this is desirable, in many cases, the person's ego and superego are unable to take over the controls previously exercised by these institutions. The police, for example, are ridiculed and not feared but provoked (frequently not without good reasons). The armies are no longer a source of strength and admiration but are despised. The courts do not inspire respect but contempt, again much of it justifiable.

54

The question is whether religion, the church, the police, the army, and the courts were any better or fairer in the past than they are at present. I think the answer is an emphatic no. If anything they were more abusive, conceited, oppressive, and discriminating than they are nowadays. These factors have not changed. Our attitudes to all these superego auxiliaries have changed. The question is again "Why?" Perhaps our increased education, information, and so on, make us (more certainly the younger generations) question their roles, their honesty, their inherent contradictions, and for some, their very validity. Yet, the lesser influence of such social organizations (with their behavior control functions) is not always supplemented by a concomitant increase in internal controls. This naturally tends to undermine to some degree the previously established social order without introducing corrective measures that, though allowing for desirable social and political changes, will keep the minimum of structure and order required for the survival of an organized society.

Conclusions

I have concentrated upon the negative or maladaptive aspects of the adolescent revolt as it affects large numbers of adolescents. The other side of this is represented by a similarly large number of adolescents who successfully sail through these turbulent waters. They emerge as mature adults quite capable of positive and constructive solutions. Our hope for the future lies at their door.

REFERENCES

Freud, S. (1892–1899). Extracts from the Fliess papers. Standard Edition, 1:177–280. London: Hogarth, 1966.
———. (1908). "Civilized" sexual morality and modern nervous illness. Standard Edition, 9:181–204. London: Hogarth, 1959.
———. (1912). Contributions to a discussion of masturbation. Standard Edition, 12:245–251. London: Hogarth, 1958.
———. (1928). Dostoevsky and parricide. Standard Edition, 21:183–196. London: Hogarth, 1961.
Kahn, M. M. R. (1963). The concept of cumulative trauma. *Psychoanalytic Study of the Child*, 18:286–306.

5] STUDIES OF PSYCHOPATHOLOGY IN ADOLESCENCE

MOSES LAUFER

The aim of this chapter is to describe some of the thinking that has gone into the setting up and development of our center [1] and to elaborate on some of the research we are undertaking and plan to undertake in the future. Though our day-to-day contact with adolescents who are experiencing a crisis in their present lives forms an important part of our work, this chapter will concentrate on the development of the center as a psychoanalytic organization interested in the study of psychological and social maladaption during adolescence. Throughout our work and thinking, our major focuses have been (1) the investigation of adolescence as a developmental stage through the study of some serious signs of psychopathology and (2) the establishment of more specific criteria for the assessment of signs of psychological crises in adolescence, so that it may be possible to prevent further pathology.

As an introduction, it seems relevant to describe some of the doubts we had at various points in our thinking, and what it was that made us decide on certain priorities. When we first planned the research work of the center, some of the staff seemed to be under considerable pressure (from newspaper reports, sociological studies, and even the concern of the government to do something about young people) to choose areas of study that would engender early results and remedies for the present state of the young generation. In our contact with people who might support our future work, there was a great deal of interest shown in some of our ideas. But, at the same time, suggestions were made that emphasized things that were very different from what we originally had in mind, suggestions such as sociological studies about people who break down when they reach a certain age, control groups to test and compare our findings, teams of professional people from different disciplines to undertake broad studies about different aspects of adolescent life, and so on. Two points emerged from these kinds of requests from people who were potentially interested in our research plans: (1) that it would take various external changes and perhaps more community services to alleviate the problems being presented by adolescents, and (2) that there was great hesitation on the part of those interested in our plans to participate in something that had to do with the unconscious and that also meant long-term financial support. Some people expressed a feeling of urgency and the belief that "doing something quickly" was more relevant to the present problems than some of the studies we were presenting.

However, these views avoided a much more basic fact, that is, that the psychological process of adolescence is itself inadequately understood. A glance at the literature soon confirms this. The most recent contributions repeat a few basic assumptions about the tasks of adolescence. We felt that the level and the quality of investigations being reported were not examining anything beyond our present knowledge, nor did we feel that such generalized umbrella concepts, which are used both in psychoanalytic thinking and in sociological studies, helped (for example, identity crisis, conflict of generations, role reversal) in any further understanding of the process of adolescence itself or of psychopathology.

It seems that some of the investigations at the study center could begin to tell us more about adolescence as a developmental stage, about the meaning of the transitory crises we observe in our contact with a large number of adolescents who come for help, about the ways of detecting the existence of pathology, and about the etiology and treatment of some psychopathological states that are usually associated with adolescence. These are the areas of uncertainty we constantly meet with in our work with adolescents and about which a great deal more needs to be known.

The main research project we are undertaking at present is entitled "Mental Breakdown in Adolescence." When the principal staff of the center [2] began planning this project, we felt that the data we would be collecting from our day-to-day contact with adolescents who came to the Brent Consultation Center for help could be used as a guide in highlighting the kinds of problems that needed more intensive study. Though the quantity of material we would obtain from our contact with a large number of adolescents each year would be enormous, we knew that a study of mental breakdown or, more specifically, of the process of adolescence itself, required data that was qualitatively different from what could be expected to be obtained from our walk-in service.

57

This first source of data will be described only in summary. The Brent Consultation Center is a walk-in service, where anybody can come in for help with any problem. Our interviewing staff consists of nine psychoanalysts and child psychotherapists who interview the adolescents who come in. The consultation center's short-term treatment program is carried out by a treatment panel consisting of the interviewing staff and twelve other psychoanalysts and child psychotherapists.[3] We also have a psychologist,[4] a doctor,[5] who is available for physical examinations of adolescents, and a lawyer,[6] who is available for legal advice to us or to adolescents. All the services offered are free.

We see about 200 adolescents each year through our walk-in service. There are fifteen adolescents, between sixteen and twenty-one years of age, in once- or twice-weekly treatment. The decision to limit our short-term treatment to the group between sixteen and twenty-one years of age is partly a practical one and partly a research one. Other community services offer treatment to children, that is, people up to the age of sixteen, and to adults, that is, people over the age of twenty-one. From a research view, we are assuming that adolescence as a developmental stage has ended by about the age of twenty-one. We are planning to collate and write up the data we obtain from our contact with this large group of adolescents who seek help, and from those of this group who then have short-term treatment. We hope to be able to describe family histories, reasons for seeking help, and the use made of short-term treatment by those adolescents who are experiencing a crisis in their lives.

The Studies of Psychopathology in Adolescence

I will return now to a description of the studies on mental breakdown that are being carried out at the Center for the Study of Adolescence.[7] In planning this project on mental breakdown in adolescence, we had as our guide the wish to collect data that would throw further light on the process of adolescence as a developmental stage. We decided on three main areas of investigation: (1) suicide attempts and self-mutilation in adolescence, (2) promiscuity in girls, (3) sudden academic or work failure.

The following observations and ideas directed us to these choices. One of the central areas in which a change must take place when the child moves into adolescence is in his relationship to his own body. Some of our experience from the treatment of disturbed adolescents

58

made us feel that a careful study of pathology revolving, to some extent, around the relationship to one's own body would make available crucial data. We felt that, whether or not the change in the relationship to one's own body seems to have a normal course or is determined by pathological factors does not alter the fact that, when physical genitality is reached, one's entire psychological structure becomes temporarily vulnerable. The manner in which one deals with stress coming from both internal and external sources will either enable one to progress on to adulthood or endanger one's entire future psychological development. The decision to kill oneself goes so completely contrary to what we assume to be the ego's efforts to perpetuate life that we begin with the assumption that a suicide attempt is always a sign of the presence of severe pathology. The conscious decision to kill oneself is something almost unknown in people before they reach adolescence; this fact, itself, made us feel that a study of a number of adolescents who have attempted suicide would tell us a great deal about adolescence and about the factors that, when they come together within the context of physical genitality, bring about an action so totally determined by a fantasy and, at the same time, that endangers the person's life in reality.

Similarly, we felt that promiscuity may also reflect a pathological relationship to one's own body, but that this kind of behavior does not actually endanger the person's life. Though both suicide attempts and promiscuity involve action rather than thought, the difference in these two forms of behavior is such that we felt that a study of a number of girls who are promiscuous might throw light on such factors as the level of object relationship reached by those girls who unconsciously feel compelled to use their bodies in this way, those factors in the preoedipal histories of these girls that contribute to a distorted development of secondary narcissism, the specific way in which the oedipal conflict has been experienced and resolved, and the relation between this kind of behavior and certain types of affective disorders that begin to show up much more clearly during adolescence.

The choice of the topic "sudden academic or work failure" was determined by similar factors, but with some additions. In discussion with a number of school principals, the point was made by them that there are a number of adolescents in their schools who suddenly seem to break down. This can be observed in the sudden deterioration of schoolwork. Everybody, including the adolescent himself, is often taken by surprise and there is no obvious explanation for this drastic change in school performance. We felt that a study of an area of functioning more related to performance in the outside world, that is, to the fulfillment of a task, would help us to explain more clearly which factors contribute to the breakdown's being isolated to a task, as compared to the breakdown's being more general, that is, one that seriously interferes with one's relationship to oneself and to the outside world (as we think is the case in suicide attempts and in promiscuity).

We are able to study, through our research, a total of twenty adolescents at any one time: eight in five-times weekly treatment who have attempted suicide; six in three-times weekly treatment who are promiscuous; six in three-times weekly treatment who have failed at school or at work.[8]

Though we consider our research to be in its preliminary stage, a number of theoretical and technical problems are beginning to be formulated and studied. What I am presenting now shows the direction of our thinking and the manner in which we intend to try to answer those questions now confronting us.

One of our first problems was to clarify which cases would better fit our research than others. In discussing, for purposes of assessment, adolescents who had attempted suicide, we found that we were being faced with material (in the diagnostic stage) we could not understand at all, which sometimes made it very difficult for us to know whether the adolescent was schizophrenic and whether he or she was treatable by psychoanalysis. One observation has interested and worried us: When seeing an adolescent soon after he has attempted suicide, it is often extremely difficult to assess the extent of pathology present; it is as though the traumatic experience of the suicide attempt temporarily does something to the ego's ability to defend against primary-process material. We have begun to ask whether those adolescents who attempt suicide have, in fact, experienced a temporary psychotic episode. We do not know. In initial interviews at the center (to decide on the suitability for treatment) we have often been struck how some of them seem to be in touch with thoughts or fantasies that, more usually, would take a long time to get to in treatment. Rita,[9] age eighteen, was seen at the center after she had been transferred to a psychiatric hospital from a general hospital. She had been admitted to the general hospital after having taken an overdose, which resulted in her being unconscious for three days. When I saw her for assessment, she was very quiet, almost ashamed of what she had done, and did not want to talk. She repeatedly stated that she was not sure if she wanted to live. Rita talked about her present and past life, but when it came to any discussion of her relationship with her mother, she withdrew and could not look at me. She was obsessed by a thought related to her mother's operation for hemorrhoids, and she could not talk about this because it related in some way to her preoccupation with her own anus. She repeatedly stated that there were certain things she could not talk about.

Independently of the meaning of this for Rita, we have noticed this attitude to "certain things" that could not be mentioned by a number of adolescents. One patient who attempted to kill herself by taking an overdose said, "I must die," with the "must" seeming to her to be related to the belief that there is no other way of getting away from one's terrible and guilt-ridden thoughts than through death. But death is, in fact, not a correct description of what some adolescents want. It is rather a removal of consciousness. The extent to which death is denied as a reality by those adolescents we are studying is noteworthy. Their attitude to their suicide attempt does not necessarily mean killing themselves. We do not as yet know what the underlying fantasies are that are related to the attack on one's own body and the attack on the internalized object, but we do seem to continue to meet this denial of death as well as the belief in the omnipotence of the action of attacking one's body.

In a recent paper (Laufer, 1968), I referred to a number of patients who had attempted suicide, and I said then that "a breakdown that manifests itself in the form of suicide or attempted suicide is an aggressive attack on the internalized parent and at the same time is an attack on the person's own body, which at that moment is experienced as separate from the rest of oneself and as not belonging to oneself. For some of these adolescents, dying means killing the body but not necessarily killing the mind." We are discovering from our study of adolescents who have attempted suicide that there may be a qualitative difference both in the regression that takes place and in the fantasy that is lived out when compared to what has been learned from the study of adults who attempt suicide. Some explanations about adult suicidal attempts do not seem to explain completely the material we are collecting from the adolescents we are studying at the center. It is as though something needs to be added to the available explanations to make sense of the clinical material.

Another observation interested us, even though we do not as yet know what this really means to the adolescent. In describing the suicide attempt, some of the adolescents seem unconsciously to view it as something special, as something that temporarily gives them the simultaneous feeling of being both very vulnerable and all-powerful. It is as though the action itself has created for them a completely new kind of internal reality in their relationships to their own bodies. However, when we, in assessment, or in treatment, convey to them that the suicide attempt is a sign of illness or severe disturbance, they often refuse to accept this and react as if they have been attacked by us. They had never thought that their behavior represented anything other than a wish to die; psychological disturbance had never been considered at all, and the way we view their actions has nothing to do with the way they view their actions. They thought we were making a lot about very little. They felt quite convinced that it was just a passing thing, and they fought very hard in the diagnostic interviews to hold on to the explanation that this had happened because of a specific event, for example, rejection by a boyfriend, or feeling a failure after having been out with a girl. But, at the same time, they are very relieved that we are not frightened by them or by what they can do.

This brings me to an observation that may have bearing on our technique in the treatment of seriously disturbed adolescents. When we first considered undertaking the study and treatment of a number of adolescents who had attempted suicide, the hesitation expressed by some of the staff about this project was not owing to the seriousness of the pathology of some of the adolescents but to the anxiety on the part of some of us at having such adolescents in treatment in the first place. There was a suggestion that we first begin on other projects and that we work our way toward the project on suicide attempts. But we went ahead. That we meet each week to discuss the material is important, both for treatment and for research. Those analysts who participate in this project have often stated that the regular discussions of the treatment material enables them to go on treating such vulnerable adolescents. But, important in the treatment is the need for the analyst to accept the fact that the treatment of such disturbed adolescents contains the possibility that the patient may, in fact, kill himself. Unless the analyst is able to accept this danger as part of the treatment, he is totally unable to treat the adolescent. The analyst cannot take the risk of interpreting certain content unless he feels sure in himself that he is doing what is right. At the same time, the adolescents seem to unconsciously detect that the analyst is either confident or frightened, and the frightened analyst, especially with adolescents who have tried to kill themselves, may provoke further action.

I want to go back to a point I made about Rita, that is, about the denial of how close she herself was to death. She at first talked about her own experience as though it was not so serious as we made it out to be. She also talked of death as though it did not concern her very much, as though she did not care whether or not she died. But when another seriously ill adolescent was admitted to the ward where Rita was, she became very upset when she observed how close this other adolescent was to death. Rita felt devastated by this, and in her sessions she could barely talk about it in any organized manner. When the other adolescent subsequently died, Rita was completely bewildered and terrified. She also observed another adolescent who could have died from her suicide attempt. While in the hospital she was very concerned about the suffering of some of these other adolescents, and she felt awful when they talked of dying. But, at the same time, she was very frightened by observing the reality that people actually do die from suicide attempts. It was as if she could not believe that she, herself, had been in a similar situation.

Those adolescents who have attempted suicide are, in a manner of speaking, in a class by themselves. That action rather than thought is considered appropriate for at least part of adolescence does not, in any way, explain what it is that enables these adolescents to choose consciously to attack their own bodies in this way and then to actually carry it out. Other adolescents we are studying use their bodies in a different way, where the action does not in any way endanger their lives. I am comparing suicide attempts either dynamically or genetically with this other form of behavior, namely, promiscuity. It is of interest that some of these promiscuous girls consider killing their bodies but never get to the point of doing it. This group of patients has not necessarily sought help because of promiscuity. Some have come because of their promiscuity, but there are others whose presenting crisis varies a great deal: trouble at home, trouble with a boyfriend, depression, fear of abnormality. It is only when we find out more about the person's whole life, either in early interviews or in treatment, that it becomes clear that one of the central problems and worries is that they have intercourse indiscriminately. But it takes even more time to discover that some of these girls are dominated by a feeling of being compelled to have intercourse. Here, too, descriptions vary a great deal: one girl may say that she does not mind having intercourse with any boy, another will describe how she feels seduced by men, a third will say that she cannot say no, and so on. It is well known that promiscuity reflects various things: worry about being abnormal, severe depression, concern about being frigid, fear of being alone, hatred of men, extreme penis envy. Still, we meet so many adolescents who fit these descriptions, but whose actual behavior is not promiscuous. There must be something more specific to explain the choice of sexual intercourse early in adolescence. The element of being compelled may be a central lead to understanding the meaning of this form of behavior.

I do not want to give the impression that we are looking for one overall explanation to account for this behavior. However, it is my impression that, in suicide attempts, there is a central fantasy lived out in the attack on the body, whereas in promiscuity (though a fantasy is certainly operative) there is something quite different going on. It is of interest to us that, in at least three of the girls being studied for promiscuity, the analysts or therapists have been concerned at one time or another during treatment about the possibility of suicide. The attitude of Joan,[10] age eighteen, toward her promiscuity shows an enormous hatred of, and contempt for men, but at the same time she feels unable to refuse any man. Her mood swings are of great concern to the therapist, varying from feeling pleased with herself to despair and feeling worthless. Lois,[11] age eighteen, has been promiscuous for some time now. She has had intercourse with many men, varying in age from seventeen or eighteen to men in their thirties. She had poliomyelitis when she was age six, which included a paralysis of the throat. Her fears of dying, and the denial of the reality of death, seem to be crucial. In addition, she has a father who considers himself a Don Juan and who constantly creates situations where he and Lois can feel close to each other, to the exclusion of the mother. Helen,[12] age eighteen, had a serious kidney infection as a child which resulted in many physical examinations, insertions of tubes into her body, and an underlying fear (shared by her parents) that she was, or would be, damaged in some way. She is a very sad girl, who often attends her sessions looking and behaving in a disorganized way. In addition to her earlier promiscuity, we learned that she is unable to travel alone (she comes to her sessions with her boyfriend) and that her mother is a seriously ill woman who recently had to be admitted to a mental hospital for a short time.

I am aware of the danger of making generalizations from insufficient material, but one observation that may prove important is that the girls included in our study "Promiscuity in Girls" have certain crucial real events in their lives that have seriously interfered with normal development. We do not know as yet whether a fantasy is fed by real events or whether real events distort what might have been an age-appropriate and normal fantasy. It may be that this is an important difference between these adolescents and those who have attempted suicide. With the latter it seems that, whatever part real events play in their memories of their earlier lives, there is an overpowering fantasy that affects their present lives in a special way.

The adolescents studied under "sudden academic or work failure" show a conglomeration of behavior that still puzzles us. For example, Mary,[13] age seventeen, sought help after having seen the social worker at the local hospital. We later learned that her doctor sent her to the hospital after a suicidal attempt. Mary left school (where she was doing very well) against her teacher's recommendation and then stopped attending technical college after six weeks. She took a job, and again left. After she left her job she took an overdose. She considers her father to be a total failure (he speaks English poorly) and also feels that her mother never grew up. The family lives with the maternal grandparents, and the head of the household is the maternal grandfather, a man whom Mary hates. Mary does not want to be like all the other failures in her family. At the same time she cannot cope with either school or work.

The treatment contains a great deal of material about Mary's feelings of worthlessness, of her hatred of herself, and of her shame of her family. Her homosexual fantasies terrify and disorganize her, and she is still not able to discuss them. She has, in fact, been very promiscuous since the age of fifteen. Her recent failure at school and at work is part of a much wider psychopathology affecting her relations to contemporaries, her achievements, and her attitudes to her body.

Another example, Bob,[14] age seventeen, a very intelligent young man, suddenly failed at school just over a year ago. He had ideas about going on for a higher education, but he suddenly became severely depressed, thought seriously of suicide, and his work dropped so badly that his principal had to tell him that, unless there were some improvement the next term, Bob would have to be asked to leave. He is constantly at war with his father, a disturbed and unhappy man who fights Bob as though he, the father, were an adolescent. Though the failure at school could be viewed as an attack on the oedipal father (and this approach in treatment has, in fact, brought about marked improvement in his schoolwork), we do not, as yet, know why it came about at this point in Bob's life.

The adolescents in short-term treatment at the Brent Consultation Center do not fit into any one of the three existing research groups. The only criterion to make short-term help available for those adolescents who live in the Borough of Brent is that we assess that a period of psychotherapy would be of help to them. It does not matter what the presenting problem is. We have recently decided to limit this short-term treatment to about one year, giving the therapist some leeway. This decision is mainly a practical one, in that our treatment then enables us to offer help to a larger number of adolescents, but at the same time it demands that the interviewer and therapist be specific about the aims of treatment. We now feel less guilty about this limit than when we first considered applying it. We have begun to see that, in many of those cases where treatment is short term, our main emphasis should be helping in the present and not expecting structural alteration. Our task with adolescents in once- or twice-weekly treatment is to facilitate any present efforts by the adolescent to meet the age-appropriate tasks. An example is that of a young man who blushes; his first reaction is to avoid girls. It may require more treatment than we are able to furnish at this moment to understand and remove the cause of his blushing. But we can, through short-term treatment, help him in his social relationships. We meet many adolescents who may show signs of disturbance that are so serious that they are really beyond the present scope of our treatment program at the Brent Consultation Center. But some seem to be able to benefit. We have found that a number of adolescents in once- or twice-weekly treatment have made quite remarkable use of it. Some have been helped to leave home; some have been helped to stay at school; some have been able, for the first time, to see the extent of their own pathology and to accept the need for more intensive help. (We are aware that, from a research point of view, the kind of data we obtain from the once- and twice-weekly treatment cannot supply us with data to study mental breakdown in adolescence. For this, we must continue to depend on material from intensive treatment.)

Method of Collecting and Organizing the Data

The data obtained from all the adolescents are categorized for future study. We have drawn up a research form that combines ordinary details about the adolescent's life with metapsychological information drawn from the adolescence profile (Laufer, 1965). Because of our method of interviewing, much of the information is not standardized. We do not collect information from the adolescent in a formal way, but obtain only information that seems to be appropriate in the interview. We are able to obtain a great deal of information about the presenting problem, education, family history, previous pathology, and so on. For those who are included in the treatment or research program, the interviewer records in detail what he considers to be the diagnosis, that is, whether the problem or diagnosis is related to transitory disturbance, simple neurotic disturbance, severe neurotic disturbance, or psychosis. We now have an enormous amount of information recorded in a way that can be studied and compared, and we are now in the process of assessing the first three years' work of the walk-in service.[15]

Members of the treatment panel write regular weekly or fortnightly reports on all the adolescents treated and/or studied through our study center and our walk-in service. Each research topic is organized into a research group, and each analyst or therapist in that study group receives the reports on the treatment of all those adolescents included in

66

any one study. This enables every analyst in any one group to follow the treatment of all the adolescents who are included in that study. It is mainly these detailed treatment reports that enable us to study various aspects of mental breakdown in adolescence.

Discussion

I have already touched on a number of observations that have interested us and that will need further study if we are to understand the process of adolescence itself. For example, we are discovering that many adolescents who present problems that seem to be of a transitory or of a simple neurotic nature turn out to be much more disturbed. In contrast, there are a number of adolescents who seem to be seriously disturbed, but their treatment reveals this is not true. Some of the material we are collecting in assessment interviews, initial and treatment interviews, should help refine our criteria for assessment.

Much of the treatment material focuses upon the adolescent's reaction to his or her physically mature body. Some of the girls had sexual intercourse very early in adolescence. This raises many questions. We now think that sexual intercourse in early adolescence should be viewed cautiously and should be considered a possible sign of disturbance. But, in fact, is it so? And, if it is so, why? The answer to this question would help us understand in metapsychological terms, the development of female sexuality and the difference between intercourse in early adolescence and intercourse in middle or late adolescence.

The presence or absence of masturbation during adolescence is another important observation. We assume that masturbation in the male adolescent fulfills an essential function which is quite different from the function it serves for the female adolescent. This observation seems confirmed from the treatment of adolescents. But, more basically, what is the function of masturbation in adolescence? When should it be viewed as normal? When is it a sign of impending pathology? When is it a sign of existing pathology? When is it a sign of the onset of a psychotic episode? The answers to these questions would enable us to be clearer about our diagnostic assessments, and we would be much more able to know early when to intervene and possibly prevent further pathology.

Some adolescents have dramatic family histories: parental illness, family breakup, illegitimate siblings, family secrets, and so on. Some who come from families with dramatic episodes seem to do well; others

67

seem convinced that their own pathology is due to the episode. What engenders these wide differences of outcome? When should these episodes be taken seriously, and when should they be dismissed as incidental? When do such episodes affect psychological development in adolescence, and when are they incidental to the person's internal life? In our discussions, it is interesting to see how many of us explain a great deal by referring to an episode, whereas other members of the staff place little importance on them. Though this kind of reasoning may reflect a staff member's own bias, it also reflects the present state of our knowledge about adolescence. We are finding that, though it is legitimate to use findings that come from the psychoanalytic study of children and adults to help us understand adolescence, this is not sufficient. There may be certain internal factors that are specific to adolescence and that may be of a different quality and a different nature than what we observe in the child or in the adult.

When we first started to treat adolescents at the center, we soon became aware that we had very little experience in the treatment of adolescents aged sixteen or seventeen to twenty. Our experiences were related either to the treatment of the young adult or to the young adolescent, and we were not quite sure how to approach the adolescent of seventeen or older. Though we use principles related to classical technique, we have to be aware of the importance of the immediate situation and be able to offer help. Many of our patients are in the midst of a serious crisis which often includes the need to make decisions affecting their future education or work. Sometimes, this type of concern (or, perhaps, what seems to be overconcern) can mistakenly be seen as a resistance, and the significance of the immediate crisis is lost. It has taken some of us a while to feel more comfortable using explanation, in active clarification of aims and limitations of treatment, and, sometimes, in actually interfering in the day-to-day lives of some adolescents who may be in danger. For example, some adolescents have had to be admitted to hospitals. In one case, the analyst insisted that his patient leave home because of the mother's mental illness, which was perceived as dangerous to the patient by the therapist. Now, we are able to do these things more readily and effectively. Still, classical analytic method is the basis of our technique; however, once we grasp the meaning of the adolescent's immediate situation and how he may be crippled by a crisis, we feel much more confident doing things that would be bad technique with young adults.

It is of interest, too, that we have had a remarkably small number of adolescents who have broken off their treatment. I would like to think that some of this is the result of good assessment and good technique.

This is certainly part of the explanation. But we must also point to the adolescent's ability to observe himself and to recognize that he is in need of help. Those adolescents who come, or are sent, to the center, do so on their own. They are not expected to attend. If they do not come, we usually write and invite them to come. But, beyond this effort, the adolescent takes the initiative in making arrangements for treatment. Once the adolescent and the interviewer have agreed upon the need for some type of help, whether nonintensive or intensive treatment, we try to start treatment immediately. We are not yet certain what the relation is of these various factors—assessment, self-observation, arrangements mainly by the adolescent, little waiting until treatment begins—to the fact that the large majority of those who start treatment continue with it. It says something about the adolescent's reaction to a crisis and the meaning of help offered at the right time and in the right way. We hope we will be able to say more about these topics as our experience accumulates.

NOTES

1. Center for the Study of Adolescence and the Brent Consultation Center, London, England. The center is supported by the Grant Foundation Inc., New York.
2. Dr. M. H. Friedman, Dr. M. Glasser, Dr. M. Laufer, Mrs. M. E. Laufer, and Dr. M. Wohl. Honorary Research Advisor: Anna Freud, C.B.E., LL.D., Sc.D.
3. Consisting of those named in note 2, and Dr. H. Bacal, Mrs. M. Burgner, Miss R. Edgcumbe, Dr. A. Hayman, Dr. T. Hillaby, Dr. A. Holder, Dr. S. Holmes, Mrs. A. Hurry, Mrs. M. Kawenoka, Dr. B. MacCarthy, Mrs. B. Mehra, Dr. K. Mehra, Dr. N. Pines, Dr. H. Stewart, Dr. S. Tischler, and Dr. R. Tyson.
4. Mr. C. Graham.
5. Dr. N. C. Mond.
6. Mr. A. Lewison.
7. The staff and treatment panel of the walk-in service are also responsible for organizing and carrying out the research of the study center.
8. There are also the fifteen adolescents in once- or twice-weekly treatment through the Brent Consultation Center (the walk-in service for adolescents).
9. In psychoanalytic treatment with Mrs. M. E. Laufer.
10. In treatment with Dr. A. Holder.
11. In treatment with Dr. N. Pines.
12. In treatment with Mrs. B. Mehra.
13. In treatment with Dr. B. MacCarthy.
14. In treatment with Mrs. B. Mehra.
15. In cooperation with the Department of Health and Social Security.

REFERENCES

Laufer, M. (1965). Assessment of adolescent disturbances: The application of Anna Freud's diagnostic profile. *Psychoanalytic Study of the Child,* 20:99–123.
———. (1968). The body image, the function of masturbation, and adolescence problems of the ownership of the body. *Psychoanalytic Study of the Child,* 23:114–137.

6] THE DRUG-DEPENDENT

ADOLESCENT

DEREK H. MILLER

It is extremely difficult to assess the extent of the problem of drug abuse, particularly as adolescents themselves are not reliable witnesses. In schools, pupils may exaggerate the incidence of drug-taking, and those who take drugs develop the idea that they must stick together and not tell tales. Studies of incidence are, however, possible with reliable cross-checking as to validity (Robins and Murphy, 1967). The conviction figures for drug offenses and clinical evidence both suggest that drug-taking among adolescents of all ages is increasing. However, the nature of this activity varies from experimentation to regular and progressive drug use, to dependence, and, in some cases, to physical addiction.

Drug experimentation need not be considered evidence of psychopathology. It can be defined as the use of a drug (which may be taken to the point of intoxication) to discover its psychological, physical, and social effects. Even though the experience may be perceived as gratifying, intoxication, with its consequent ego regression and conscious awareness of lack of control, is felt by adolescents as psychologically threatening. In order to restore a feeling of self-mastery and a sense of control of ego functions, drug experimentation is likely to be repeated four or five times after an actual intoxication experience.

Though drug experimentation in itself may not be pathological, drug responses are likely to be unpredictable and idiosyncratic. In particular, intoxicant effects related to the use of hallucinogens may be felt as intensely threatening psychologically and ego disintegrating.

Both early and midadolescent drug experimentation are vulnerable to a "halo" effect; the more drugs are talked about and taught about, the more likely adolescents are to use them. Identification with a valued nondrug-using adult is more likely to lead to abstinence than antidrug propaganda or classroom teaching.

Regular drug usage is the more or less regular use of drugs because of their sedative and/or intoxicant effect. In this category is included the regular use of tobacco, alcohol, marijuana, and any hallucinogenic or mood-changing drug, whatever its frequency. The regular user may be psychologically dependent on a drug or may intermittently crave its use to relieve tension. The fact that an individual may be able to withdraw from a drug with no apparent ill effect does not mean that its use is other than pathological.

Progressive drug usage implies a variation of drug use from "softer" to "harder" drugs, for example, cigarettes to alcohol and marijuana, or in some social groups to glue-sniffing. A variety of synthetic or natural hallucinogens, stimulants, and sedatives, and ultimately heroin, other opium derivatives, or cocaine may be taken. Adolescents who take cocktail mixtures of drugs in an effort to avoid the toxic effects or addictive qualities of any one of them are progressive drug users. Commonly, but not necessarily, such individuals ultimately change from taking drugs by mouth or sniffing them, to their injection, either intravenously or subcutaneously. Any chronic drug abuse, either regular or progressive, that may lead to drug dependence can best be understood as an unconsciously sought ego regression (Weider and Kaplan, 1969).

The terminology of drug abuse is confused. The term "addiction" has been defined as a "chronic intoxication produced by the repeated consumption of a drug." Its characteristics are said to include a compulsion to continue taking a drug, a tendency to increase the dose, and psychological and sometimes physical dependency on its effects. "Habituation" is said to differ from "addiction" in that it creates a desire but not a compulsion to continue taking a drug because of the increased sense of well-being it may produce.

Obviously there is no clear distinction between the meanings of "habituation" and "addiction," and in 1965 the World Health Organization recommended the term "drug dependence" be substituted for both. Nevertheless, in 1966 the U.N. Commission on Narcotic Drugs decided to keep the old definitions (Office of Health Economics, 1969).

Some unsuccessful attempts have been made to equate various types of pharmacological effects of drugs with different levels of ego regression. Mahler (1968) equated the results of opium-taking with the psychic state common in the characteristic behavior pattern of the second half of the first year of life. However, it is probably impossible to draw hard and fast lines as to what the psychic effect of any one drug might be, particularly as the psychological and toxicological effects often seem idiosyncratic.

Adolescents are particularly likely to become dependent on drugs. When they do, they tend to show a significant degree of total personality involvement with drugs and the people who use them. They crave the relief of psychic tension that the drug gives them, or they seek a specific psychological sensation (Chein *et al.*, 1964). When they take drugs, adolescents seem to be seeking satiation and contentment in the same way a baby demands his bottle. When they have taken a drug their expression resembles that of babies who have just been fed. The concept of the drug-dependent adolescent who is intolerant of frustration and is unable to make affectionate and meaningful object relationships would appear to be valid (Hartmann, 1969).

Early Adolescent Drug-Taking

The psychic turbulence of puberty, which lasts for three or four years, is a time at which early adolescents in Western culture experiment with mood-changing drugs. In particular, they use those drugs about which the adult world has mixed feelings, drugs that adults use to induce more or less ego regression. Though the age norms are unsatisfactory, children between the ages of eleven and thirteen typically experiment with alcohol and tobacco.

Smoking and drinking are both related to peer-group expectations, but alcohol, other than wine, is usually rejected because the early adolescent does not like the taste of beer or spirits. Wines, particularly those with a sweet, fruity flavor, are often enjoyed but are rarely abused by adolescents. There are many reasons for this. Wine drinking is surrounded by many cultural controls. It may be taken as part of a family, religious, or mealtime ritual. Thus, wine-taking is surrounded with strong external ego controls provided both by parents and society. It is therefore rarely used by adolescents as part of a rebellious acting out of hostile wishes toward their parents. Furthermore, the unpleasant hangover associated with excessive intake spoils it as an unconsciously sought ego regression.

On the other hand, though its taste may not be initially enjoyed, tobacco may be abused more or less regularly from early adolescence onward. As is much drug-taking, cigarette smoking is related to parental behavior. Parental attitudes to cigarette use are similar to those toward sexuality: It is said to be acceptable only as adult behavior. Furthermore, its equation with danger in the future allows adolescents to rein-force their own sense of immortality with what has come to be felt as death-defying behavior. Perhaps not surprisingly, both early adolescent boys and girls with mothers who smoke are more likely to become de-pendent on cigarettes than those who have nonsmoking parents (Emery *et al.*, 1967). Similarly, adolescents with older siblings who smoke are more likely to use cigarettes during early adolescence than others.

Early adolescent drug experimentation is associated with early ado-lescent experimentation with sexuality. Just as the pubertal child deals with the reawakening of sexual impulses by re-experimentation with the masturbatory activity of infancy and childhood (Miller, 1969), so drug-taking is associated with the revival of the omnipotent dependent wishes of infants. Any drug about which adults have mixed feelings, which in-duces ego regression, and which is widely and easily available, is likely to be tried by early adolescents. During recent years the ambivalent feelings felt by adults and late adolescents about tobacco and alcohol have become associated with marijuana usage. As a result, in some parts of the world, marijuana is added to the drugs used in junior high schools.

Early adolescents who do not experiment with smoking, drinking, or other drugs do not necessarily have particularly strong ego controls. On the contrary, in the assessment of the place of drug-taking in the psy-chopathology of early adolescents, failure to experiment with the drugs at all may be understood in the same way as the failure to re-experi-ment with infantile sexuality. However, before significance is ascribed to the fact that an adolescent cannot allow any self-experimentation that induces ego regression, cultural and social class attitudes need to be taken into account. A powerful parental external superego figure may negate the use of drugs; some early adolescents may not experiment with drugs because though intensely dependent on a peer group, the lat-ter may exert a pressure that negates the use of drugs. The ego ideal of adolescents may forbid experimentation with intoxicants; some individ-uals do not try drugs because of religious convictions, either their own, those of parents, or those of other important adults with whom they have meaningful emotional contacts. Those religious groups that cannot allow oral regression may force individuals within them to attempt to resolve conflicts about this with various types of reaction formation, for example, being excessively puritanical.

Some cultural and religious groups cannot allow regressive sexual ac-tivity. When adolescents are forbidden to experiment with infantile types of sexuality, such as masturbation, many solutions are sought. The interdiction may be ignored; repression may be intense with consequent

73

affective isolation; or in some conflict is solved with early sexual inter-course. Masturbation is then replaced by an apparent heterosexuality, which is, in reality, masturbatory in nature. A girl may become the ve-hicle for a boy's demonstrating to himself his capacity to control his own ego regression and also his feelings of sexual excitement. In other adolescents a failure to masturbate may be associated with late develop-ment into puberty.

Middle-Stage Adolescent Drug-Taking

After the flurry of experimentation early in the pubertal period, toward the end of the first year of midadolescence, the period of identification and self-realization, there is a new episode of drug re-experimentation (Miller, 1969). This is more related to community and peer-group atti-tudes toward drugs and expectation of drug use than is early adolescent experimentation. During early adolescence, drug experimentation can be an initiation rite to the adolescent group; the midadolescent who be-comes a regular user of intoxicants may do this to reinforce a tenuous sense of personal identity by continuing intense peer-group involve-ment. Because of this need, such middle-stage young people are more likely to seek out new drugs. The drug used may depend on the current peer-group fashionable norm. It is less significantly related to parental behavior and attitudes than is the case in puberty, but is more signifi-cantly related to the behavior of older adolescents. Early adolescent drug-taking tends to be an imitation of adult norms; midadolescents who abuse drugs act in defiance of these norms. Socioculturally, drugs may be used as part of a phony war against adults. Adolescents who group together to use drugs often appear to believe that they are a group of nonconformists fighting a corrupt and conformist adult society that wishes to attack them. It is, however, ironic that the adolescent who is least sure of his capacity to be independent is most likely to take drugs and become dependent on them.

The difference between the use of alcohol and marijuana appears to be that adolescents often take alcohol not to get drunk but to partici-pate in what they see to be an acceptable adult ritual. They may also like the taste. Marijuana is rarely used in low dosage when its intoxi-cant effect is mild, unless joints are handed around at pop concerts and the like. It commonly is used in greater dosage for its intoxicant effects, though some adolescents attempt to titrate the degree of intoxication they may experience (Hollister, 1968). Those adolescents who tried alcohol and cigarettes at the beginning of puberty and then stopped may become regular users of either or both at midadolescence. Those young people who were regular users of cigarettes during early adolescence may now become intensely dependent on them.

The wish for the experience of drug intoxication in midadolescence is not necessarily pathological. It may represent an individual's wish to try out new feelings of self-control. This is not unlike one of the reasons for the midadolescent's active seeking of heterosexual relationships, a wish to demonstrate to oneself a newly acquired potency.

Adolescent Drug Use

The type of drugs used by adolescents depends on their personal history of drug-taking. Early adolescents who become regular users of marijuana seem more likely during midadolescence, or sooner, to try other hallucinogenics. For example, midadolescents who use LSD seem to have a history of more than a previous experimental use of marijuana. The drug used also varies from country to country, within institutions in any given society, and in different social groups. Drug abuse appears to vary with fashion. Amphetamine derivatives may be preferred at one time and in one culture; at another hallucinogens appear to be the drugs of choice. Early adolescents use glue and paint thinners for their intoxicant effect in parts of the United States and Continental Europe. In Britain their use is rare except in penal institutions. Marijuana was used in Sweden many years before it was used in its neighbor Finland. Its use is common among students in Britain and in the United States and among deprived and black adolescents in the ghettos of American cities. The British working class used amphetamines for years and only more recently began to use hashish.

STIMULANTS

Stimulant pills used by British working-class youth have special names, such as "black bombers" (Durophet), "purple hearts" (Dexamyl). In the United States, stimulant pills are "bennies," "dex," "crystals," "dominoes," "minstrels," "purple hearts"; Dexamyl is known as "Christmas trees." In the United States, all stimulants carry the generic name of "speed." In Britain, this name is reserved for Methedrine. In the United States, those young people who inject Methedrine are usually known as "speed freaks." In Britain, speed is always injected; when

Methedrine ampoules were taken out of the pharmacopeia in Britain, those individuals who used it injected the powdered tablets.

When the use of mood-changing and mind-bending drugs spread out of the black ghetto and the world of jazz music in the United States to the white population, the first drugs to be widely abused were the stimulants, in particular, amphetamine derivatives. Prior to 1955, these drugs had something of a vogue among students in order that they might cope more adequately with examinations. In America, stimulants began to be pervasively used among middle-class white adolescents at about that time. About three years later they began to be the drug of choice among working-class British youth. By 1960, the use of amphetamine-barbiturate mixtures was common in large cities and in new towns in Britain. Since middle-class use of amphetamines was more culturally aberrant than working-class use, the few academic middle-class young people who used them were more likely to be severely psychologically disturbed than the working-class people taking a similar dosage. In the United States, there is no social-class delimitation to stimulant drug usage.

Initially, the amphetamine derivatives were prescribed by physicians mostly for middle-aged women as antidepressants and appetite suppressors. Methedrine for injection was usually used to facilitate psychiatric abreactions and in the treatment of the coma caused by alcoholism; the tablet was also given as an appetite suppressor. Methedrine is abused specifically for its side effects, which include restlessness, euphoria, and extreme talkativeness. Up to eight injections a day are taken by addicts who go on jags that last up to six days. Individual doses may be very large, and while on the jag the subject does not eat or sleep. Each injection sends an intensely pleasurable orgasmic flush throughout the whole body, and the user becomes fascinated with his own thoughts and feelings.

In the aggressive and sexual activity of disturbed adolescents, there is often a relationship between the implicit and explicit message parents give their children and the latter's explicit behavior. The same is true for drug abuse. Parents must say that they do not wish their children to take drugs, but they act as if they do:

Larry, a fifteen-year-old school boy, was hospitalized because of his aggressive, antisocial behavior. He began to abuse amphetamines at the age of thirteen. He was first given them by his doctor father because he slept excessively when having to work for an examination. The boy felt that his father was "always giving me pills." He used this behavior to justify his own drug abuse. The father was told about this by the psychiatric social worker and asked not to give the boy drugs. During a visit, the boy complained to his father of headaches. The latter immediately gave him some aspirin. The same day the boy absconded from the hospital and was picked up by the police one week later in a commune of boys, all of whom were drug toxic.

Sometimes children are offered drugs by their mothers when, feeling unsure of themselves, they complain of boredom, emptiness, and depression. The underworld rapidly discovered that adolescents would take stimulants in excessive dosage and that there were enormous profits to be made.

In large doses, the typical symptoms of amphetamine use are tachycardia and peripheral vasoconstriction with dryness of the mouth. Along with a transient euphoria, sleeplessness is quite common. If amphetamines are taken over several days, their psychic effect seems to be similar to that experienced when any individual stays awake past the usual barrier of fatigue. Preludin (phenmetrazine) and the amphetamines both can cause psychosis. Connell (1958) found forty-two cases of individuals who became psychotic after a single dose of amphetamines, thirty-two after several doses.

Most adolescents appear not to suffer permanent damage in their circulatory systems, though abnormal electrocardiographs have been reported in adolescents on such stimulants. Recently necrotizing angiitis has been reported in young drug abusers who used methamphetamine alone or with heroin or LSD (Citron, 1970). Some individuals die from Methedrine overdosage, but most adolescents appear not to suffer permanent damage to their circulatory system. After overdosage, stimulant users may be restless, overexcited, and difficult to control some twenty-four hours after the last dose has been taken.

In a toxic psychosis owing to an overdose of amphetamines the individual is typically paranoid:

A fifteen-year-old boy ran away from a school for delinquent boys and was later picked up by the police "blocked" on speed. The police called the principal of the school who collected the boy in his car. As he was driving back, the boy suddenly tried to wrench the steering wheel from his hands, screaming, "We must get out. We are being attacked by a gang of murderers who are firing machine guns at us from the sidewalk."

The use of stimulants is as particular to the age range of adolescents as is juvenile delinquency. Gibbens (1968) showed that, statistically, those adolescents who engage in delinquent acts for the first time at the end of puberty are likely to be conforming to the accepted social norms of society by the time they are twenty-one. The explanation would appear to be that delinquent acts are typically associated with the struggle for a secure identity in a socioeconomically underprivileged boy

77

(Miller, 1965). On the basis of this idea, Miller (1965) showed that in a penal setting a social system designed to enhance a boy's feelings of identity produced less recidivism after discharge than the usual more punitive setting.

Providing they are able to make meaningful emotional relationships with others, most disturbed adolescents with identity problems tend to consolidate some more or less secure feelings of self by young adulthood. There is then a built-in recovery process to antisocial behavior. Like delinquent activity, drug abuse, particularly of stimulants, appears to be related to a search for a secure identity.

It would appear that many adolescents who abuse amphetamines during their adolescent years may give them up in association with some type of adult adjustment and more secure identity at the age of nineteen to twenty-one. Thus, just as many adolescents grow out of criminal activity, many appear to spontaneously recover from drug abuse.

HALLUCINOGENS

Marijuana

Marijuana, whose active principal is tetrahydrocannabinol (THC) derived from the hemp plant Cannabis sativa, has been the subject of controversy since ancient times. However, it remained in the U.S. pharmacopeia until 1937 and was used for a variety of psychosomatic symptoms, in particular, asthma, dysmenorrhea, and migraine.

Drugs prepared from hemp vary in potency depending on the climate, the soil, the type of cultivation, and the method of preparation. The drug is obtained almost exclusively from the female plant. In Britain, where most marijuana comes from the Middle East and is of fairly similar potency, the terms "grass" and "hashish" were used fairly interchangeably. In the United States, where much of the drug is obtained from the leaves of the uncultivated plants, this tends to be called "grass." The extract of the plant resin "hash" is usually more potent than grass. In the United States the best hashish is thought to come from Mexico and is sometimes called "Acapulco gold."

Among young people, marijuana has long been associated with a drop out from the established norms of society. In the Middle East in the eleventh century the protest was violent. Hasan Sabah formed a secret society of Mohammedan Ismaelites to spread a new doctrine through an authoritarian yet loosely integrated environment. A compact force that could strike suddenly at the authority of the state would lead to its disintegration, and the new doctrine would take over. This group, with its grand master, terrorized Persia and Egypt for centuries by its sudden and effective assassinations; it became a state within a state.

Hasan motivated these young men by feeding them hashish after their murderous attacks. The intention was to give them a glimpse of the sensual joys that awaited them in heaven. Ultimately they obeyed him with robot-like obedience.

The Crusaders came into contact with this group during the twelfth century. They learned to know them as assassins (Hashishans) from the part that hashish played in the life of the young novice. The analogy with the present century is more than apparent. Marijuana is the drug of the rebellious young in all Western societies in which it is used. In itself, it is not normally associated with violence.

When marijuana is eaten, it seems to last about twice as long as when it is smoked, five to twelve hours. The cigarette, or "joint," usually gives an effect that lasts about two to four hours. The amount smoked affects the degree of intoxication, but unlike wine, it is rarely used only for its taste. The taste is thought by some to be quite revolting. One boy said, "Now I know why it is called 'shit'." The price of marijuana varies depending on the available supply. It is very often given by adolescents to one another rather than sold, and it is usually smoked in groups. It is not unusual for young adults to give marijuana cigarettes to younger adolescents. There is a distinct sweet smell to the drug that can be noticed on the breath and clothing of smokers, sometimes for a day after it has been smoked.

Typically, the intoxication of marijuana is initiated by an anxious period that lasts for about ten to thirty minutes. Because of this, many individuals who suffer from nonspecific anxiety attacks use marijuana as a way of giving themselves a realistic reason for their anxiety. After this initial anxiety, the individual may become calm and euphoric; the body may feel light; visual and auditory perception is sometimes enhanced. Just as with alcohol, the individual may feel that his conversation is particularly brilliant. This is, in fact, a type of "chattering," and the individual who is high on marijuana is not making a meaningful emotional communication with others. Time sense is distorted, and depersonalization and splitting are common. Paranoid ideas are not unusual, yet the individual may appear quite bland about them. Under the influence of marijuana, adolescents often appear dreamy and uncaring, though they can also feel impotent. Marijuana leads to a psychological withdrawal from involvement in the world outside the self and is associated with a preoccupation with a fantasy world.

The psychological effect of marijuana depends on whether it is taken as part of a group experience and on the mood of the user. When adolescents feel depressed or anxious before taking the drug, it is often said to make this worse. Occasionally adolescents report vivid, aggressive fantasies while under the influence of marijuana. One boy insisted that he had stabbed another to death, and another that he had drowned a girl in the local river. In neither case was there any evidence that this had happened.

The effects of marijuana are highly variable and the results of studies of its effects contradictory (Grinspoon, 1969). The drug has less effect on driving skills than does alcohol, but clinical studies do not take note of a volitional disinclination to pay attention, an aspect of driving that is reported by many patients. The drug has not been studied on people who have used it in large quantities over a long period of time, and the amount of active principal in any joint is, of course, variable. Intellectual functioning, when marijuana is taken repeatedly, seems to be impaired as measured by academic progress; but there are some students who appear to do better in their schoolwork when they are chronically intoxicated.

Adolescents who become dependent on marijuana may spend most of their days in a state of intoxication. They can make no satisfactory relationships. This total drug dependence is associated with an inability to cope with the complexities of life. It has been said that marijuana is less habit forming than tobacco, but the clinical evidence suggests that this is not true for adolescents.

Eighteen-year-old Robert smoked six joints daily, ate inadequately, and dropped out of school. He was hospitalized because of his inability to care for himself. He was not able to smoke marijuana and his intense passive-dependent needs were automatically met by being in the hospital. Diagnostically he was thought to be a borderline psychotic, and his electroencephalogram showed abnormalities typical of marijuana overdosage and rapid beta waves (Brill, 1969). He had no obvious heterosexual wishes, but experienced an intermittent craving to "get blasted on hash." Three weeks after discharge from the hospital, while in twice weekly psychotherapy, he began to smoke grass again. Within two weeks he was back on large doses of hashish and he sought rehospitalization because he felt he could not stop taking marijuana without such support.

There is no evidence of physical dependence on marijuana, but emotional dependence can be intense. Marijuana use may be symptomatic, as with alcohol, when emotionally vulnerable human beings use it as an escape from conflict. Alternatively, it may be essential when it fulfills a personality need. In many ways its use is then psychologically very similar to that of a perversion.

It would appear from clinical evidence that once marijuana is regularly smoked, dependence on it becomes more likely. In this way it became used by a moderately depressed boy of eighteen each weekend because, "I find the strain of life intolerable." Its use as a transitional object to meet profound emotional needs is demonstrated by a fifteen-year-old boy who smoked grass once following an acute traumatic episode and then began to smoke five joints of hashish daily. He was noticed because of a sudden decline in his schoolwork.

The knowledge that marijuana is not addictive may lead to adults not taking the pleas for help from adolescents, implicit when they get themselves caught with drugs, sufficiently seriously. The following example illustrates the consonance between sexual perversion and drug dependence.

Wendy began to smoke grass when she was eleven in association with multiple traumata; a friend of the same age was killed in a road accident, her parents separated, and her mother was in the hospital. By the time she was twelve, she was sexually promiscuous and smoking hashish three times weekly. She was either given joints by older boys or bought the drugs from pushers. At thirteen she tried some pills, but she gave these up. At age fourteen, she began to use LSD. She was frightened by the effect of this, though she was on a trip with many other young people, and so she continued only on marijuana. From time to time she would use sleeping pills that had been prescribed for her mother.

She sought help in the following way: She was caught smoking cigarettes in the school lavatory and as punishment was told to write an essay on the evils of tobacco. She sent in an essay full of incomprehensible jargon. She was then seen by her class teacher whom she told she was smoking marijuana. The teacher warned her of the harmful effects, but did nothing. Three weeks later, in a severely confused state, she was hospitalized and diagnostically was thought to be suffering from a hysterical personality disorder.

Lysergic Acid Diethylamide (LSD)

Still the most commonly used synthetic hallucinogen carrying the generic name "acid" is LSD-25. It was synthesized in 1938 and discovered to be a hallucinogen in 1943. It is one of the most potent mind-affecting substances known. One hundred to 250 micrograms given by mouth causes symptoms in 30 to 45 minutes; if it is given intramuscularly symptoms appear in 15 to 20 minutes. In small doses, it seems to act as a psychic stimulant; in larger doses, it ultimately becomes a depressant. The experience associated with taking LSD lasts from one to four hours whether it is taken as a clear liquid, a tablet, or as an intravenous injection. Repeating the dose of LSD-25 while still on a trip does not enhance the hallucinating experience, though it may increase the duration of its effect. After a trip a mild fatigue is common (Hoffer and Osmond, 1967). Specifically, the effects of LSD-25 have been divided into six stages, but these grossly overlap. In a general way the experience varies from a flight of ideas with tension, irritability, and perceptual changes to a state of preoccupation with somatic discomfort.

81

This is often followed by confusion, perceptual distortion, and paranoia. This may slide into a stage in which there is a sort of dual reality in which the patient feels as though his inner world is being explored.

The effects of LSD can be summarized by saying that the drug basically impairs ego functions, and there is then a burst through of primary-process thinking.

There is an apparent connection between the hallucinatory state induced by LSD and schizophrenia. It was for this reason that it was used experimentally by Hoffer and Osmond (1967) for a period of time on volunteer subjects to try to induce schizophrenia chemically. LSD had a vogue during the early 1960's in a type of abreactive therapy, but the results did not justify the initial enthusiasm. It now appears to be the treatment of choice in few if any psychiatric illnesses, and the drug is now banned from legal production in both the United States and Britain. It was first used illicitly in the United States and is also now used in this way in Britain and Europe. Sometimes a mixture of LSD and strychnine is taken, as supposedly this gives especially vivid hallucinatory effects.

Psilocybin and Mescaline

Other hallucinogens in common use are psilocybin and mescaline, the latter being in more common use. Psilocybin is very similar to LSD and is the active psychotomimetic of a mushroom from Mexico. It was used originally by the Aztecs. It is likely to produce a chronic toxic psychosis and the visions it produces are rich in color patterns. It is, however, notable in that there are never reports of erotic experiences. A cross tolerance to psilocybin and LSD may develop. Mescaline is also used as part of Indian religious rituals in the form of peyote, of which it is the active principal. It was isolated in 1896 from mescal buttons, which are used in South and Central America. Its typically toxic effect is that it allows the individual to feel removed from earthly cares. The hallucinations are particularly concerned with perceptual changes, particularly in the areas of hearing, smell, and taste. Quite often these are pleasant, and very prolonged reactions are common.

The use of hallucinogenic drugs is most common among late adolescents, often university students and drop outs, but it is not rare among thirteen- and fourteen-year-olds. Often philosophical constructs are given to hallucinogenic usage. Many adolescents who take LSD and other drugs begin to be intensely preoccupied with a type of pseudoexistentialist philosophy. Hallucinogens are particularly associated with a conscious desire on the part of adolescents to opt out of society because of its corruption. Often adolescents who take such hallucinogens appear to suffer from somewhat passive-aggressive personality styles, but it is difficult to know whether a chronic user of hallucinogens could have dealt with the complexities of society in any case. Many hallucinogenic fantasies are highly unpleasant. Pleasant fantasies, erotic and otherwise, are relatively rare depending on the drug used. The pleasant fantasies may last for only a short period of time in any hallucinogenic experience, which itself may last for hours.

Some adolescents, perhaps as an idiosyncratic response, perhaps because they were previously suffering from a borderline psychosis, appear to suffer prolonged psychological disorder after taking the hallucinogens. A particular symptom that is noticed in adolescents who have taken many doses of hallucinogens, and some patients claim to have had up to 300 acid trips, is that they appear to be quite affectless. This can be noticed when they are talking even though they have not taken the drug recently. It becomes extremely difficult for them to make meaningful emotional contacts with others. One adolescent described this as an experience of feeling like a tape recorder. Often they suffer from a subtle confusional state which the interviewer recognizes because after some minutes he realizes that the patient's thoughts do not hang together. Of all the drugs on which intense psychological dependence is possible, the hallucinogens appear to be the most dangerous. There are two reasons for this: (1) The users of hallucinogens, particularly LSD-takers, are one of the few groups of young people who when they do become drug dependent and are aware of it often have no conscious wishes to stop. (2) A marked aftereffect which may last for years, flashbacks, is quite common. For example, one doctor reported getting a flashback effect for a year on hearing the same piece of music that had been playing on the one occasion when the drug was taken.

Some adolescents show clinical evidence of organic brain damage after many trips. One youth reported that he could no longer multiply 6×6, but had to add the 6's together. Concrete thinking becomes common, and the capacity to make abstractions appears to be impaired. On the other hand, adolescents who appear to become dependent on LSD, taking frequent trips, may appear to be making satisfactory life adjustments with no treatment some two to three years later after they have stopped taking the drug. Suicide on LSD trips is not rare, and bursts of wild maniacal excitement have been observed:

A seventeen-year-old boy was having intercourse with his girlfriend while under the influence of LSD. He suddenly became extremely violent, attacked her, and then completely destroyed the furniture in the apartment (his father's, in which he was staying). The girl locked herself in the bathroom for several hours and the boy was in a catatonic-like stupor for two to three hours after having ingested the drug. The apartment had to be broken into in order to help him and his girl.

As might be expected, the chemical effect of the drug brings preexisting pathology to the surface of consciousness. Diagnostically this patient was suffering from acute identity confusion. The destruction of the family furniture in this state is a well-known phenomenon.

OPIUM DERIVATIVES

An unknown number of adolescents involved in progressive drug usage move from marijuana or stimulant pills to Methedrine injections and opium derivatives. There is no evidence that marijuana causes heroin addiction, though almost all heroin addicts have previously been regular, as distinct from experimental, users of marijuana. Since almost all adolescents experiment with cigarettes and alcohol, a previous experimental use of marijuana would not in itself be significant. Emotional dependence on marijuana may follow addiction to heroin after its withdrawal, as many heroin users withdrawn with methadone substitute marijuana for heroin.

Heroin addiction may lead to physical deterioration and ultimately to the death of the addict, though the rate of physical deterioration is idiosyncratic. It also appears to depend on the technique by which heroin is used, for example, whether clean or dirty syringes are used.

A twenty-year-old youth was offered and took heroin while under the influence of marijuana. He liked the effect and began to think he could safely use heroin. He was brought by a friend to a house which was full of people who were on the drug. He called a psychiatrist who had seen him previously and said, "I must have help, I cannot become like them."

It is not possible to predict the dosage of heroin that will lead to physical dependence on such drugs as heroin and other opium derivatives. Some adolescents claim to have injected two or three grains of heroin daily for a period of weeks, either under their skin, "popping," or into their veins, "mainlining," without being dependent on the drug. On the other hand, addiction with one-sixth of a grain daily has been observed. Some adolescents will know of one person who has taken himself off the drug with no apparent ill effects. They may then reject the truth that the risk of heroin addiction is a reason for avoiding the drug. With no withdrawal symptoms, it may well be that the dosage of heroin was small. However, addicts usually can tell the strength from the type of "high" that they obtain when they inject the drug. It is usual, for example, for the popularity of any one dealer to decrease if the heroin caps become weaker.

Britain has a particular problem with hard drugs because it is possible to become a registered addict. Since there is no way of telling the exact amount that any one addict may need, and since addicts are very often unable to mobilize themselves to earn a living, such addicts tend to live by selling spare drugs because they have obtained an amount greater than their need. Sometimes adolescents in Britain are introduced to drug-taking by being given heroin by registered addict friends.

A fourteen-year-old boy who had taken heroin only once insisted that he managed to get himself registered as an addict. He said that he was given two grains of heroin and four ampoules of Methedrine daily by the drug clinic.

In the United States, adolescents commonly graduate to heroin from Methedrine. As younger adolescents become involved in regular and then progressive drug use, the spread of heroin addiction to early adolescents becomes inevitable.

The Psychology of Drug Abuse

A variety of possible stresses will produce drug abuse. Experiments with drugs in present-day society should not in itself be considered evidence of psychopathology. Regular and progressive drug usage is always a form of self-medication. There are three etiological reasons for drug abuse which to some extent overlap. They are associated with problems of identity, sexual conflict, and the relief of intrapsychic pain. The extent of drug use is not necessarily indicative of very severe personal pathology, and progressive drug users are not necessarily suffering from syndromes whose etiology is based on very early deprivation.

PROBLEMS OF IDENTITY

Drugs may be used in an attempt to facilitate maturation and to free the self from infantile dependence on parents or parent figures. These are adolescents who without drugs may experience feelings of loss of individual autonomy in relationship to authority figures. Such young people also tend, when off drugs, to complain of feelings of depression, anxiety, or emptiness. Before the present pandemic of drug abuse, those adolescents who suffered from identity diffusion (Erikson, 1968) behaved symptomatically in different ways; they were often delinquent, sexually promiscuous, or academic failures owing to underachievement.

The most usual cause of a failure of psychological maturation in an adolescent is isolation from extraparental adults. The most common reason for adolescents being unable to make significant relationships outside the immediate family is not just the personal psychopathology of the individual. Stable extraparental adult relationships are becoming increasingly difficult to obtain because of social instability resulting from the vertical and horizontal mobility of society (Miller, 1969). When important human relationships are made by early adolescents, especially with a teacher, school counselor, or social worker, the structural organization of the school system makes it highly likely that the chosen adult will be lost to the adolescent. The pupil may then drop out of an attempt to make an attachment, just as a two-year-old who experiences parental separation (Bowlby, 1969).

Individual psychopathology can, of course, be significant in a failure to make extraparental adult and peer-group relationships. Those children whose early attachments within the family were impaired on reaching adolescence are likely to find it hard to establish a trusting relationship with anyone. A stable network of extraparental relationships may protect adolescents from a disturbed parental relationship, but it is less likely to protect them from the effects of severe early deprivation. Those adolescents who do not make significant emotional relationships with extraparental adults, whom both they and society feel as valuable and significant, find it difficult to develop a sense of personal autonomy. Without attachments to such grownups, adolescents may remain overdependent on parents, consciously often an intolerable psychic stress. More usually such young people continue to be overdependent on peer relationships through the whole of adolescence in a manner that is more usual with early adolescents.

A typical group process of early adolescence is to seek the experience of being aware of commonly held feelings with peers. It is not unusual in some cultures for groups of early adolescent males to masturbate together; thus, they become aware that others can obtain the same feeling of sexual excitement as they themselves. This awareness may also be acquired through the intensive intimacy of early adolescent friendships. In midadolescence, if psychological development is proceeding satisfactorily, a group of young people may use alcohol not to get intoxicated but to facilitate interpersonal relationships. Depending on its strength and the amount used, marijuana, which is often used with the same intent, may produce an essentially masturbatory type of relationship. With his peer group the adolescent toxic on marijuana is more preoccupied with his own internal imagery and the feeling that others have a similar experience than he is with an emotionally meaningful interpersonal relationship. In this behavior, which so parallels the passivity of television watching, midadolescents who do not develop a satisfactory sense of self continue by the use of such drugs the type of interpersonal group relationships that are typical of the earlier adolescent age period. It is also reasonable to hypothesize that the regular use of marijuana by early adolescent groups may reinforce their masturbatory type of relationship and so inhibit the development of more mature types of interpersonal communication.

Within groups, some individuals who may have difficulty establishing relationships and establishing a sense of their own identity may not become drug involved even if drugs are available. People whose psychological orientation is more passive are likely to graduate to drugs alone; some, on the other hand, may become radicalized; some high school pupils seek an identity by becoming "greasers" (or in Britain "skin heads"), who may anathematize drug-taking. Adolescents in groups who do not have adult relationships are extremely vulnerable to group contagion; a changing fashion about drug usage is likely to be as rapidly transmitted as is a variation in language, dress, or delinquent activity.

Adolescents who are in an acute identity crisis become introduced to drugs and may deteriorate because of the drug rather than because of their fundamental emotional instability.

SEXUAL CONFLICT

Along with drug use to attempt to facilitate emotional maturation and a sense of identity, drugs may be used in an attempt to resolve conflicts about sexuality in the following ways. Drugs may be used as a substitute for sexual intercourse, to allay anxiety about possible impotence, to potentiate masturbatory activity, or to resolve conflicts about heterosexuality.

Marijuana appears to reduce the push that individuals feel toward resolving conflicts about sexual activity. Boys whose sexual advances are initially rejected by a girl are less likely to be insistent when "stoned"; girls are less likely to reject a boy's sexual advances. Boys with homosexual conflicts are more likely to allow themselves to be seduced.

Some boys with sexual conflicts typically take large doses of amphetamines on weekends. In American and European culture this is the typical time for dating, so boys with sexual anxieties can use the chemical impotence of amphetamines both to save face with their peers and to avoid the anxiety they might experience because of sexual incompetence or disinterest. Some adolescents who are consciously aware of sexual anxieties, which without drugs the processes of psychological maturation might have resolved, may deliberately use amphetamines and Methedrine to inhibit potency. It therefore becomes possible for these young people to say that they use drugs and therefore do not need to use sex (Miller, 1969). In small doses amphetamines are said to enhance a boy's capacity to maintain a penile erection; in large doses no erection is possible. The association between the use of stimulants and sexual anxieties in girls is also evident.

Jane was a seventeen-year-old suffering from an infantile personality disorder, with many hysterical features. Initially, she took many drugs and was also sexually promiscuous. When she caught syphilis, she took seriously the injunction that she should not have intercourse. Then she began to inject drugs, saying that the feeling she obtained from the injection was like the feeling of having intercourse. She was hospitalized for a short time and then absconded. She went to live with a boy who would punish her when she angered him by refusing to have intercourse. Whenever he did this, she would go and buy some speed and take it by mouth.

The price paid by the individual is that psychological maturation is almost certainly inhibited but not necessarily permanently impaired. Without treatment other than intermittent supportive psychotherapy, by the age of nineteen Jane had given up drugs, finished her high school education, and established a semipermanent relationship with a stable young man of twenty-five.

Heroin and cocaine are often associated with homosexual fantasies in both sexes. Heroin may produce prolonged erection during intercourse for the male, with an inability to ejaculate. Women may behave with less inhibition when "done-up" with heroin. Though there is an apparent relationship between mainlining and sexual activity, the phallic injection has the same meaning as the use of a penis to a girl with a hysterical or infantile personality; what is really being sought is the omnipotent oneness that is obtained with infantile sucking.

Among the hallucinogens, LSD is sometimes described as giving special erotic parameters to sexual intercourse; more often it appears to be associated with masturbatory activity. Psilocybin obliterates erotic experiences and so psychologically has a similar effect to the chemical blocking of large doses of amphetamines.

THE RELIEF OF INTRAPSYCHIC PAIN

Drugs are commonly used by adolescents as a defensive medication to avoid the experience of anxiety. With this type of behavior young people are very directly imitating the behavior of the adult population. Drug-taking in adolescence may often occur following the traumatic loss of a love object: parents by death or divorce, loved adults, or peer-group members. Since the awareness of death is a threat to an adolescent's necessary feeling of immortality, the toxic effect of drug usage defends against this by allowing a return to omnipotent infantile feelings. Since excessive drug usage is also dangerous to life, adolescents may also use drugs self-destructively, playing a game of Russian roulette with their bodily and psychic health. It is as though they defy destruction by playing with danger. The injection of morphine derivatives was used in this way by one seventeen-year-old patient, both of whose parents died when he was ten. He said, "When I shoot up, I feel at first as if I am going to die. Then I feel sleepy and warm and comfortable." So drug-taking can be an attempt to work through a mourning process.

Those adolescents who suffer from severe chronic ego disintegration or who diagnostically suffer from a variety of borderline states may use drugs as tranquilizers. If they use hallucinogens such as mescaline and LSD, or stimulants, their overt clinical condition worsens though they are apparently less aware of psychic tension. Those adolescents who take large doses of marijuana, for example three or four pipes of hashish daily, and who continue to function with a high degree of competence in academic or other work, clinically often appear to be suffering from either schizophrenic or borderline psychotic states. Though it is said to produce psychosis, the toxic effect of marijuana at least as commonly may provide a defense against ego disintegration.

As well as defending against the experience of anxiety, drugs can also be used as a defense against severe chronic feelings of deprivation. In adolescents suffering from an anaclitic type of depression, in which they cannot make object relationships because of early traumata, drug toxicity may become a substitute for a loving mother or act as a transitional object (Winnicott, 1953). A patient described his LSD trip in a way that clearly symbolized his omnipotent wish to be mothered:

I feel as if I am in a room manufactured by the government given to all its citizens which will take care of all my survival functions; eating, air, living. It will prevent me from hurting myself, and it can even hold my hand. In the room I have nothing to worry about. Everything is done for me; I have no fear of bodily harm. It is a great place to trip.

A seventeen-year-old boy who came into treatment because of heroin addiction was withdrawn from heroin by the use of methadone. He then became highly dependent on hashish, which he smoked each evening. The following interchange occurred in his therapy, as he described having taken heroin:

He said, "I feel when I take smack as though I am hugging a teddy bear." While making this statement, he was playing with his mouth and the therapist said, "I guess you really want to feel loved." The reply was, "I cannot bear to be pushed around," to which the therapist said, "No, I did not mean that, I meant loved as your mother might love you as a small child." To which the boy replied that he wanted nothing better than to be able to curl up into a small ball and be looked after.

Psychotherapeutic Problems

Adolescence is an action-oriented age and significant communication is often nonverbal. Rarely do adolescents ask for help in words; much more commonly the request is through an activity, often one that society sees as antisocial. It is not then surprising that early adolescents commonly seem to be caught taking drugs deliberately by an exhibitionistic disturbance. So, when drugs are available, young people may become intoxicated in front of teachers, school counselors, social workers, and parents. Many such adolescents are not helped because the meaning of this behavior is not recognized; the adult response is symptomatic and may be only controlling or punitive. When adolescents misbehave as part of an unconscious request for help, often the agency used appears to depend on symptom change; so disturbed adolescents may see a member of a social agency, a psychiatrist, or a juvenile court official. Even with early adolescents pediatricians are rarely involved.

Unlike younger adolescents, middle and late stage youths may ask for help in words rather than action. However, this depends on the way of life of their social environment, the availability of helping people, and whether pseudomagical solutions such as drugs are available. In addition, the ability to ask for assistance in words depends on an adolescent's perception of helping adults and the image that such adults have generally among the adolescent group. Because of the oversold image that adults cannot be helpful, adolescents often use informal so-called peer-group networks from which they seek assistance. These rarely are able to offer highly technical assistance; mostly they are supportive and useful for some.

There is no evidence that an episode of acute toxic confusion, for example, a bad trip, necessarily leads to an attempt to stop drug use in those people who are regular or progressive drug users. As might be expected, fear is not a deterrent, though it may lead to a change in the type of drug used.

Apart from drug toxicity representing a plea for assistance in those adolescents who are not in treatment, a not unusual problem in modern therapy is for an adolescent to appear for his session intoxicated on one of a variety of drugs. The therapist then has to make a decision as to whether specific medical intervention is necessary. An additional area of concern is that the adolescent does not always know what has been taken. Many young people appear not to care what they buy, and they tend to try anything offered. Drug dealers often lie as to what they are selling; THC is not available outside a few research centers. Many adolescents know this but will still buy mixtures carrying this name. A therapist, when a patient appears toxic, almost inevitably must have doubts about his physical safety. Particularly for nonmedical therapists, the possible complications of the transference do not justify a failure to take an individual to the nearest hospital emergency room if there is any doubt at all as to what might have been taken or its possible effects. This is a necessity if the patient has taken a large number of "downers," which may be any one of a number of barbiturates. Drug toxicity complicates psychotherapy in other ways. Patients who are high on marijuana probably do not have enough observing ego to use a therapy session; in many respects the problem is similar to that of a patient who appears drunk on alcohol. The therapist then has to decide whether to continue a session from which the patient has so effectively chemically removed himself.

When patients are high on a hallucinogen, these are always finite states. Fifty milligrams of chlorpromazine will end a trip but an assurance of adequate liver function is needed. Valium (diazepam) in small doses of five milligrams by mouth relieves the tension associated with a trip but does not oversedate the patient. However, the therapist has to decide the implicit message he gives his patient as he becomes the dispenser of downers; so a question of clinical judgment as to whether to interfere psychochemically is involved. An LSD trip requires someone to be with the patient and to be generally reassuring until the episode is over. Since therapists are usually time bound because of their commitment to other patients, this may mean mass cancellations or finding a "baby sitter." Intoxication on LSD can lead to apparently unbearable anxiety for the patient, particularly because of the possible loss of body image boundaries. Some individuals then obtain enormous reassurance by having their bodies touched and stroked. The meaning of this as an equivalent to cuddling a frightened child is obvious. LSD can, however, potentiate homosexual anxieties; so a misguided cuddling equivalent can throw the patient into a panic. It is easy to see how in psychotherapy a patient who becomes high on acid is acting out a regressive fantasy in which the therapist is cast in a maternal role.

Heroin addiction causes a different psychotherapeutic and medical problem. Addicts may be withdrawn as outpatients if they are sufficiently motivated by the use of a five-day course of methadone in which the dosage partially depends on the amount of heroin taken. If an addict's motivation is in some doubt, or the patient is an early adolescent, hospitalization is always necessary. Unless liver function tests can be given, it is probably unwise to give chlorpromazine to abate the possibility of cold turkey, but Librium (chlordiazepoxidehydrochloride), in doses of twenty-five- to fifty-milligram tablets three to four times daily, effectively makes withdrawal a smooth process.

The particular psychotherapeutic problem of drug dependency is on the one hand to make an adequate diagnosis of its cause and on the other to assess its significance as a symptom. If drug-taking is an experimental act that can be part of the process of psychological maturation in a society that makes drugs freely available, it may have little more significance than the first cigarette. If drug abuse is regular or progressive, this always indicates some degree of psychopathology which influences treatment planning and goals.

There are specific complications of drug abuse that are particularly relevant to the therapist. The drug itself may produce chemical toxicity; alternately, it may potentiate underlying psychopathology. Motivation for therapy may be influenced because of the apparent magical solution offered by a drug, and drug abuse may be part of a resistance in ongoing psychotherapy. In either case, drug withdrawal is necessary before the underlying psychopathology can be treated. The paradox is that the causes of drug dependence often cannot be treated until drug withdrawal has occurred.

Insofar as motivation is concerned, when psychotherapeutic help is sought for adolescent patients it is always rare for early adolescents in particular to be consciously motivated. This is explicable. It is not unusual for family psychopathology to show itself under the guise of adolescent maladjustment when the adolescent is the ticket of admission for the family in order for them to obtain help. In addition, the pubertal adolescent is narcissistically involved with the self, so feelings and conflicts are inevitably projected into the adult world. Quite apart from any possible drug dependence there are special difficulties in the therapy of early adolescents. A pubertal adolescent is experiencing psychic dissolution (Spiegel, 1951). Many such adolescents are particularly preoccupied with the need to gain control over themselves because of the physiological changes of puberty. They have hardly any capacity for self-observation (Eissler, 1958).

Any anxiety that may be produced by referral for psychiatric help is a further threat to a tenuously developing ego, because of the implication of dependence and incompetence in such a referral. Both these are threats to adolescent self-esteem.

Prior to the onset of the present pandemic of drug abuse, conscious motivation for therapy became more likely in midadolescence, the stage of identification, and was very likely by late adolescence, the period of psychic consolidation. As the complexity of society has increased, in particular as social networks have deteriorated, individual adolescents have tended to isolate themselves more and more from adults. Without adult support, middle- and late-stage adolescents who are psychologically disturbed find it increasingly difficult to separate themselves from the regressive dependency needs of childhood. They are then particularly likely to see psychiatrists as the hostile representatives of an alienating world. These are the adolescents who are particularly likely to involve themselves in the drug culture. They are often consciously unmotivated for therapy even into young adulthood, a situation that in the past would typically be expected from early adolescents. Insofar as the problem of drug dependence is a problem of motivation, the psychiatrist is in a similar position to that in which he may have been with an actively destructive or delinquent adolescent. The psychiatrist may have to be prepared to arrange for the protection of the young person directly, with all the complications of thus taking over a magical omnipotent role.

An initial goal of therapy with the nonmotivated adolescent, usually those suffering from a variety of characterological distortions who are consciously satisfied with their ways of handling reality and making interpersonal relationships, is to try to help them become consciously motivated to change. One aim of the opening stages of therapy is to show the patient, affectively as well as intellectually, that his style of personality functioning is not helpful to himself. This requires a capacity to make a positive relationship with a therapist and to tolerate within this a preparedness to suspend destructive acting out (Miller, 1968). However, adolescents who have learned to medicate themselves with drugs often appear to prefer ego regression to the frustration inherent in psychotherapy.

Drugs are a complex factor in changing the adolescent's capacity for self-observation, which in any case varies with the extent of personality maturation and with their capacity to make a meaningful relationship. A boy or girl who has made many LSD trips may for a long time be quite incapable of making a relationship unless offered other emotional support, usually by being hospitalized. Outpatient psychotherapy is only possible if a therapist is able to make a meaningful alliance with the patient; this is particularly true for those individuals who in any case find it difficult to make object relationships. In such a situation the patient may be able to suspend significant drug abuse because of the initial idealization of the therapist. To make ongoing therapy possible, however, the adolescent must begin to understand that his projection of an idealized mother onto the therapist is unreal; it represents the patient's wish to retain his own omnipotence. The frustration involved in this recognition is the point at which efforts at psychotherapy break down and destructive acting out of the wish for omnipotence ensues. It is at this point that drug-taking, which has previously been suspended, may resume. The therapeutic dilemma is that, on the one hand, the therapist has to use the omnipotence given him by the patient as part of this idealization; on the other, he has to carefully titrate the ending of this phase of treatment. Otherwise, the patient is exposed to an intolerable level of psychic frustration, as the therapist becomes the representative of a frustrating world that denies the patient satisfaction. The patient needs to be able to abandon the use of drugs because of his infantile loving feelings for the therapist.

In the initial stages of therapy, drug-dependent adolescents may need to be seen daily if they are to be able to give up drug abuse. At the same time, it is necessary to interpret both the patient's wish to have an omnipotent therapist and the patient's hostility to the therapist because he is not omnipotent. The goal is, as the patient is abandoning an idealization of the therapist as an omnipotent projection of the patient's internal mother figure, that therapy becomes valued at a more mature level, so that it will be worth keeping and not lost in a fog of drug toxicity. The nonmotivated delinquent adolescent character disorder, in the days prior to the present drug pandemic, similarly had to abandon the gratification of his impulse-ridden behavior to avoid the risk of a jail sentence and so preserve therapy. Once the problem of idealization is being worked through, the frequency of psychotherapy can be reduced to more manageable proportions. Depending on the extent of the patient's characterological difficulties, this may vary from three-times-weekly intensive psychotherapy to psychoanalysis. The particular difficulty is to interpret the patient's feelings of rejection at the same time as he perceives a rejection. A therapist's vacation at this time will almost certainly be catastrophic in these patients, as they then are particularly likely to return to drug toxicity.

Those adolescents who are only potentially able to make object relationships, and are not consciously motivated to abandon drug dependence, are psychotherapeutically inaccessible unless an authority figure other than the therapist is primarily responsible for their coming into treatment. This must be either parents or representatives of society at large. The superegos of such drug-dependent adolescents tend to be harsh and weak. They are rarely powerful enough to control impulse discharge. Neither is the ego capable of handling ego regression without its functions being overwhelmed. If early in therapy the therapist becomes identified with this harsh, weak superego, the patient will attempt

94

to escape from the therapist as he does from his own superego pressures. Therapy then becomes impossible.

The nonmotivated drug-dependent adolescent will almost certainly have to be hospitalized, and the parents must make arrangements for this, with or without the support of legal processes, preferably the former. As such a step threatens the intrafamilial libidinal equilibrium (Aichhorn, 1949), it is often very difficult for a parent to support the hospitalization of a drug-dependent adolescent (Miller, 1958). If such an adolescent is hospitalized, the hospital may in itself become a representative of the early omnipotent mother, and psychotherapeutic movement may not take place. This is because the individual is in the same situation, in many ways, as the person who is drug toxic; he has no motivation to move from a state of idealized dependence. It is probable that successful psychotherapy of the hospitalized drug-dependent adolescent is only possible with a therapist who in the first instance works interpretively with the patient in his life space and is prepared to intervene, a continuation of administrative therapy and psychotherapy. Later this needs to be converted to more usual psychotherapy in which there is no direct involvement with the patient's life style. At this transitional point, which has the same hazards as the shift in outpatient therapy from the situation in which the concept of an idealized transference figure is abandoned, the patient must agree to exercise his own ego controls without the therapist acting as an external ego for him.

Because of the chemical and psychological insults to the personality involved in drug abuse, not all drug toxic, drug-dependent adolescents who appear to be unable to make affectionate and meaningful object ties (Rado, 1926) are necessarily unable to do this when drugs are removed and they dry out. Those adolescents who are suffering from identity diffusion may be significantly helped by once-weekly expressive-supportive individual psychotherapy, which may need to last over a period of two or three years. Adolescents who have become drug-dependent as a result of a psychic traumata late in childhood or early in adolescence may be significantly helped by brief focal intensive psychotherapy once they are withdrawn from drugs.

Conclusions

Hallucinogenic and other intoxicating drugs may be used as a resistance in psychotherapy and psychoanalysis in the same way as alcohol or barbiturates. Providing there is no idiosyncratic response to the drugs, the situation needs to be dealt with by interpretation in the same way as any other resistance. However, because of the number of dangerous drugs currently easily available, adolescents may act out in therapy in such a way as to cause the therapist to counteract. Drug toxicity may be the storm center in which otherwise successful psychotherapy may founder. In any case, accurate and well-timed interpretations do not necessarily control acting out in adolescence, and drugs may destroy therapy that would otherwise have been successful. Of all the ages of man, adolescence is the most favorable time for treatment. Therapists need to understand the adolescent's need for self-assertion, to form judgments, achieve bodily competence, and prove adulthood. The adolescent must also find a place for himself or herself in relation to the opposite sex and to society at large (Zachary, 1945). Drug abuse has added a complex parameter to adolescent therapy; it has made some adolescents apparently unreachable, but it has not made the majority who are so involved psychotherapeutically untouchable.

REFERENCES

Aichhorn, A. (1949). Quoted by R. S. Eissler. Scapegoats of society. In: *Searchlights on Delinquency,* ed. K. R. Eissler. New York: International Universities Press, pp. 288–306.

Bowlby, J. (1969). *Attachment and Loss.* Vol. 1. Attachment. London: Hogarth.

Brill, H. (1969). EEG abnormalities in marijuana overdosages. *Proceedings of the New York State Narcotic Addiction Control Commission.*

Chein, I., *et al.* (1964). *Narcotics, Delinquency and Social Policy.* London: Tavistock.

Citron, P. B. (1970). Necrotizing angiitis associated with drug abuse. *New England Journal of Medicine,* 283:1003–1011.

Connell, P. H. (1958). *Amphetamine Psychosis.* London: Chapman & Hall.

Eissler, K. R. (1958). Notes on problems of technique in the psychoanalytic treatment of adolescents: With some remarks on perversions. *Psychoanalytic Study of the Child,* 13:223–255.

Emery, F. E., *et al.* (1967). *Affect Control and the Use of Drugs.* London: Tavistock.

Erikson, E. H. (1968). *Identity: Youth and Crisis.* New York: Norton.

Gibbens, T. (1968). *The Psychiatric Offender.* London: Routledge & Kegan Paul.

Grinspoon, L. (1969). Marijuana. *Scientific American,* 221(6):17–25.

Hartmann, D. (1969). A study of drug-taking adolescents. *Psychoanalytic Study of the Child,* 24:348–399.

Hoffer, A., and Osmond, H. (1967). *The Hallucinogens.* New York: Academic Press.

Hollister, L. E. (1968). *Chemical Psychosis—LSD and Related Drugs.* Springfield, Ill.: Charles C Thomas.

Mahler, M. S. (1968). On human symbiosis and the vicissitudes of individuation. In: *Infantile Psychosis.* Vol. 1. New York: International Universities Press.

Miller, D. (1958). Family interaction in the therapy of adolescent patients. *Psychiatry,* 21:3.

———. (1965). *Growth to Freedom.* Bloomfield: Indiana University Press.

———. (1966). A model of an institution for treating adolescent delinquent boys. In:

Changing Concepts of Cure and Its Treatment, ed. Hugh Klare. London: Pergamon Press, pp. 97–117.

———. (1968). Principles of psychotherapy in adolescence. *Wiss. Leitschinft Der Universitat Rosvock,* pp. 625–628.

———. (1969). *The Age Between Adolescents in a Disturbed Society.* London: Hutchinson.

Office of Health Economics (1969). London. p. 324.

Rado, S. (1926). The psychic effects of intoxicants. *International Journal of Psychoanalysis,* 7.

Robins, L. N., and Murphy, E. G. (1967). Drug use in a normal population in Negro men. *American Journal of Public Health,* 57:9.

Spiegel, L. A. (1951). A review of contributions to a psychoanalytic theory of adolescence: Individual aspects. *Psychoanalytic Study of the Child,* 6:375–395.

Weider, H., and Kaplan, E. H. (1969). Drug use in adolescents. *Psychoanalytic Study of the Child,* 24:399–432.

Winnicott, D. W. (1953). Transitional objects and transitional phenomena. *International Journal of Psychoanalysis,* 31:89–97.

Zachary, C. B. (1945). A new tool in psychotherapy with adolescents. In: *Modern Trends in Child Psychiatry,* ed. L. N. Pacella. New York: International Universities Press.

7] ON TELLING THE TRUTH

> Nashville, Tenn. (UPI) A muscular convict whose mother said "he'll be dead when he tells the truth" Sunday recanted a confession that he slew two young women near Ann Arbor, Mich. *The Nashville Tennessean* quoted Mrs. Ernest Sims in a copyrighted story: "He has never told the truth in his life. He never would live right."
>
> *Chicago Sun Times,* June 1969.

Obviously telling the truth is easier for some than for others. A delineation of the development of the processes involved in truth-telling and their relationship to living right is necessary for understanding why this is so. Sometimes concepts or terms that are less than clearly understood in our daily practice emerge and come into better focus when subjected to a careful clinical examination and metapsychological assessment. The emphasis in this chapter will be on the development of truth-telling. The corollary concepts to truth-telling involve such phenomena as lying and being lied to as well as reality testing, illusion, and delusions. At one or another time each of these must be considered in assessing whether the truth is being told. Of course, this is quite aside from the philosophical implications as to whether there is such a thing as truth in the abstract sense. For our purpose, we shall merely utilize the working definition of truth as correspondence to fact.

Lying perhaps is not so self-evident a phenomenon as we might hope it to be. For one it is usually thought of as occurring between two or more people, and thus is a transaction or an interpersonal process. From a psychoanalytic point of view, however, we must concentrate on the intrapsychic and differentiate the liar with intent to lie from the person who experiences a lie. It goes without saying that not all intentional truth-telling or intentional deception is experienced as such, and the experiencer of a lie cannot be too hasty in judging the sender. For a psychoanalyst this means that a careful metapsychological assessment of the lie must preclude a reaction to it.

This, of course, necessitates the continual monitoring of material in psychoanalysis which is considered true or false on many levels. Patients involved with fantasy may feel they are truthful when they are not. There are levels of truth that become clarified in analysis. If the infantile fantasy is thought of as a lie, then Ferenczi (1927) was accurate in stating that full and complete free association and thus complete truth can be fulfilled only at the end of analysis. He quoted Freud as saying that sometimes an approaching cure is signaled by the patient saying that during his illness he was shamming.

The capacity to tell the truth involves a multitude of factors beginning with being able to know the truth coupled with the ability to conceal it or reveal it. This capacity then moves onto the adaptational sphere regarding the wisdom of communicating such knowledge in an interpersonal arena. Lying is an ubiquitous phenomenon and can hardly be considered as pathological per se. However, lying does strain reality testing if it is conscious, and thus its maintenance is quite vulnerable.

The question often posed as to why people lie may be more profitably considered in terms of why and how people tell the truth. Truth-telling is a psychological development from the earliest ability to differentiate truth from falsity through a realistic utilization of truth to the not uncommon disorder of pathological truth-telling. The problem of telling the truth is one of longitudinal development proceeding from the inability to conceive of the truth to the capacity not to tell the truth to a multitude of uses of the truth. It is related to the growth from narcissistic to real objects as well as the development of each of these separate developmental lines. Being untruthful is not an absolute sign of pathology, nor is truthfulness a criterion of analyzability.

Adolescence often presents a unique challenge in assessing development, and the phenomenon of truth-telling offers an interesting gauge in this assessment. For the adolescent, moral issues, such as lying, often take on intense and passionate associations. It seems self-evident that truth-telling, especially in adolescence, is not a clear indicator of pathology; this age group often is profoundly honest with peers and happily dishonest with parents. Only a re-examination of the truth-telling issue clearly separated from considerations of mental illness allows us to consider the developmental significance of the issue as it emerges in a variety of forms in the adolescent.

Review of Literature

The psychoanalytic literature that devotes itself directly to the problem of truth-telling is not easily summarized. The assumption that patients naturally tell the truth in free associating is unwarranted since such a formulation of the rules of psychoanalysis is not made to patients. At one point Freud does state that "you must be absolutely honest and never leave anything out" and thus interchanges truth and completeness. In the presentation of a case of obsessional neurosis, Freud (1909) noted Rat Man's request not to tell the details of the horrible punishment, but Freud stated it was beyond his power to grant this dispensation. Again, the basic rule is that you say everything that comes to mind. This case of Freud and his reference to another case wherein a request was made to conceal state secrets (Freud, 1913) are both characteristic of patients who for one or another reason choose not to be truthful without in any way being considered liars. Dora (Freud, 1905), however, deceived Freud by not telling of her plans for terminating treatment (yet she did not lie). The rest of the classical psychoanalytic literature deals mainly with the truth-telling problems in terms of the problem of lying.

Much that has been written about lying is in terms of its being pathology; however, a few authors stress its role in development. Anna Freud (1965) distinguished three types of lying in terms of stages of development: (1) innocuous lying, (2) fantasy lying, (3) delinquent lying. The first she considered a primitive defense mechanism of ignoring or denying pain. The second was seen as a part of a regressive process owing to frustration in response to the inability to cope with reality. The third involved a more advanced ego development with truth distortion having motives relating to some conflict. Most lying seen in children and adolescents involves a combination of these three forms.

Tausk (1919) noted that the period assigning omniscience to the parents ends with the child's first successful lie. He states: "The striving to have secrets from which the parents are excluded is one of the most powerful factors in the formation of the ego, especially in establishing and carrying out one's own will." In his discussion of the development of this sequence he states:

The period before the first successful lie occurs very early in infancy. Lies fabricated in the first year of life are nothing unusual; they can be observed especially in children who resent the regular elimination of bodily wastes . . . . The child, to gain forbidden pleasure, begins to enjoy the practice of lying. Children learn to lie from parents and upbringers, who by misrepresentations and unkept promises make the child obey and teach him to disguise his true purposes. Many children continually test God with regard to his omniscience and not frequently actually succeed in unmasking him as a phantom of the dethroned parental power.

In this discussion Tausk attributed lying to a preoedipal era and more particularly to anal involvement. He cited lying as a part of normal development and indicated that children learn to lie from their parents, owing to a disillusionment in the parental powers.

This is made more metapsychologically precise by Kohut (1966) who stated "Every shortcoming detected in the idealized parent leads to a corresponding internal preservation of the externally lost quality of the object. A child's lie remains undetected; and thus one aspect of the omniscient idealized object is lost; but omniscience is introjected as a minute aspect of the drive-controlling matrix and as a significant aspect of the all-seeing eye, the superego." Thus Kohut indicated that internal structure is formed by the successful phase, specific loss of illusion or failure of idealization. Loss or inadequacy or failure of parents becomes transformed into internal regulation. In this view as well as that of Tausk, lying is considered as a part of the process of development. That is, the ability and capacity to lie allows for growth. To put it another way, the child who is able to lie can reveal primarily to himself the existence of a shortcoming in his parents and can thus allow himself to assume a function or regulation previously within the parents' domain.

Winnicott (1953) supported this point of view in his consideration of transitional objects. These bridging objects and experiences allow for phase-specific separation from the supporting psychological object and thus move to gradual assumption of self-regulation. Winnicott underlined the normal or necessary stage of transitional objects or phenomena and pointed to their persistence as involved in pathological lying.

There is an overall lack of emphasis in the literature on the normal development of telling the truth. A simplistic moral position is taken that the goal of growth is to be truthful and deviations from the truth are weaknesses or inadequacies or pathology. However, it can be seen that lying has its normative functions as well as its pathology and so does telling the truth.

A poignant note by Winnicott (1964), in his review of an autobiography of Jung, directs our attention to the psychopathological side of lying:

When Jung deliberately lied to Freud he became a unit with a capacity to hide secrets instead of a split personality with no place to hide anything. In this way perhaps Freud did perform some service for Jung, albeit without knowing it . . . it does not matter much what the lie was about. At some point, however, Jung had to lie to Freud, or else he had to start an analysis with him, one that could not possibly have led to cure, though it might have led to a flight from psychosis to sanity or to psychoneuroses.

Winnicott told us of the protective function of lying, in this case necessitated by a rather severe form of pathology, that is, perhaps a deliberate falsehood allowed a self-delineation and avoided a regressive merger.

Ferenczi (1927) utilized the developmental scheme of original infantile amorality associated with lying while the transition to subsequent morality is associated with a feeling of unpleasure at hypocrisy or untruth. In a case illustration Ferenczi demonstrated how a lying patient with a memory disturbance suffered from a "split in his personality."

Dickes (1967), reviewing the analytic literature on the subject of lying, referred to single articles by Freud and Brunswick mainly on the psychopathology of lying. Both these papers concentrated on oedipal issues, with Freud emphasizing the incestuous relationship of a girl for her father and Brunswick emphasizing the phallic phase. Dickes's own contribution brought modern structural theory into consideration with his emphasis on the role of the superego. He likewise stressed the preoedipal fixations in the development of lying, particularly those of the anal phase.

The analytic literature has, of course, made many more contributions to the study of lying but mainly in the form of work on reality testing and the phenomenon of denial or disavowal. In his "Fetishism" (Freud, 1927) and "A Disturbance of Memory on the Acropolis" (1936), Freud outlined the psychological phenomena of both believing and not believing at one and the same time. Freud's own clarification of disavowal is best seen in his quotation from the Spanish poem about the last caliph of Granada; "Letters had reached him telling him that Alhambra was taken. He threw the letters in the fire and killed the messenger." This brings home to us that this powerful mechanism allows us to lie to ourselves or at least a part of us does so allow. Freud explained that the phenomenon of splitting allows a part of the ego that knows reality to coexist with a part that must, in effect, lie about it. Though usually the parts are not in contact and not simultaneously available to conscious scrutiny, the lie is but a step beyond what may be called an illusion. The progression from delusion, wherein the truth may not be "known," to illusion, wherein the truth is unconscious, to a lie, wherein we both know and do not know, is a progression based on this splitting process.

Glover (1956) stated that rationalizing our own maladaptions plus turning a blind eye to any idiosyncrasies that make us uncomfortable and allowing "these two mechanisms to run harmoniously together in consciousness, ends in, for all practical purposes, a lie." This is the analyst's attempt to clarify the intrapsychic makeup of the lie. When we consider the liar we thus need to evaluate the extent of disavowal operating.

The most precise and novel recent addition to the psychoanalytic literature on the phenomena of lying has been contributed by Kohut (1966) in his formulation on the grandiose self as a form of narcissism. His explanation of pseudologica fantastica involves the overexpansiveness of the grandiose self in its exhibitionism and megalomania. The testing of reality is suspended as the grandiose self merges with objects of narcissistic investment, and the problem of intentional deception is less an issue than that of the limitlessness of the self-experience. Here too, however, disavowal is usually operating, and the individual both knows and does not know.

Developmental Considerations

The earliest formation of psychic structure has been formulated by various writers and is either conceptualized as involving an undifferentiated ego-id matrix (Hartmann, Kris, and Loewenstein, 1946), a nonintegrated arrangement of ego nuclei (Glover, 1956), a nondifferentiated self-object fusion (Jacobson, 1964), or some other representation of a primitive arrangement of stimuli impinging on an apparatus not yet able to organize and adjust its responses. In this state of affairs issues of truth or falsehood are not germane. Pathological parallels of the primitive psychic apparatus (considered with some latitude) would involve severe schizophrenic reactions or processes, and here too the question of telling the truth has little relevance. Seen from the point of view of disparate aspects of the self or ego, there can be communication inward and outward from one area with little or no connection whatsoever with another and perhaps contrary area. Likewise such reparative processes as delusions render irrelevant the matter of truth or lying since the necessary developmental processes are not in operation.

A clinical example of this may clarify the point. A psychotic patient told me that he had known me previously though this was our first interview. He likewise knew that we had never met before, but the two supposed contradictory statements could live together because they were not connected, and it would be foolhardy to confront the patient with the contradiction. My clinical assessment was that at some point he felt familiar with me, and thus he "knew me" from before but at another point he recognized my unfamiliarity.

The delusion, of course, is a resolution of some of the many confusing and contradictory feelings of the disorganized psyche. The patient just mentioned might resolve his dilemma by "discovering" that I had disguised myself or perhaps some other explanation could handle the discontinuity.

After some cohesive establishment of the self the most clarifying metapsychological description of the psychic apparatus is that of the self or ego in relation to narcissistic objects. This state can be conceptualized as that of the need-satisfying object noted by Anna Freud (1965) or some form of the grandiose self described by Kohut (1966). Regardless of the preferred metapsychological formulations, the cohesive self is not at first clearly separated from the archaic objects and the differentiation of self and object is not obtained until further development has occurred. This differentiation, according to Zetzel (1965), is considered a requisite for analyzability.

Though the psychological phenomena of lying may be observed at this point in both normal childhood development (the innocent lying of Anna Freud) and its pathological counterparts in the adult, there can be no intentional lying or intentional truth-telling. Dickes (1967) correctly argued that lying involves secret keeping. This capacity presupposes intentionality and thus demands separation of self from object and a different state of needs in self from object. The pseudologica fantastica described by Kohut as a pathological manifestation of the grandiose self is based on a merger with the surrounding objects. Thus, once again the issue of truth or falsehood is not relevant or pertinent.

For an example of the phenomenon of the temporary manifestation of the grandiose self, I freely borrow from Kohut who described the analytic candidate who says he has read a book though he has not. The momentary expansiveness of his grandiosity does not allow for truth to prevail; but only a careful evaluation of this narcissistic imbalance allows one to consider him an intentional liar or someone for whom truth is temporarily unavailable.

Another form of lying noted before the complete functional differentiation of self from object involves still another problem of narcissism, that of the maintenance of a relationship to an idealized (archaic or transitional) object. From the little boy who insists his father is the strongest or smartest or wealthiest man in the world to the patient who insists on his analyst's omniscience, the search for an idealized parental image is aided by "lying" about the other's shortcomings. The genesis of the pathogenic fixation of patients on an idealized parental image has been described by Kohut as relating to the enmeshment within the narcissistic web of the parent's personality.

Parents who have lied to children to maintain their own grandiosity will necessarily not be told the truth by the child as he attempts to recapture or maintain the idealization. To be sure, parents can meet a child's lie by simply allowing it or by challenging it with the truth. The multitude of interactions between parent and child over the issue of truthfulness usually are directed to aspects of the child's health and well-being. The child who says he can fly might be allowed this fantasy until he tries to take off from a rooftop. Often, however, the crucial ingredient becomes the degree of threat to the parent's narcissism.

An amusing and illustrative story told by a patient involved her little boy of three who lied to her. He said that he had just spoken to the doctor who said the boy was not to eat any vegetables. The mother said she would call the doctor to find out if this meant the particular vegetables she had prepared that day. The boy said he had just spoken to the doctor who said he could not eat those particular vegetables. The mother said that he obviously did not understand the specialness of these vegetables and would call to clarify it with the doctor. At this point the little boy blurted out that the doctor had just died.

The story is a family gem and is hardly felt to be an item of concern. However, a crucial point in the anecdote is that both child and mother were lying to one another; the mother was obviously better at it, and the child was driven to a small act of desperation. Interestingly, the mother is chronically incapable of telling the truth, and the little boy has grown up with a variant of the problems Winnicott (1953) connects to transitional objects, pathological drug addiction.

As development proceeds to the formation of a superego responsible for internal regulation, the problem of telling the truth becomes an internal one based on successful adaptation (normal) or based on an expression of neurotic conflict (pathological). Before this developmental step the need state of the self and its relationship to archaic or transitional objects often make truth-telling an impossible task. Any attempt to conceptualize a primitive merger of self and narcissistic objects, with resulting blurring of truth in terms of deliberate concealment or deception, is doomed to failure. However, at the point of structural integrity of an internal regulating system, the pertinence of telling the truth is subject to meaningful scrutiny. This particular form of communication becomes an interpersonal one based on effectiveness of the message and agreement with the moral standards and ideals of the superego. Indeed there is no particular biological or psychological reason to tell the truth, and a supposedly healthy superego allows a variety of deceptions, concealments, and white lies.[1]

Pathological truth-telling or the need never to lie is probably indicative of a stern superego struggling with hostility and guilt. Much hostility and aggression may be discharged under the guise of always being truthful. The inability to not tell the truth (the George Washington syndrome) is a neurotic manifestation. A perhaps common example of this pathology was offered by a patient who complained of his inability to hold a job. He described himself as forthright and honest but possibly a trifle too blunt. His compulsive neurotic character manifested itself in a conscientious work performance and a scrupulous attention to detail. His calling his superiors' attention to their minor derelictions of duty often irritated them and led to his dismissal though he was only being honest. A hostile attitude to paternal surrogates was nicely expressed via his virtuous stance.

The problem of determining whether lying is a defense against truth or vice versa necessitates a more comprehensive view than merely concluding that lying is a symptom. At early points in development any new found capacity functions in an experimental mode. This later is drawn into the varieties of psychic function so that an assessment of the multiple functioning of any behavior reveals it sometimes more as a discharge, sometimes more as a defense, and sometimes more as conflict free. Thus, telling the truth as a behavioral phenomenon serves a variety of masters.

It may need emphasis that certain patients close to primary-process material may view other individuals' defenses as being manifestations of hypocrisy. Such a position equates the unconscious with truth and overlooks the necessary role of the ego in regulating and adjusting what is true.

Adolescence and Truth-Telling

As noted, there are crucial periods in development when telling the truth or lying are of paramount significance. These often occur around the anal struggle and the preoccupation with concealment of body function as well as the oedipal period with its own particular quality of concealment of instinctual wishes and oedipal fantasies. For the most part, the preoedipal manifestations of lying have to do with narcissistic objects with the resultant relative inability to be truthful, whereas oedipal lying is more classically neurotic and associated with a problem of the superego. This corresponds to Anna Freud's (1965) delinquent lying. The pathological concern with truth-telling is most common in obsessive-compulsive neurotics in whom the struggle is a neurotic one with superego conflict and libidinal regression to anal fixation points emphasizing those qualities of retention, hostility, and concomitant dishonesty that may characterize this period.

Another period in which there is a recurrence of interest in being truthful is that of adolescence. Adolescents often are very interested in questions of truth or deception and also show marked interest in their parents' honesty. A most common and bitter complaint directed against parents is that they are dishonest, corrupt, deceptive, and so on. Parents of adolescents often are able to verbalize the fact that they do not always know when or how to be honest with their children and are often caught in a morass of deception and its consequences. Thus, careful examination of the issues reveal that projection of the adolescent's wish to conceal onto the parent is not the complete answer.

The adolescent struggle over ideals nicely demonstrates the problem. Ideal figures are usually imbued with many qualities, one of which is honesty. Ideal persons never lie. The superego may tell you not to lie, but the idealizing quality makes you proud of this accomplishment (Kohut, 1966).

The adolescent re-experiences his search for an external ideal, but likewise re-encounters his fallible parent. The molding and modification of the internal psychological structures takes place as the parent is seen as less than ideal; the sought-for ideal is internalized, and a realistic relationship with the parent ensues. Thus, at one stage of this process (which unfortunately for parental comfort is not a stepwise progression but an oscillation), the parent is idealized, then debunked, then someone else is idealized and usually more slowly brought to ground. The lost qualities of parents become the internal ideals, so that the parent who accepts and allows awareness of his limits in truth-telling will likely have a child who idealizes truth-telling.

One case illustrative of this concerns an eighteen-year-old young man seen in consultation for mixed symptomatology of lying and stealing. His family consisted of a working mother, an overworked father, and a younger sister. The father cared for the children, did the laundry, cleaned the house, and carried out his full-time job. The mother was involved in her own outside employment, and her son told me that when she was home her major activity was criticism.

I suggested a family interview to better assess the interaction of the members. The father called and said that he and the sister would come, but the mother refused to expose herself to what she suspected would be blame for her son's difficulty. One can only theorize (but perhaps accurately) that this parent could not serve the necessary function in development for her adolescent son. She could not be alternately idealized and debunked in a partial stepwise manner to allow formation of an internal set of reasonable ideals in the child's psyche. Her own extreme sensitivity manifested in her outflow of criticism made her unavailable for the crucial developmental task. No doubt the father's passivity also contributed to the son's inability to internalize ideals and his subsequent symptomatology.

Adolescents recapitulate all the problems of development in their transition to adulthood. The psychic stresses met with may result in fragmentation of the self, which leads to noncohesiveness and may be manifested as lying, but is more readily appreciated as a lack of internal integration and communication. The precarious cohesiveness of the self and its relation to archaic objects may demonstrate lack of truthfulness based on merger of the grandiose self or a need to overidealize the parental image. Again, the lack of truthfulness of this stage is not based on deliberate deception but on lack of self-object differentiation.

The struggle over truthfulness often mirrors the struggle over separation with an oscillation between merger with an external object and internalization. Only after such internalization does truthfulness and lying allow relevant scrutiny as neurotic symptoms showing compromises between impulse and defense in a relationship of object love.

Adolescents often manifest overscrupulosity in a manner of familiarizing themselves with this new internal agency. Here we see pathological truth-telling. Only when adulthood is entered is there a parallel entrance to the use of truthfulness in a manner appropriate to adaptation and thus not based on superego struggles or preoedipal problems. The clinician who works with adolescents is familiar with the variability of responses, since structure is fluid and runs the gamut of these developmental stages. No period better illustrates the inexact correlation of truth-telling with pathology and potential for treatment. Likewise, no period better demonstrates the idea that lying is as much a part of normal growth and development as is telling the truth.

Clinical Consideration

The basic rule of psychoanalysis is simply to say whatever comes to mind with no requirement to be truthful about it. This avoids deliberate concealments and secrets, and when these do occur there is some manifestation of resistance or else a regression to a state of psychic organization characteristic of a period before truth-telling is possible. To comprehend the problem in its developmental and metapsychologic meaning leads to the realization that criticism is out of place, and analysis either of an early narcissistic merger or a neurotic superego problem is called for.

The countertransference reactions of repugnance and anger at being lied to usually involve some narcissistic problem of the analyst, who required more from the patient than can be therapeutically accomplished at the time. To be sure, patients who persist in lying more likely suffer from narcissistic disorders with a relative inability to appreciate separate objects irrespective of their own needs. However, this does not necessarily preclude an analytic stance. The usual reaction revolves around the analyst's struggle over not being recognized as a distinct person or an object with unique qualities. This usually relates to the analyst's meaningfulness being literally disavowed, that is, his not being recognized, appreciated, or valued. The necessity of such a defense and its accompanying split in the self is obvious in order to maintain the integrity of the remaining psyche. The phenomena may be subject to conscious awareness or, more commonly they remain unconscious. However, the experience of the analyst ranges from boredom to outrage as he feels totally insignificant and unimportant. There usually is some personal variation on the theme of "How dare you do this to me" as the narcissistic position of the analyst is threatened by an untruthful patient.[2]

Perhaps a more intriguing question revolves around the analyst's telling the truth to the patient. There is no doubt little outright lying to patients except for occasions of specific neurotic problems of the analyst. However, the issues of deliberate concealment, keeping secrets, telling only partial truths are all part of analytic lore. For one, the analyst often purposefully conceals much about his private and personal life, feelings, judgments, and values from the patient. This is accepted practice in analytic technique and is designed to foster a transference neurosis with a minimum of interference from the real qualities of the analyst. There is no doubt that this is often subject to abuse because of the analyst's conviction that concealment is not only in the best interests of the patient but also that such areas of curiosity are not properly part of the analytic material or are simply none of the patient's business. It may well be that this at times reflects a defensive position on the part of the analyst, whose fantasied idealized picture of himself vis-à-vis the patient is threatened.

Moreover, the overzealous truth-telling or self-revealing analyst does truly often conceal more than he reveals (Kohut, 1966) and again may be protecting a narcissistic image of himself or defending against the patients transference to the analyst as an idealized parent. Here, too, we may see evidence of a neurotic conflict of the analyst involving hostility to the patient. Some narcissistic problems of analysts involve their inability to see the patient in their own web of grandiosity.

Concealments or lack of telling the truth on the analyst's part, of course, include material about the patient as well as the analyst. Analysts rarely tell patients all they know. Perhaps only at certain periods of analytic work, when analyst and analysand mutually share association to analytic material, does there exist something approaching complete truth-telling. We are reminded of Winnicott's (1953) consideration of transitional objects as those that are shared without being owned by either party. Perhaps even more tellingly relevant is Kohut's (1966) description of empathy as one kind of narcissistic transformation that involves the gathering of psychological data and that is necessary for good analytic work. That is, the analyst's narcissism has matured to allow a merger or mutuality under the control of the ego of the analyst and thus can be used for understanding the patient. Perhaps the capacity to be objectively truthful to the analysand is a measuring stick of analytic understanding and a balance between cure by love or cure by objective dosing of interpretations.

Summary

Truthfulness in society is essentially related to moral behavior and ethical ideas. This is the mature end of the developmental line of the concept. As such the history of truthfulness is the history of civilized man and often a barometer of the degree or extent of civilization. The art and literature of our world—from Polonius's famous advice to his son (which, I feel, is basically untrue), to the maddening riddles of Pirandello, to the mystery of Rashomon—reflect a preoccupation with this concept.

The concern with the concept of truthfulness has been mainly a religious one. Hindu ethics regard truthfulness as virtue and states that one must not hurt others since the purpose of truthfulness is the welfare of others. The wise remain silent if this purpose cannot be served. The Christian ethic of man's primary obligation being to love one another manifests itself in a network through which love must be expressed. Thus man must adjust his love impulse in a responsible manner and truthfulness is always subsumed under this basic obligation. The dominant trait in Jewish ethics is the law, and there exists a pluralism of the mood and manner of Jewish experience as related to truthfulness since the source of Jewish ethics derives from both Bible and Talmud.

Such philosophical schools as pragmatism indicate that ideals are simply hypotheses and moral standards must change with changing social conditions. Indeed a positivist study of the concept of truth always reduces it to a relative matching of facts, that is, truth has no ethical relevance in this view. The whole problem about objective falsehoods arises from thinking of facts or falsehoods too literally as objects or entities. There are no negative facts at all since fact has meaning only as parts of the phrase "it is a fact that" and a negative fact simply says "it is not the case." Modern logic has evolved other devices for dealing with negation and eliminates it as a problem.

At some time we see the often described freshness and openness of adolescents who can be amazingly free and honest. There is a marvelous appeal and seductiveness to such candidness and at times this becomes raised to a kind of philosophy. In its simplest form it is merely the statement that people should be completely honest with one another and hold nothing back. This then will lead to a state of true understanding of mankind. Sometimes this is carried over into various forms of psychotherapy, especially in groups wherein everyone is encouraged to speak out and say whatever is on one's mind. I suspect one of the turning points from adolescence to adulthood is learning that openness often is cruelty and saying whatever is in one's mind is an indulgence that no adult can afford.

Thus, we must conclude that truthfulness consists of telling the facts to someone whom one wishes to know them. It involves both the capacity to do so acquired in the course of development plus the judgment to behave with maximal adaptiveness to the situation. It is not necessarily a higher order of behavior nor an ethical good. The final outcome of the developmental line of truth-telling is thus an admixture of facts and fictions that best meet the situation. As Hartmann (1960) said,

Analysis is as little a never-failing key to morality, as it is (as Freud was the first to realize) a reliable key to happiness. [However] just because we are psychoanalysts, we have a desire for greater clarity as to these [moral and ethical] problems, even where they transcend our immediate clinical, theoretical, and technical concern.

NOTES

1. An example of truth-telling free of conflict is the television program "To Tell the Truth," wherein participants try to determine which one of four contestants is being

honest. Here the situation is one of plan without any necessarily meaningful pathological connections.

2. Kohut in a personal communication has likened the passion for truth to a feeling of firmness of the self.

REFERENCES

Basch, M. F. (1967). Unpublished manuscript. Chicago, Illinois.

Dickes, R. (1967). Some observations on lying as a derivative of secrecy. *Journal of the Hillside Hospital*, 6:94–109.

Ferenczi, S. (1927). The problem of termination in analysis. In: *Final Contribution to the Problems and Methods of Psychoanalysis*. New York: Basic Books, pp. 77–86.

Freud, A. (1965). *Normality and Pathology in Childhood*. New York: International Universities Press.

Freud, S. (1905). Fragment of an analysis of a case of hysteria. Standard Edition, 12:105. London: Hogarth, 1953.

———. (1909). Notes upon a case of obsessional neurosis. Standard Edition, 10:153–249. London: Hogarth, 1955.

———. (1913). On beginning the treatment. Standard Edition, 12:123–143. London: Hogarth, 1958.

———. (1927). Fetishism. Standard Edition, 21:152–157. London: Hogarth, 1961.

———. (1936). A disturbance of memory on the Acropolis. Standard Edition, 21:239–248. London: Hogarth, 1964.

Glover, E. (1956). *On the Early Development of Mind*. New York: International Universities Press.

Hartmann, H. (1960). *Psychoanalysis and Moral Values*. New York: International Universities Press.

———, Kris, E., and Loewenstein, R. M. (1946). Comments on the formation of psychic structure. *Psychoanalytic Study of the Child*, 2:11–38.

Jacobson, E. (1964). The self and the object world. *Journal of the American Psychoanalytic Association*, monograph series 2.

Kohut, H. (1966). Forms and transformation of narcissism. *Journal of the American Psychoanalytic Association*, 14(2):243–272.

———. (1971). *The Analysis of the Self*. New York: International Universities Press.

Tausk, V. (1919). On the origin of the "influencing machine" in schizophrenia. *Psychoanalytic Quarterly*, 2:319.

Winnicott, D. W. (1953). Transitional objects and transitional phenomena. *International Journal of Psychoanalysis*, 31:89–97.

———. (1964). Book review: C. G. Jung: Memories, Dreams, Reflections. *International Journal of Psychoanalysis*, 45:450–455.

Zetzel, E. (1965). The theory of therapy in relation to a developmental model of the psychic apparatus. *International Journal of Psychoanalysis*, 46:39–52.

8] THE YOUTH CULTURE,
FUTURE ADULTHOOD,
AND SOCIETAL CHANGE

ERWIN R. SMARR AND PHILIP J. ESCOLL

The New Values and Adulthood

Erikson, in *Identity: Youth and Crisis* (1968), wrote about the cultural and technological consolidation that characterizes an era's way of doing things, a mode of being adult with which youth identifies. He was speaking about the vast compact majority, who are able to combine the existent dominant techniques with their own identity development and become what they do. This process seems apt for consideration of the present tensions experienced by late adolescents toward joining society. They are pointedly saying they want their adulthood to be defined differently from that of their parents. They do not want to have to do and be what their parents are and do. We wish to consider what impact the current value conflicts focused on by youth may have on their particular patterns of adulthood to be.

We learn of the traumatic effect of future shock not only from Alvin Toffler (1970), but also Waelder (1967), who wrote of how the rate of scientific and technical change threatens to create a rapid obsolescence beyond the human biological capacity of adaptation. Such change destroys economic, social, legal, and emotional security. New technology, together with rebellion against tradition, changes adult role expectations. Waelder predicted there will be nothing constant but change, which also means no enduring relationships, the prerequisites for mental health. We are seeing these effects on today's youth. We must examine the meanings of these changes for their influence on mental health, personality and character development, and society. We can expect, as usual, to see these changes reflected not only in pathology but also in norms of the healthy.

It is acknowledged widely in psychiatric circles that there has been a progressive change in the personality structure, and hence the type of psychopathology, of Americans during the middle half of this century, along with a progressive reduction of authoritarianism in society. The rigid Victorian moralistic superego has been modified; we now frequently see predominantly characterological problems in adults instead of psychoneurotic symptoms in the classical repressive mode. In a workshop discussion at the American Psychoanalytic Association meetings, December 1970, for example, it was readily agreed that there is now much more acting out (in the broad use of that term) of what used to be repressed, and repression is now directed not so much against genitality as against object relationships, a defense against early traumatic object loss. The clinical picture produced is of the cool, affectless, narcissistic character, obsessively driven to transient liaisons and to distracting activity and drugs, with impairment of capacity for object constancy and little interest in introspection. Accompanying this change is the so-called new morality, which rejects sexual restraint and marriage as the primary conditions of heterosexual intimacy and emphasizes present conscious feeling as the basis for authenticity in relationships. The philosophical antecedents of this rejection of the old order of authoritarian and rational controls are found in the writings of the German philosophers of romantic antirationalism from Kant to Marcuse (1955) and are also reflected in the therapeutic philosophies of D. H. Lawrence and W. Reich (Rieff, 1966).

Along with these changes have also come the social effects of affluence, prolonged education, an unpopular and demoralizing war, the bomb, the pill, masses of students influenced by intellectuals, as well as an antiauthoritarian political spirit. These have culminated in a social movement of opposition to scientific progressive rationalism, called "neohumanism." These three forces, the narcissistic character, the new morality, and neohumanism, have coalesced to form a living style being tried widely in adolescent role playing, emphasizing libertarian rights of existential individuality.

Instead of identifying with the official predominant generational pattern of ideology set by their parents, there has been an attempt to "do their own thing" or, as Erikson (1968) put it, "to ritualize life for themselves, and by themselves, against us." They do not want to do as the compact majority, "combine the dominant [cultural] techniques with their identity development and become what they do."

We would like to consider the influence of this value system on the life style of the developing adult and for other American youth. For as Erikson (1968) has also pointed out, "in revolutionary times, the over-privileged and the under-privileged often reach out to each other, being both marginal to the vast consolidations of the compact majority."

This seeming coalition in the youth culture styles of living may be misleading. While both, for different reasons, take an anti-establishment stance and use common symbols of that opposition, their motives and needs may differ as much as they overlap. The underprivileged, while also rebelling against a futile life of work, cannot do so from the same base of economic security as the children of affluence, who reject the competitiveness of an economy of scarcity because they think it is no longer necessary for them to sacrifice pleasure for the sake of future security; they can have both, now as well as later. This change in values, from an impulse-delay psychology renouncing some pleasure for sublimation into work to one of more immediate gratification and rejection of material rewards for work, affects both personal character structure and future role preparation.

Since what is normal bears some relationship to what is statistically most frequent, are we seeing an emergence of a life style of young adults which represents a new norm, especially since it offers so much libidinal, passive-aggressive gratification?

So much gratification always upsets a parental generation, which feels deprived by its own sacrifices, past, present, and future, whether real or fantasied, and there is always, therefore, an envy of the youth generation who will displace it, as well as envy of its privilege without responsibility. Parental superegos, acquired at the cost of libidinal repression, cannot tolerate so much freedom and therefore the older generation feels punitive toward youth. One form of this envy and punishment focuses on the immaturity of the young, predicting that they cannot become mature adults and meet adult role requirements and that some tragic fate will certainly befall them. Another method, prevalent among mental health professionals, is to consider their character structure a fixed norm and declare that the less rigidly constructed young are or will become mentally ill. The rigid, parental superego and ego ideal are considered prerequisites for mental health. Can today's youth work out an adult life style satisfactory for their needs, but with different values and goals with a less repressive ethic, and still be considered mature and adult?

Adulthood, as distinguished from youth, has been characterized chiefly by commitment to roles that carry responsibility—for self, mate, offspring, and society, in part or in toto. The first responsibility, for self, implies separation and independence from parents emotionally, physically, and financially. Responsibility for a mate implies a capacity for sustained and enduring heterosexual genital relationship with love and tenderness, and a capacity to endure necessary adversity without abandonment of the mate, especially when the original romantic conditions for love become complicated by life's other realities. The responsibility to offspring implies a contribution to and investment in the future of the race and society, as well as a further acceptance of responsibility for the care and identity formation of the next generation. The last responsibility involves taking one's place somewhere in society, in accordance with the needs and motivations relevant to one's self and one's dependents. Responsibility means that one must respond to the needs of others (or self). It requires a perspective of consideration of others, of reality beyond the self-centered and pleasure-oriented perspective of youth, and a reliance largely on one's own resources. These are all aspects of ego and superego maturity, and require identification with responsible parental imagoes. They represent traditional Judeo-Christian Western adulthood.

The new ethic follows in part the moral doctrines of D. H. Lawrence, "neither an ethics of responsibility nor of conscience, but an ethics of action," and of W. Reich, the ideal of the "unafraid individual . . . who satisfies his strong libidinal needs" (Rieff, 1966). Both stress the need to overthrow the repressive old internalizing order by the cultivation of a "private sense of well-being, divorced from an ethic of social responsibility based on the guilt feeling of the private man" (Rieff, 1966, p. 196). Combining the sexual revolutionary aims of Reich with the mystical religion of sexual union proferred by Lawrence, there is, at times, a complete turning away from responsibility to anyone but the self. Curiously combined with this, however, is an emphasis on deep emotional sharing with one partner. None of this is new, but it is a superego change in middle-class America. It is the overthrow of puritanism and the Protestant ethic. The question is "how will this affect the patterns of adulthood to be of this generation?"

The Group for the Advancement of Psychiatry (1968) report on normal adolescence, in defining the resolution of adolescence, specifies six criteria: (1) the attainment of separation and independence from the parents; (2) establishment of a sexual identity; (3) the capacity for lasting relationships and for both tender and genital sexual love in heterosexual relationships; (4) the development of a personal moral value system; (5) the commitment to work; (6) a return to the parents in a new relationship based on a relative equality.

We shall examine the ways in which present changes affect these criteria of resolving adolescence and, reciprocally, examine whether these criteria are all still relevant for tomorrow's middle-class adults. Let us consider each of these criteria in the light of both intrapsychic and social aspects of adolescent and future adult personality.

Separation and Independence from Parents

Supported by the combination of affluence, freedom to postpone work, ever-spiraling needs of the society for specialists, and an inability to absorb untrained manpower into the economy, the earlier foreclosure of adolescence out of economic necessity has changed to a prolonged moratorium on adulthood for middle-class youth. In Marcusean philosophy, this should ultimately progress to a society free of external compulsion, where a pleasure ethic can predominate. Many of today's youth act as if that state were already here. Though this has freed youth to develop its critical faculties and to test and challenge society further than ever before in modern times, in what respects has it promoted and/or hindered ego growth toward self-sufficiency, experience of reality, and resolution of dependence on parents? Related to this is the lessened certainty in parental definition and values. Adolescents do not have clear guidelines set for their impulses and behavior. This leads to difficulty in separation-individuation and can contribute to impairment in the development of the ego's capacity to deal effectively with the demands of the internal and external world. There is a wide variation in the ego adequacy of an adolescent. Blos (1969) points out that the disorganization of social structures may act like a psychonoxious agent on the consolidation process of late adolescence, in which "defective structure of social institutions lays bare in many adolescents an ego deviancy of early childhood which was contained as long as the child remained part of the family."

Most authors seem to agree that one striking influence on middle-class youth is affluence. Children of depression parents are, in a sense, living the depression in reverse. With affluence, there is a tendency to gratify the child without expecting him to contribute or to produce. He may not receive the pleasure of achievement and mastery and the related sense of competence and ability to deal with stress (Settlage, 1969). He may not be sufficiently exposed to frustration, and may receive gratification (of drives) without experiencing delays and have difficulty in developing the very important and necessary mechanism of sublimation.

An example is that of a nineteen-year-old girl whose parents struggled through many difficulties to achieve financial success. She was much indulged throughout her childhood materialistically and otherwise. At thirteen, she expressed a desire to follow an older friend and live in Greenwich Village for a time. Her parents readily assented. At fifteen, she became interested in the Navajo Indian culture. One afternoon, a virtual library of books on the subject was delivered to her home. She found the stress of typing applications for college trying, so mother and father volunteered to do it. At seventeen, she was accepted for early admission to college. She eagerly looked forward to going away from home but as the date drew closer she became increasingly anxious. Subsequently, she showed severe personality disorganization requiring hospitalization. In the hospital, she vacillated between expecting her roommate to care for her or caring for her roommate. She was uneasy and expressed feelings of self-depreciation and worthlessness when asked to make her bed; yet, in one of her fantasies, she saw herself as a princess.

These adolescents lack the capacity to wait or postpone; they may be impulse ridden and lack confidence and self-esteem because of not having the experience of coping with frustration and stress. They may feel exploited in being used as narcissistic adornments by their parents. In addition, the overstimulation of earlier years makes the present reality disappointing; it imposes stress, and it does not offer the previously experienced immediate gratification. They may view themselves as exceptions, not governed by the reality principle. When such individuals present themselves for treatment, symptoms such as lack of self-esteem, vague dissatisfaction with their lives, and depression are common. Their character structure is basically a narcissistic one, and it is difficult for them to sustain object relationships with all the narcissistic wounds and vicissitudes involved.

For some, perhaps many, upper middle-class youth, the fantasy that their wishes can be always satisfied does have some material reality, just as it was always true for second-generation children of wealth, whose parents had sufficient means to provide for their scions without the adoption of a work ethic. The generation that inherits wealth usually does not develop the character strength of its competitive parents' generation. Many have turned to alcohol, or run afoul of the law when marriage placed more demands on them than they were able to meet. Today's substitute or supplement for alcohol is drugs.

On the other hand, some adolescents who have felt secure economically, and whose parents did not respond as previously described, are not materialistically oriented. Their ego ideal does not include the acquisition of wealth and achievement of material success but rather may incorporate the ideal of contributing in a constructive fashion to society. These characteristics are often seen when they become adults. Since these values are not primarily acquired rebelliously in opposition to the parents, they have a more lasting basis and often satisfy values implicitly shared by the parents. A recent follow-up study of several of the Berkeley radicals found them to be serious, gainfully employed adults, devoted to social causes.

A twenty-four-year-old young man was reared in an affluent family. In college, pursuing a course of study to prepare him to follow his father into the family business, he experienced a sense of dissatisfaction with his existence and depression. He used marijuana extensively to cope with anxiety related to feelings of failure. Subsequently, having had some group therapy, he conducted group sessions for drug users. He showed considerable skill and sensitivity, and later was able to secure employment as a drug educator in a community mental health center. He was content, feeling he had found something meaningful. In a dream, he saw himself working for an older man who thoroughly approved of his efforts. The patient remembered that his father had expressed a wish to leave his business and devote himself fully to a social agency for which he did some volunteer work.

In such instances the freedom from scarcity permits the fulfillment of a previously suppressed ideal, provided the son succeeds in finding a new reality-based identity and has a basically healthy ego. This case also highlights the problems of the protracted adolescence characteristic of today's society. A prolonged period of education and training is necessary before the individual is considered to be capable of assuming adult status. As a result, some adolescents are in limbo, partially emancipated but unable to fully resolve their emotional dependency on the parents. In adulthood, such individuals may demonstrate a spurious independence, but may have serious gaps in their self-esteem. The superego may not be able to accept this. They may find the disparity between the independent ideal self and the dependent actual self quite painful.

A twenty-eight-year-old man, trained in physics, could not find the employment he desired without an advanced degree. Becoming discouraged, he then studied architecture. When told by an instructor that he needed to develop his artistic creativity, he enrolled in art courses for a year. He married during this period and saw himself as independent. Many of his depressive feelings, however, related to superego condemnations for still depending on his parents for economic support and for not measuring up to his ego ideal.

Passive-receptive wishes may be intensified by prolonged adolescence; the person may demand that the environment continue gratifying him. Sometimes these wishes are repressed, and reaction formations develop. These passive longings are often satisfied by drugs. Drugs give some adolescents a sense of the security and safety of earlier years, and this usage can continue into adulthood. Drug usage is certainly common in adolescent society today, and we can expect to see its influence in adults.

A beginning college student was having conflicts with his family and often used drugs, particularly in times of stress. He progressed well in treatment and went on to medical school. Now, when he experiences anxiety studying, he uses marijuana, even though it interferes with concentration.

Identification with contemporaries often provides a pathway to sustained ego interests that otherwise might have disappeared if adolescence ended more abruptly. Keniston (1968) has emphasized this point. Such youths may be able to effectively maintain their position as constructive observers and movers of an adult society from which they are to some extent detached spectators because of protracted adolescence. Their lack of adult heroes with whom to identify is compensated for by their identification with one another and with young adults of similar persuasion.

Another problem often results, paradoxically, from the lessened identification with authority. Some adolescents, because of the absence of valid authority figures, find it difficult to feel comfortable with their own impulses. They may develop rigid defenses and punitive superegos. In adulthood, such an individual, should he be devoted to a cause, might be exceedingly severe with colleagues who deviated from his standards, and he would react strongly to criticism. Thus, lessened authority identification does not guarantee the disappearance of the authoritarian personality.

A twenty-year-old college student's father was a very mild-mannered professor who set few rules at home and who expressed no concern when the patient and his brothers destroyed household possessions. The patient was exceedingly active in peace-directed, antiwar organizations. He described his activities in some detail and with considerable pride, before disclosing that he was always fearful that he might hurt someone. He recalled his contempt for colleagues who left the organizations and described the scathing denunciation of righteous indignation he administered to a friend who declined to go on a march. He feared he might injure someone by his wrath, and he was plagued by frightening dreams in which he was involved in violence and brutality.

Of course, less authoritarianism might be internalized as a reasonable, tolerant superego, leading an adult to be flexible in his judgment of himself and others. Some adults to be may find it difficult to appropriately exercise authority in their work and with their families, for example, the adult who declined a position of leadership as being too authoritarian for his ethic. This is one of the patterns contemporary youth are showing, a preference for agrarian crafts and blue-collar jobs, anything but competitive authoritarian rules.

Is it possible, however, that ego and superego development are promoted in these circumstances? This depends on the stability of psychic organization. With a well-functioning ego he may respond to uncertainty and the lack of absolutes by being stimulated and challenged to develop his capacities further. His superego may be less archaic and harsh and may function in harmony with other psychic structures, permitting acceptance and expression of emotions.

In summary, we see the following spectrum of patterns of late adolescents from affluent families:

1. Secure adolescents making successful adaptations: (a) conventional youths who identify with the "compact majority" and are preparing for traditional career roles (according to Offer [1969], the majority); (b) less materialistically driven, idealistic youths, with more socially constructive ideals implicitly shared by parents, and not chosen in rebellious opposition; (c) youths who make socially constructive identifications with other youths and their values rather than their parents, and are able to move society because of their detached positions; (d) passive-dependent youths successfully sublimating into a vocation.

2. Immature, insecure adolescents who may show: (a) ego deficiencies, with insufficient mastery of frustration, underdeveloped sublimation, decompensating under loss of dependency; (b) impulse-ridden, narcissistic personalities, subject to depression and unsustained object relationships; (c) passive-dependent personalities unsuccessfully coping; (d) reactively rigid authoritarian personalities, with behavior sometimes displaced into militancy; (e) reactive depressions over inability to achieve independence because of vocational delay and emancipation difficulties.

Any or all of these personalities today may use drugs, to a lesser or greater degree, dependent upon the intensity of anxiety to stress. In a somewhat similar fashion, the new social values, neohumanism and the new morality, can be used as modes of expressing adolescent conflicts and function as vehicles of defense. This fact tends to confuse and obscure the problem of whether these values have some validity and authenticity for adult maturity and society in their own right.

Establishment of Sexual Identity and Capacity for Love

For males it seems that the competitive model based on the warrior-hunter, or on machismo, has been abandoned in favor of the "feminine," noncompetitive traits of sentimentality, sensitivity, and tenderness. Occupational achievement as a measure of manhood, especially the earning of money as a status symbol, is decried. With it, also, have gone other forms of sublimated aggression that heretofore were parts of the masculine identity, including the desire and willingness to look after and be responsible for someone else's economic well-being. The permissive, perhaps even valued, emphasis placed on overt homosexuality and bisexuality, not to mention the influence of the "liberated" woman who rejects the role of homemaker, causes us to wonder about the pattern of family life of the future. Are sexual roles becoming less distinct to the point that the differences between maternal and paternal are being obliterated? Will we learn that anatomy is not necessarily destiny as regards active and passive, even in a purely genital sense? How will the oedipus complex be resolved in the children of these adolescents whose own resolutions are different from those of their parents?

Though sociological data show that the vast majority of young women still expect to marry, there has been a notable increase in couples living together without marriage. Will the opportunity to experiment with marriage without legal commitment promote or retard development toward a better capacity for mature love and durable mating? We note that our criteria for adulthood do not specifically include marriage. Is the institution, the outgrowth first of the change from a nomadic to an agricultural society and later, in medieval society, of the need for social order, on the way out in this technotronic age? The concerns of overpopulation, the pill, and the availability of abortion portend to make marriage less necessary as a vehicle of security and child-rearing. How much, then, will marriage continue as a pure manifestation of people's needs for exclusive possession of a love object, overriding all other negative considerations? If so, will the change in character structure permit a less ambivalent, less tense relationship between mates after marriage? Will the trial marriage promote more maturity in this respect? It is a question of whether a healthier capacity for object love can develop when compulsory marriage is eliminated and people are freer to live out their adolescent narcissism.

One would expect adolescents who not only verbalize a concept of sexuality relating to emotional intimacy and closeness but actually experience it to be adults who have achieved a high level of comfortable functioning regarding sexual impulses. In others, verbalizing may be a rationalization, defending against anxiety and perpetuating conflicts that will linger, though masked, into adulthood. The freedom to experiment sexually does not necessarily overcome anxiety about sex. It may only obscure underlying pregenital fixations. The intense narcissism of many adolescents is also masked through denial and rationalization and is not, therefore, worked through, leading to sexual and other difficulties in close dyadic relationships which are characterized by sharing and giving.

We are already seeing some of the effects of the lessening of sharply defined female and male role models. To some, this lack of distinction leads to confusion regarding masculine or feminine identification; in others, there is a less rigid, less defensive internal conceptualization of male and female ideals and a comfortable acceptance of passive and aggressive attitudes in the self together with greater capacity for empathy with the opposite sex.

Helene Deutsch (1969) has pointed out that with early sexual gratification the inner work of alteration of narcissism into object relationship may not fully occur. Also, difficulties in identifying with a mother who has abandoned her traditional role, and who relates as a sister may lead to masculine identifications. The preoedipal relationship with father is intensified, and the tendency for identification with him is marked. The inadequate maternal ego ideal may lead to problems in marriage and motherhood. Here again, there may be a more flexible, less stereotyped, less rigid female ego ideal than that constructed in the traditional maternal relationship.

Perhaps we will see fidelity and monogamy prevail with or without marriage and remain a criterion of adulthood, because the sense of isolation in the absence of object love is too painful. Perhaps, too, woman's inborn need to fill her inner space with the right person will continue to compel generativity by reproduction, and thus continue the race despite a lack of belief in the species.

We have to conclude that current value shifts show propensities that favor both growth and development of the ego, as well as fixation and regression. For some, a higher degree of personal growth may be promoted, with greater freedom and capacity to love; for others, more predisposed to fixation, unconscious compulsions will be acted out, instead of being repressed. This will be simply a change in form but not substance, though the difference may have social consequences.

Personal Moral Value System

There is no doubt that present youth are cultivating a personal moral value system with a vengeance. They are trying to change the scientific-progressive-technological course of society to one emphasizing concern for human feelings, for nature, and for basic emotional security. It is very easy to use romantic humanism as a rationalization for prolonged dependency and a refusal to share in the world's work. But is there not also real need for this value change in a world facing nuclear destruction and a society that dehumanizes? Is there not an equal need to change the distortion of values that places such a high premium on violence and aggression, while hypocritically repressing sex? Yet, does not this neohumanism also serve as a romantic denial of reality? At the same time who is really more adult, the one who unquestioningly accepts a life of stultifying occupation, in a successful compromise between social and economic reality and his own ideology, or the one who refuses it at the price of material and social security? Not everyone has the competitive resources to succeed ultimately in converting hardship to security. We have tended to call the rigid ideologue, who wants to retain his humanism, an unresolved adolescent, because he refused to accept the status quo. But if reality changes, and he participates in changing it, history calls him mature, even if he is martyred in the process. The current question is not so much whether the personal moral values of youth are right, but whether they are authentic and whether they can be integrated into an adult life style, suitable to them in the immediate future and in the wider sense beneficial for society in making a better world.

Commitment to Work

The capacity to work is based on sublimation of pleasurable but renounced play impulses and reaction formation. At best, it acquires a secondary pleasure and is not inherently a human desire. Aggressivity and mastery of the environment are also involved in work. Adulthood has required, in the past, the attainment of a work-oriented character, which is at odds with an ethic of pleasure and narcissistic primacy. We have recently seen vast hordes of youth living marginally, often close to starvation and disease, who manifest not only an unwillingness to work but a complete incapacity to do so, because of ego defects and drug damage. Yet, even among the healthier upper middle-class youths, there is a disinclination to assume a life of work if the rewards are going to be a life similar to their parents'. Only very recently has the economic base that allows them this luxury been threatened, and at this point they find the employment market sharply restricted.

Insofar as commitment to work is not an economic necessity, there is no reason why it should be made, if the future can be guaranteed. History refers to many creative and productive people who did not have to work. Work, according to Freud, binds the psyche to reality, and in that respect nonworking adults would be considered less mature, but we must remember that maturity has no absoluteness; it is always relative to some culture-bound ideals. Perhaps the future will not require so much reality-binding. In that case, the protest generation is a harbinger.

In any event, it seems that youth are not always protesting work per se, but work for goals that seem unworthy.

Return to the Parents in Relative Equality

Achievement of equality is the outcome of emotional maturity. Will noncompetitive identification, with its welcome relief of tensions, still occur when patterns of living and moral values differ from generation to generation, and both marriage and child-bearing are either foregone or reduced in frequency? Identity will probably become even more conflictual and will have to be actively struggled for, consciously, because it cannot be unconsciously acquired. Conversely, there may develop, after this generation, increasing acceptance of intergenerational differences, future adults being more accustomed to rapid change. In any event, Erikson (1968) said, "rapid technological change makes it impossible for any traditional way of being older to become so institutionalized that the younger generation can step right into it." Will today's youth create adult roles that will bring to their children the necessary prerequisites of an identity, or will identity be even more elusive because of society's inability to maintain a constant enough consolidation of cultural forms?

It appears that as long as economic stability prevails, there will be increased variations of life style, particularly within a neohumanistic and sexual ethic, which does not necessarily center around responsibility or material gain. Young people will basically meet the six criteria of adulthood except in two respects: (1) complete financial and emotional separation and independence from the parents may be harder to attain because of economic dependence; (2) it is unlikely that the "return to the parents in a new relationship based on relative equality" will be possible until the parental generations accept the inevitability of change of values in their offspring as a norm. Whether, even then, generational change can ever occur without rebellion, is a question that hinges on narcissism and the nature of adolescence.

REFERENCES

Blos, P. (1969). In: A. J. Solnit, C. F. Settlage, S. Goodman, and P. Blos, Youth unrest: A symposium. *American Journal of Psychiatry*, 125(9):1145–1159.

Deutsch, H. (1969). The contemporary adolescent girl. *Seminars in Psychiatry*, 1(1): 99–112.

Erikson, E. H. (1968). *Identity: Youth and Crisis*. New York: Norton.

Group for the Advancement of Psychiatry (1968). *Normal Adolescence*, Vol. 6, report no. 68. New York: Group for the Advancement of Psychiatry.

Keniston, K. (1968). *Young Radicals*. New York: Harcourt, Brace & Jovanovich.

Marcuse, H. (1955). *Eros and Civilization*. Boston: Beacon Press.

Offer, D. (1969). *The Psychological World of the Teen-Ager*. New York: Basic Books.

———. (1971). *Toward a New Definition of Maturity?* Paper presented at workshop at Third Annual Meeting, American Society for Adolescent Psychiatry, Washington, D. C., May 1971.

Rieff, P. (1966). *The Triumph of the Therapeutic*. New York: Harper & Row.

Settlage, C. F. (1969). In: A. J. Solnit, C. F. Settlage, S. Goodman, and P. Blos, Youth unrest: A symposium. *American Journal of Psychiatry*, 125(9):1145–1159.

Toffler, A. (1970). *Future Shock*. New York: Random House.

Waelder, R. (1967). *Progress and Revolution*. New York: International Universities Press.

PART II

SEXUALITY
IN
ADOLESCENCE

INTRODUCTION

As is generally recognized, sexuality is an important aspect of the adolescent process. Whether its study is conducted in terms of developmental goals, focusing upon resolution and working through of oedipal struggles, or from a physiological perspective concentrating upon hormonal changes and secondary sexual characteristics, sex is crucial to adolescent development and causes, next to aggression, the most concern.

Gene H. Borowitz presents a chapter that contributes an important insight into the development of mature object relations by tracing the development of object constancy from its autoerotic and narcissistic roots to the maintenance of conscious object relationships. Borowitz focuses upon the defensive meanings of episodic outbursts of homosexual activity as responses to maternal sexual stimulation. Viewing masturbation as a transitional sexual activity, Borowitz discusses the developmental importance of achieving the capacity to masturbate alone.

Lawrence E. Newman's chapter refers to transsexualism. Differentiating transsexualism from transvestism, effeminate homosexuality, and biological intersex states, Newman presents a case history which elucidates developmental determinants as they contribute to the adolescent crisis and sexual identity. Diagnostic and treatment approaches, both with the individual and the family, are discussed.

The major portion of this section is devoted to the adolescent sexual revolution, an examination of changes in sexual mores, and their effects on behavior. In her introduction, Malvina W. Kremer discusses the beginning phases of this revolution, or evolution. A series of papers presented at a Joint Meeting of the American Society for Adolescent Psychiatry and the American Orthopsychiatric Association follow.

In summary, this section emphasizes once again the crucial aspects of the adolescent process as they contribute to the consolidation of character and the establishment of identity, especially sexual identity.

9] THE CAPACITY TO MASTURBATE ALONE IN ADOLESCENCE

GENE H. BOROWITZ

This chapter considers several aspects of genital masturbation in males during adolescence. The capacity to masturbate alone during adolescence is a developmental achievement, an important way station in the transition from infantile sexuality to adult genitality and from narcissism to object relatedness.

Clinical Material

Stanley was placed at a residential treatment school when he was eleven because of incorrigible stealing. His stealing became apparent when he was six and had increased in frequency, complexity, and magnitude over the intervening five years. Preadmission psychological testing revealed Stanley had high average intelligence, with no indications of organicity or schizophrenia. He was diagnosed as suffering from a severe character disorder.

Stanley had a chaotic childhood: His mother, a prostitute, frequently left him in the care of others and his father was an alcoholic who deserted the home repeatedly for long periods of time.

When Stanley entered the residential treatment school he soiled continuously and had regular nocturnal enuresis. After several months his soiling and enuresis became episodic though he was noticed to masturbate frequently. For the most part he masturbated alone; occasionally he would engage in mutual masturbation; on rare occasions he would engage in fellatio and pederasty, primarily as the passive partner.

Stanley masturbated following any form of internal distress; homosexual behavior appeared to follow situations that provoked intense rage and/or anxiety in him. One such stimulus was a typical visit with his mother during which there would be a great deal of mutual kissing, petting, and fondling. While he was with his mother, Stanley appeared happy and excited, but after she left he would masturbate for long periods, only occasionally participating in homosexual activity.

When he was thirteen there was a dramatic change in Stanley's sexual behavior; he became frenetically involved in homosexual behavior while his masturbation seemed to disappear completely. When asked about the masturbation he said that he had stopped masturbating alone when he was frightened by his first ejaculation.

After about a year at the school, Stanley, now twelve, entered individual psychotherapy. In treatment he related in a hostile, depreciating manner, trying to maintain a grown-up, wise-guy attitude. After about seven months he began to regress markedly during his sessions and to relate as a helpless, defenseless child who needed to be fed, protected, and kept warm. There was a great deal of body contact, clinging, and holding. These helpless attitudes alternated with seeing the therapist as a frightening persecutor. During these times Stanley would become provocative and destructive, forcing the therapist to hold him for extended periods of time.

His associations and play during these phases of therapy centered about his intense neediness and greediness. He would associate himself with devouring hungry animals who were constantly on the prowl for food. The animals were always female. His play began to focus on his destructive rage toward women and his confusion and lack of differentiation between the women and himself. At first he focused much of his rage and fear on his cottage mother, but later the focus shifted to his therapist whom he now hated and was afraid of and yet felt that he needed for actual survival. A constant theme in Stanley's play fantasies was obvious sexual activity in a wide variety of explicit forms, which invariably resulted in a violent fight leading to the death of one or both of the partners.

After several months in therapy, Stanley began to rub his genitals whenever upset by his play, by his associations, or by interactions with the therapist. The genital manipulation was not associated with any particular content or affects, but seemed more generalized.

While Stanley was involved in seeing his therapist as a persecutor, his external behavior changed; his masturbation disappeared, and there was a profound increase in his homosexual behavior. His genital manipulations disappeared from his therapy sessions. He became even more regressed; his play was largely fragmentary and his associations disorganized. His destructiveness and provocativeness increased, and most of his therapy sessions were spent with his being held by the therapist. Despite the intense and prolonged physical contact, there was nothing that suggested erotic interplay.

This behavior began to abate when Stanley was almost fourteen. He began to talk about his tremendous need to grow up and take care of his mother. He reported how she frequently would tell him that his father was not at home so she needed her "little man" to come home and take care of her. He said he had taken several jobs in the past, saved all his money, and sent it to her. Yet he had still felt driven to steal, too, to provide enough money for her. It was increasingly evident that Stanley felt that he was his mother's husband and had to fulfill a role that his father was unable to; however, he was extremely afraid that he would not be able to live up to her needs and expectations and that she would become disappointed and angry at him and abandon him completely. During this time his homosexual activity decreased, and his behavior was more adaptive in school and social activities.

A phone call from his mother precipitated another period of intense homosexual behavior. She was going to divorce his father and wanted him to come home. He appealed to his therapist to help him curb his homosexual behavior, which he experienced as disturbing and frightening. He talked about how he felt he had to go home and take care of his mother, and, with an expression of terror, he asked the therapist if that meant that he would have to have intercourse with her. Over the next several weeks he elaborated his fantasies about intercourse as a destructive act in which he would be killed. The fantasies had two foci: the first, of being swallowed by the vagina; and the second, of the female performing fellatio on him and beginning to eat his genitals and continuing to eat him until he was totally devoured.

Then his homosexual behavior changed. After several episodes of masturbation while with several other boys, he began to masturbate alone. He was embarrassed to talk about his masturbation, but on a few occasions he did speak briefly and sketchily about his masturbation fantasies. These involved suckling on a woman's breasts and active and passive beating fantasies.

Unfortunately, when Stanley was fifteen his therapist left the institution, and therapy data were no longer available. We do know that at about sixteen Stanley became interested in girls and then obsessed with heterosexual activity. This driven heterosexual activity resulted in many absences from the school and his eventual discharge.

Summarizing his sexual behavior at the school, he began to demonstrate a good deal of genital play alone and occasional homosexual ac-

tivity until his first ejaculation. He then became involved in frenetic homosexual behavior, and his masturbation alone disappeared. After a
period of six months there was a decrease in his homosexual behavior,
he masturbated alone in the presence of several boys and then began to
masturbate alone with fantasies. After several years he became involved
in driven heterosexual activity.

Supplementary clinical material was derived from a peripheral investigation of some psychophysiological correlates of sexual arousal in
"normal" men. The sketch which follows describes Mr. A, a subject
from that study.

Mr. A was a handsome, bright, articulate, twenty-five-year-old Negro
who was at the time of the interview an outstanding student in nursing
school. His father had died when Mr. A was one and one-half years
old, but his mother had maintained the family of six children by teaching
in a high school and with the help of relatives and the older children.
Mr. A had done well enough in school to enter college on a combination athletic and scholastic scholarship, but after one year he became
unsure of his future and dropped out. He went to work as an attendant
in a hospital. Several years later he applied and was accepted to a nursing school.

Memories of his sexual history begin with recall of masturbating
when he was two or three years old. He remembers "sleeping in a room
with my mother; she's in a bed, and I'm in a small bed. I remember
masturbating with the pillow, and I remember her telling me to be still
when I was rocking the bed. I remember me on top of the pillow as in
normal sexual relations." This activity continued until he was about six
or seven. He then became involved in frequent genital play with a girl
several years his senior. He remembers his first ejaculation occurring
while engaging in genital play and "intercourse" with this girl when he
was ten. He continued to engage in intercourse with the same girl for
several years. He commented that he masturbated once after that, when
he was about twelve. This episode involved mutual masturbation with a
male classmate. He did not enjoy it, found it difficult to ejaculate, and
stated that from that time on his sexual contacts were with girls. He
gave a long and complex heterosexual history and realized that he had
an inner need to have intercourse with so many different girls. He felt
the reason he never masturbated alone in adolescence was his seduction
by and interest in the older girl and, then later, the ready availability of
other girls.

He described his experiences during foreplay and intercourse as follows: During foreplay he would focus on his partner, he would enjoy
the mutuality of their activities, and he would not engage in fantasy. As

133

his excitement increased, shortly before or on beginning intercourse, he would begin to actively fantasize. The fantasies included a wide variety of activities, almost always with another girl. The fantasies were most intense at ejaculation and then quickly disappeared. During the postcoital period, he would again focus his attention on his partner and enjoy her presence.

Discussion

Blos (1962), in his excellent discussion of masturbation in adolescence, states:

Genital masturbation during adolescence is the phase specific sexual activity which divests pregenital drives of their independent aims and progressively subjugates them to genitality. This is to say that these drives become relegated to an initiatory rather than satiatory role, the latter being focused in the genital aim. Any function of masturbation which furthers this development represents its positive aspects. The ultimate achievement of adolescent masturbation lies in the elaboration of forepleasure.

In clearly defining adolescent masturbation as a phase-specific developmental task that must be mastered in order to achieve genitality, he shifts the emphasis from the usual consideration of the pathologic elements reflected in the masturbation fantasies of adolescence. He comments on the fact that there has been little attention paid to the factors involved in the achievement and resolution of this phase-specific developmental task when he discusses individuals who reveal a total absence of masturbation during adolescence. He believes that this indicates an incapacity to deal with pubertal drives and further indicates that memories of infantile masturbation have been repressed to such a degree that the necessary alignment of pregenital drives with genital sexuality cannot be accomplished.

The work of Blos (1962) and most other authors focused on the vicissitudes of an adolescent masturbating alone. Since we are aware that frequently adolescents begin their masturbating with mutual masturbation, it might be profitable to investigate some of the factors involved in the development of the capacity to masturbate alone in adolescence.

Winnicott (1953) called attention to a number of factors involved in the development of the capacity to be alone. He believes that its earliest determinants are the experiences of the infant and small child of being alone in the presence of the mother. Sufficient positive experiences of this kind contribute to the development of a good internal object so that at a later time the child, and later the adult, is never alone, intrapsychically. Winnicott postulates that the development of the capacity to be alone provides a matrix within which id tensions may be experienced and integrated. If the capacity is insufficiently developed, id tensions will be experienced as disruptive and lead to disintegration rather than higher levels of integration. In these considerations he provides further metapsychological foundations for Erikson's (1950) concept of basic trust and Benedek's (1938) concept of confidence.

Winnicott (1958) then traces the determinants of the capacity to be alone forward to the primal scene. He postulates that an individual's capacity to be alone also depends on his ability to deal with the feelings aroused by the primal scene:

In the primal scene an excited relationship between the parents is perceived or imagined, and this is accepted by the child who is healthy and who is able to master the hate and to gather it into the service of masturbation. In masturbation the whole responsibility for the conscious and unconscious fantasy is accepted by the individual child, who is the third person in a three-body or triangular relationship. To be able to be alone in these circumstances implies a maturity of erotic development, a genital potency or the corresponding female acceptance; it implies fusion of the aggressive and erotic impulses and ideas, and it implies a tolerance of ambivalence; along with all of this there would naturally be a capacity on the part of the individual to identify with each of the parents.

Our attention here is directed to the hierarchical elaboration of masturbation intercorrelated with the organization of object relationships and the interrelationships of the capacity to be alone, masturbate, and fantasy.

In considering the masturbation of the phallic-oedipal phase, Freud (1905) commented: "It is in the world of ideas, however, that the choice of an object is accomplished at first; and the sexual life of maturing youth is almost entirely restricted to indulging in fantasies. . . ."

Spitz (1949) compared three groups of children, using as the two variables the mother-child relationship, and autoerotic activities. He observed that during the first year of life, where there was a good mother-child relationship, genital play was regularly observed; where the mother-child relationship was "problematic," genital play was infrequently observed and other autoerotic activity such as fecal play was prevalent; where the mother-child relationship was absent, genital play was completely missing and the prominent autoerotic activities involved repetitive body movements such as head-banging and body-rocking. Spitz (1949) distinguished between autoerotic genital play and masturbation.

Nagera (1964) distinguished three different levels of autoerotism and autoerotic phenomena, which he attempted to correlate with the three earliest phases in the development of object relations: autoerotism, primary narcissism, and true object relationships. He commented that in the phase of object relationships, after the development of a stable internal object, an object-related fantasy life develops that attaches itself to autoerotic activities.

Freud, Winnicott, Spitz, and Nagera all pointed to the importance of early object relationships in regard to the development of autoerotic activities and the interrelationships of object relationships, autoerotic activities, and fantasy. Winnicott and Spitz called particular attention to the importance of infant-mother interactions for the development of the capacity to move to object-related fantasy.

In usual male development, phallic-oedipal masturbation becomes one of the major methods of dealing with the affects and conflicts of the oedipal situation through a repetitive working through of fantasies, leading to an integrative resolution. In latency, genital play with fantasy continues but with a profound increase in the utilization of fantasy in attempted conflict resolution. The increased drive tension of puberty causes further fantasy production and genital play as efforts at working through are intensified. Blos (1962) commented that adolescent masturbation "is an indispensable transitory sexual activity which normally brings infantile autoerotic experiences into contact with objects through . . . fantasy." In normal development, adolescent masturbation with fantasy gives way to the finding of a real object and genital sexual object-related activity with the absence of conscious fantasy. In the male, genitality can be defined, in part, by the ability to engage in genital sexuality while consciously focusing on the partner.

To this line of normal development another frequently seen phase should now be added, the phase of mutual masturbation or masturbating in another's presence. This is a frequent occurrence among pubertal boys and is often a boy's initiation to ejaculation. This phenomenon has been attributed to sharing the guilt, seemingly an important aspect of the phenomenon. However, I believe that there is another important determinant, namely, the utilization of an external object as an aid to tolerate id tension. This is identical to the mechanism of the transitional object described by Winnicott (1953). The transitional object (here the sexual object) is utilized in a variety of ways; occasionally the object need only be present, in other cases, with mutual masturbation, actual body contact is necessary. In either case the object serves as a focus for attention; the boy attends to the object while masturbating and does not focus on conscious fantasy. The object thus aids in defending against those fantasies associated with the increased drive tensions (see Giovacchini, 1971).

A great deal has been written on the subject of masturbation fantasies during adolescence, and I will not attempt to review all of this rich material here. Suffice it to say that there is a repetition and reworking of pregenital fantasies with progressive elaboration of those that are further and further removed from preoedipal and oedipal objects and pregenital modes of gratification. In normal development, pregenital fantasies can be tolerated and integrated, but in cases of pathological development this is not the case. Disturbing fantasies, because they can not be integrated, lead to fragmentation instead of structuralization. Defensive operations and external adaptations may be called into play to prevent the emergence of these disruptive fantasies.

In light of these considerations, I would like to discuss some aspects of the clinical material presented earlier.

Stanley's prepubertal masturbation became apparent following his admission to the residential treatment school. His masturbation did not appear to be linked to sexual fantasies or to an attempt to achieve sexual pleasure, but rather it was an attempt to relieve himself of a painful state of anxious excitation. While he masturbated frequently, in response to a wide variety of internal and external stimuli, his masturbation became more frequent in therapy sessions when his play focused on sexual activity, which became contaminated with aggressive destructive acts and often led to the death of one or both of the imagined participants. His masturbation also increased in frequency following any visit with his mother during which a great deal of kissing, petting, and fondling occurred. In both situations, Stanley was sexually aroused and responded with masturbation. His masturbation assumed a compulsive character and did not appear to be soothing or gratifying.

Kramer (1954, 1962) discussed similar situations. Since the prepubertal male does not possess orgastic capacity, the attempt to rid himself of a state of painful excitation through masturbation is doomed to failure. Kramer (1954) traces several outcomes of such circumstances, one being compulsive masturbation in adulthood, another, the development of a personality characterized by driving restlessness, the incapacity to be alone, impulsiveness, and constant seeking of stimuli. Stanley was markedly and persistently sexually hyperstimulated in childhood; on many occasions he observed his mother engage in a wide variety of sexual practices. Throughout his life he engaged in mutual petting, fondling, and caressing with his mother. Kramer (1954) comments on this:

The description of intensive masturbation without relief in childhood indeed impresses one with its profound, and at times nearly catastrophic, effects. In the cases that I could study, such experiences ended in reactions varying from stormy discharges on levels other than genital to fainting. Explosive involuntary bowel movements, vomiting, convulsive crying, and motor phenomena described as terrifying shaking occurred. . . .

[At] the same time important and far-reaching affective reactions take place, destined to influence the character development significantly. There is a feeling of utter helplessness and inadequacy difficult to describe. There is also an inescapable engulfing sense of shame, which from then on permeates the life of the individual and contributes to the formation of the person's character. . . . Throughout life, the patient reproduces the patterns which had been forced on him by the combination of external circumstances (overstimulation) and the pressure of instinctual needs physiologically incapable of relief in childhood. . . .

These considerations appear applicable to Stanley. Stanley's prepubertal masturbation did not appear to be that normally seen in latency, postphallic, oedipal masturbation; rather it seemed derived from earlier stages in which self-object differentiation was insecurely established and a triangular erotic love and hate relationship weakly, if at all, achieved. Though fantasies of the primal scene appeared in the play, this was not the phallic-oedipal primal scene but a primitive two-party fantasy primarily conceived of in terms of oral rage and destructiveness. Stanley's prepubertal masturbation, then, was not like erotic-based, pleasurable, latency masturbation; instead it was an attempt, largely unsuccessful, to decrease painful internal excitation. He was usually able to masturbate alone, but on occasion his internal excitement and the accompanying disturbing fantasies led to his masturbating in the presence of others, and at other times, to homosexual behavior including mutual masturbation, fellatio, and pederasty.

With pubertal changes and his first ejaculation Stanley's behavior changed abruptly. He commented that he was frightened when masturbation led to ejaculation. He became involved in regular and repeated homosexual behavior. Coincident with these changes was a marked change in his behavior in therapy. Where formerly he had seen his therapist as a needed persecutor with whom he played out his disturbing internal fantasies, his behavior now became chaotic; he was unable to organize his play in either form or sequence for any period of time, his behavior became markedly destructive and led to his therapist holding him for most of the sessions. This persisted for several months and then only slowly abated.

Considering these phenomena from the framework offered by Winnicott (1958), Stanley did not have a sufficient matrix or ego structuralization to experience and integrate the drive tension and release associated with pubertal masturbation. Rather, the experience of the drive tension and release led to fragmentation and an intense regression to a state in which self-object differentiation was, at best, tenuous. During this time Stanley was only able to experience genital drive discharge through homosexual activity, focusing on the external objects and not experiencing conscious fantasy. He did not enjoy his experiences; he claimed they were frightening, upsetting, and out of his control. As in his prepubertal masturbation, the stimuli for his homosexual behavior did not appear to be erotic; frequently it appeared stimulated by rage at overstimulation or rejection.

Among the determinants of Stanley's homosexual behavior were his identification with his mother, his sexual confusion, and his rage at his mother stemming from her inconsistent care and overstimulation. In part, his homosexuality was a flight from his fear of his mother largely determined by his projected rage.

Another factor was also condensed in this behavior: an attempt to maintain contact with external reality through intimate contact with an external object, thus affording a focus for external perception as a means of avoiding conscious, disturbing fantasy. This mechanism bears many similarities to Winnicott's (1953) concept of the transitional object and transitional phenomena. Transitional phenomena refer to an "intermediate area of experiencing to which inner reality and external life both contribute . . . the intermediate area between the subjective and that which is objectively perceived." The transitional object and phenomena lie between illusion and objective perception based on reality testing. Stanley's utilization of the object helped him to prevent regression to illusion and hallucination while not recognizing or testing the reality of the external object.

These considerations of Stanley's homosexuality may be of value in understanding some forms of adult homosexuality. A frequent pattern of adult homosexual behavior involves an individual who is primarily heterosexual but who, during times of internal stress, seeks homosexual activity. Often mechanisms similar to those described above seem operative. Following a situation in which intense rage at a female is experienced, this type of individual begins to masturbate. Primitive oral destructive fantasies become manifest and the individual becomes panicky. The masturbation is stopped in an attempt to suppress the disturbing fantasies. The person remains panicky and at this time seeks homosexual contact with an anonymous partner. During the homosexual activity attention is focused on the partner, and no conscious fantasy is experienced. Drive discharge is achieved without leading to persistent further disintegration.

Stanley's transition from homosexual behavior to the capacity to masturbate alone was coincidental with a change in the transference from regressed symbiosis to a phase in which there was increasing self-object differentiation and a capacity to see his therapist as a nurturant helper.

During this phase of the treatment, he spoke of his mother's need for him and his fears that he would not be able to live up to his mother's expectations or meet her needs. He was concerned that she would become disappointed and angry at him and abandon him completely.

Stanley's homosexual activity decreased in frequency and intensity during this period only to recur following the phone call from his mother asking him to come home. In therapy he was slowly able to elaborate his terrifying fantasies of intercourse in which he would be swallowed by the vagina or orally devoured. Though manifestations of these fantasies had been seen repeatedly during his prepubertal play, regularly followed by disintegration, the verbal expression of the fantasies in the present state of the transference led to integration. Stanley began to engage in masturbation; at first, in the presence of others and apparently without fantasy. He then began to masturbate alone with fantasy. At this time he became reticent and ashamed to talk of his masturbation or his masturbation fantasies. The available fantasies were of suckling on a woman's breast and active and passive beating fantasies with a woman. The fantasies are clearly prephallic but were experienced alone during genital masturbation with ejaculation and were accompanied by apparent personality integration.

Unlike Stanley, who demonstrated severe pathology with marked maladaptive behavior, Mr. A has shown a high degree of adaptive behavior and an absence of disrupting symptomatology. Mr. A never masturbated alone in adolescence; his drive discharge involved precocious heterosexuality. In his current heterosexual behavior, Mr. A shifts repeatedly from one girl to another and during intercourse engages in a wide repertoire of fantasy. In discussing similar cases Blos (1962) states:

Certain adolescents, in whom the homosexual drive is overwhelmingly strong, completely sidestep masturbation and enter into a heterosexual relationship at an early age. The compulsive urgency with which heterosexuality is pursued, in conjunction with a persistent lack of object relatedness, reveals the defensive nature of the sexual act.

While sufficient data are not available, these considerations seem applicable to Mr. A. This case material also calls our attention to the utilization of an object in order to defend against or tolerate fantasies during drive discharge.

Freud (1905), Tausk (1951), Orlow (1953), Anna Freud (1965), Reich (1951), Eidelberg (1952), and Hammerman (1961) have all discussed different facets of masturbation fantasies, focusing primarily on symptoms and character formation. Blos (1962), in his considerations of adolescent masturbation, pointed to some of the mechanisms and functions of the fantasies. He observed that the masturbator "experiences fluctuating self and object representations, since he is simultaneously subject and object, male and female, active and passive." Spiegel (1958) alluded to similar mechanisms when he referred to the observation that a dichotomy of the self exists during adolescent masturbation; the object-directed fantasies represent the genital aspect of the self, and the narcissistic aspect of the self takes the genital as the object.

Wermer (1967) studied the influence of growth and development in altering the content of masturbation fantasies. He elaborated on the differences between masturbation fantasies at different developmental phases. Differences between preadolescent and adolescent fantasies have been discussed from the points of view of content and drive discharge. Blos's (1962) and Spiegel's (1958) contributions suggest another area requiring further study, namely, the investigation of the association of masturbation fantasy and maturation in cognitive development. Piaget (1963) postulated that a qualitative shift in cognitive development takes place during adolescence, a shift in representational thinking from, in his terms, "concrete operations" to "formal operations." He believed that this maturational shift occurs between ages eleven and fourteen. The main characteristic of the phase of formal operations is the capacity for abstract operational thinking in that the child can form abstract concepts and can reason from hypothesis, thus having the basis for scientific thinking. With this maturational shift, the adolescent has the cognitive capacity in his fantasies to progressively abstract his fantasies from his oedipal and preoedipal representations and to rapidly reverse sequences, thus reworking his preoedipal and oedipal latency self and object representations and modes of drive discharge. Cognitive operations, fantasy content, and modes of drive discharge are all involved in the determination of masturbation fantasies at different developmental phases.

Summary

The capacity to masturbate alone in adolescence is a developmental achievement. The determinants of this capacity can be traced to vicissitudes of ego development and autoerotic activity during the first year of life, when the internalization of objects become interrelated with auto-erotic activities and object-related fantasies gradually replace actual object contact in relation to autoerotic activities. Object-related fantasies become the foci of masturbation fantasies during the anal, phallic-oedi-pal, and latency periods.

With pubertal changes and the development of the capacity of orgas-tic discharge, adolescent masturbation fantasies may become a source of psychic trauma. In some cases, an external object is utilized in order to tolerate and/or defend against fantasy in adolescence. This frequently serves as a transition to the capacity to masturbate alone.

Early object relationships form a matrix in which drive tension may be experienced and integrated. If early object relationships are dis-turbed, the capacity to tolerate and integrate drive discharge may be in-adequately developed. In such situations this may be manifested in the incapacity to masturbate alone. The capacity to masturbate alone pro-vides a setting in which working through by the use of fantasies of pre-adolescent self and object representations and modes of drive discharge may occur. This leads to the establishment of heterosexual object choice with genital sexual activity in which the individual focuses on the object without conscious fantasy. I believe the capacity to masturbate alone in adolescence is a developmental achievement, a way station in the transi-tion from infantile sexuality to adult genitality and, in another frame of reference, from narcissism to object relatedness.

REFERENCES

Benedek, T. (1938). Adaptation to reality in early infancy. *Psychoanalytic Quarterly,* 7:200–214.

Blos, P. (1962). *On Adolescence: A Psychoanalytic Interpretation.* New York: The Free Press.

Eidelberg. L. (1952). *A Contribution to the Study of the Masturbation Phantasy Studies in Psychoanalysis.* 2d ed.; New York: International Universities Press.

Erikson, E. H. (1950). *Childhood and Society.* New York: Norton.

Freud, A. (1965). *Normality and Pathology in Childhood: Assessments of Development.* New York: International Universities Press.

Freud, S. (1905). Three essays on the theory of sexuality. Standard Edition, 7:125–243. London: Hogarth, 1953.

Giovacchini, P. L. (1971). Fantasy formation, ego defect, and identity problems. *This Annual,* 1:329–342.

Hammerman, S. (1961). Masturbation and character. *Journal of the American Psycho-analytic Association,* 9:287–311.

Kramer, P. (1954). Early capacity for orgastic discharge and character formation. *Psychoanalytic Study of the Child,* 9:128–141.

———. (1962). Report on a case of compulsive masturbation. In: Panel on Masturbation at American Psychoanalytic Association, *Journal of the American Psychoanalytic Association,* 10:91–101.

Levin, S. (1963). A review of Freud's contributions to the topic of masturbation. *Bulletin of the Philadelphia Association of Psychoanalysis,* 13:15–24.

Nagera, H. (1964). Autoerotism, autoerotic activities, and ego development. *Psychoanalytic Study of the Child,* 19:240–255.

Orlow, A. (1953). Masturbation and symptom formation. *Journal of the American Psychoanalytic Association,* 1:45–58.

Piaget, J. (1963). *The Developmental Psychology of Jean Piaget,* ed. J. Flavell. New York: Van Nostrand Reinhold.

Reich, A. (1951). The discussion of 1912 on masturbation and our present-day views. *Psychoanalytic Study of the Child,* 6:80–94.

Spiegel, L. A. (1958). Comments on the psychoanalytic psychology of adolescence. *Psychoanalytic Study of the Child,* 13:296–308.

Spitz, R. (1949). Autoerotism: Some empirical findings and hypotheses on three of its manifestations in the first year of life. *Psychoanalytic Study of the Child,* 3/4:85–120.

Tausk, V. (1951). On masturbation. *Psychoanalytic Study of the Child,* 6:61.

Wermer, H., and Levin, S. (1967). Masturbation fantasies. Their changes with growth and development. *Psychoanalytic Study of the Child,* 22:315.

Winnicott, D. W. (1953). Transitional objects and transitional phenomena. *International Journal of Psycho-Analysis,* 34:89.

———. (1958). The capacity to be alone. *International Journal of Psycho-Analysis,* 39:416.

10] TRANSSEXUALISM IN ADOLESCENCE: PROBLEMS IN EVALUATION AND TREATMENT

LAWRENCE E. NEWMAN

In the treatment of the transsexual the clinician faces unique problems. This is especially true for the adolescent transsexual who finds himself in conflict inwardly because of the impact of pubertal development he does not want and outwardly because of the opposition of his family and society to his cross-gender aspirations. Problems arise for therapists in diagnosing the disorder in adolescence, in conceptualizing the nature of transsexualism and its development, and in providing a feasible and humane treatment program. The following report, based on the study of child, adolescent, and adult transsexuals at the Gender Identity Research and Treatment Clinic of the University of California at Los Angeles, offers one approach to these difficulties.[1]

Transsexualism is a unique condition in which an individual of one sex, because of a profound identification with the opposite sex, chooses to live his life as a member of that sex (Benjamin, 1966). The male transsexual feels inwardly like a woman though he acknowledges that his body is physically male. These are the persons who seek sex transformation procedures: estrogen administration to feminize the contours of the body, electrolysis for the removal of facial hair, and surgery to remove the male genitalia with construction of an artificial vagina (the so-called sex-change operation). The male transsexual is profoundly and naturally feminine in behavior, including nuances of gesture and expression, so that once cross-dressing begins he passes undetected in society as a female. In contrast, when dressed as a male he feels awkward and

Reprinted with permission from *Archives of General Psychiatry*, 23 (August 1970) and Lawrence E. Newman.

miserable and is identified by others as a deviant because of his feminine mannerisms. Following surgery most male transsexuals live conventionally and without fanfare as women, secure in the knowledge that accidental disclosure of their "male" sex status is no longer possible. To complete the transformation in all respects they attempt to have their sex designation on all legal documents changed to read "female."

Female transsexualism, somewhat rarer in clinical experience than male transsexualism, is manifested by profound and normal-appearing masculinity in a physically normal woman. In thought, behavior, and sense of identity she is as thoroughly masculine as her male counterpart is feminine. She lives as a man, is accepted by society in this role, and feels inwardly that she is a man despite her female body. In order to masculinize their bodies, female transsexuals seek bilateral mastectomy, hysterectomy, and androgen hormone administration. They would like to have a functioning penis, but surgical construction of this organ is not technically possible at present.

Advances in endocrinology and surgery have made apparent sex change a possibility only in our own time. The phenomenon we call transsexualism, however, is much older. Descriptions of persons similar in all respects to the transsexuals we see today can be found in the records of ancient European societies and in other, less developed, cultures (Green, 1966). In our own time, transsexualism first received worldwide attention in 1953 with the publicity given the case of Christine Jorgenson and the report of successful sex-reassignment surgery by her physicians (Hamburger, 1953). These doctors later reported on the flood of letters they received from transsexuals the world over, which gave testimony to the profound unhappiness and despair of these individuals (Hamburger, 1953).

Infancy and Childhood

What causes the transsexual to become so completely identified with the opposite sex? Primate studies have indicated that sex-hormone levels during the prenatal period are of critical importance in determining postnatal gender-role orientation (Goy, 1968; Harris, 1948). A similar process may occur in some cases of transsexualism (Baker and Stoller, 1968), but so far no one has been able to demonstrate an organic etiology for the disorder.

Another line of research has emphasized the importance of early learning in determining gender identity in humans. Money and his coworkers demonstrated, through their studies of hermaphroditic children, that the way a child is reared during his first two to three years of life will determine thereafter whether he feels himself to be a male or a female (Money, Hampson, and Hampson, 1955). This process, which they consider to be analogous to imprinting, determines the child's gender-role orientation regardless of the actual biological sex (Money, Hampson, and Hampson, 1957). Following this discovery, Stoller demonstrated a specific combination of family circumstances that lead to the development of profound femininity in boys (Stoller, 1968). An unhappy woman, unsure of her femininity and envious of men, involved in a stable but loveless marriage, comes to life, as it were, with the birth of the transsexual-to-be son. She finds him exquisitely beautiful and showers all her attention on him. He is smiled at, cuddled, held against the mother's body blissfully many hours a day well beyond the second year of life. The frustration essential for normal separation and individuation is not permitted to occur, the mother instantly gratifying all the child's needs. In order for this exceptional mother-son relationship to take place the child must be attractive enough to evoke the mother's all-consuming attention (in fact these children are exceptionally good looking) and passive enough to sustain the endless closeness with mother that follows. The father, passive and physically absent during this critical period, most often does not interfere in any way with the mother's relationship with the son, nor is he available to provide an alternate model for identification.

In consequence, a profound identification with the mother occurs. This is later manifested in the little boy's insistence on wearing girls' clothing, in his feminine mannerisms, and in his preference for girls' games: playing with dolls or playing house. He expresses his disappointment with being a boy and openly states his wish to grow up to be a woman. Typically, the parents are remarkably accepting of their son's femininity in childhood, rationalizing that it is only a phase that will eventually pass. In fact, our studies of such families indicate that the parents may covertly encourage their son's feminine behavior without consciously being aware that they are doing so. Subjected to the taunts of being a sissy by his male peers at school, the transsexual boy retreats to the security of the family where his feminine interests are allowed to flourish.

We do not know the family dynamics of the female transsexual, but there are indications that a similar process in reverse may occur at least with some of the extremely masculine little girls. In the case of one very boy-like little girl, for example, who insisted that she would grow up to be a man, the mother was absent and the child had been reared by an overly close and solicitous father.

Adolescence

The following discussion concerns the male transsexual but applies similarly to the female.

Adolescence is typically the time of life in which one struggles with the issues of personal identity: "Who am I?" "What will I be?" The inner experience of the self must be reconciled with the way one is perceived by others. The development of a meaningful social role, which is the continuous task of the adolescent, must reflect a synthesis of the private, internal view of the self and the reality of the way one is perceived by others. For the transsexual, adolescence is a time of crisis. A masculine role consistent with the expectations of others is impossible for him because it is a negation of everything he inwardly feels himself to be. To live as a feminine male, for example, within the homosexual community is more acceptable because it allows for expression of some femininity. But for the transsexual it is unsatisfactory because he is still identified socially as a man. In some cultures, as, for example, in some of the American Indian tribes, the profoundly feminine male is provided with a socially acceptable role. He is known as *berdache* and is allowed to live completely as a woman (Green, 1966). No similar role is available in any major Western or Eastern culture for the transsexual male. The radical step of actually becoming a woman seems to the transsexual to be the most satisfactory synthesis. Most have read about Christine Jorgenson (Jorgenson, 1967) and know that this is possible. To live as a woman satisfies the inner experience of the self, which has been feminine since infancy. Similarly the transsexual discovers that society finds his femininity much more acceptable when he is passing as a woman than it does when he is identifiable as a feminine male. Transsexuals will report with pleasure that the low esteem in which they were held as sissy males is replaced by stares of admiration when they begin to pass as women. But if he is to live as a woman, the transsexual must disguise completely any evidence of his true biological sex or risk the devastating embarrassment of disclosure. Before he can live completely as a woman he must overcome the opposition of his family to this change, or else run away. Urgency is added to the situation by another harsh reality: With puberty his body begins to develop in a masculine

147

direction, and he is aware that each change—the deepening of his voice, the rapid increase in height, the appearance of facial stubble—decreases the possibility that he ever will be able to live undetected as a woman. Moreover, these changes create conflict about the feminine image he has of himself, which was established in infancy and sustained throughout childhood. The penis, as the cardinal sign of maleness, becomes increasingly offensive, because with puberty it has acquired an increasing capacity for sustained erections and can no longer be ignored.

Illustrative Case Report

The patient, an intelligent fifteen-year-old boy (whom I will call by the fictitious name of George) was initially seen after a serious suicide attempt. For several months prior to this he had been depressed, irritable, and withdrawn, refusing to attend school or to tell his family what was troubling him. In his psychotherapy sessions the patient revealed for the first time that he had, on several occasions during the prior year, dressed up in his sister's clothing and gone out on dates with young men who assumed him to be a girl. To be accepted in society as a girl had been, he reported, the source of his greatest happiness. He had avoided intimacies of any kind on these dates, kissing included, for fear that in an embrace his male status might accidentally be discovered. Dressing in female clothing did not cause him to become sexually excited, and he denied penile masturbation at any time. The patient said that he felt inwardly like a girl and that he yearned to be allowed to live like one. The following are quotes taken from one of his sessions.

"I really realized how different I was when I got to be around ten or eleven. I tried to play kickball with the boys—everybody expected me to—but I always hated it. The boys always knew I wasn't like them, I think. They used to call me 'girl' because of the way I walked and talked. I hated gym especially. I hated to shower and let them see my body. Once I even broke my hand on purpose so I wouldn't have to go to gym." (The fact that he had indeed broken his hand, supposedly accidentally, was confirmed by the parents.)

"Last year I started dressing up and going out. I waited until everybody was out of the house and then I put on my sister's dress and shoes. I used some eye liner I had bought and my sister's mascara. I knew that what I was doing was dangerous, but I felt that time was growing short. I always felt like a girl from as far back as I can remember, and I knew that if I didn't do something now I'd never have the chance. I knew the changes had started. You know—this hair growing on my legs and underarms. I was desperate. I was going to go out and be a girl for once in my life before all the changes. I planned to live as much as I could as a girl before the changes made it impossible. Then I planned a suicide. When I went out it was what I wanted. I looked like a girl and people accepted me as a girl. One guy I met even liked me a lot and wanted to come to my house to pick me up. But of course I couldn't let him. It's all so terrible."

Physical examination revealed the patient to be a healthy, normally proportioned young man with signs of early pubertal development. The penis was of normal size, testes were descended and normal to palpation and copious hair had appeared in the pubic area, upper thighs, and axillae. Chromatin pattern was XY and hormone studies were within normal limits for the male. However, in gesture and expression, in postures while sitting and walking, in tone of voice and in mannerism, the patient gave the impression of softness and femininity. Mental status examination gave no evidence of delusional thinking, hallucination, or stigmata of schizophrenia. Nor did psychological testing give any indication of a thought disorder.

In childhood, the parents reported, the patient had preferred dressing up in his sister's clothes to all other activities. He enjoyed playing with dolls, helping his mother with housework, and actively avoided all boyish games and activities throughout childhood. Despite this the family had continued to reassure themselves that he would "grow out of it" and had never previously sought professional help.*

Not all transsexuals find puberty as intolerable as did George, though all suffer to some degree for similar reasons. Some transsexuals with more masculinity in their personalities may resign themselves to pubertal changes and try for years to fit their bodies and to behave in accordance with the expectations of society. Those who are successful in suppressing these feelings I suppose we never see. Those that we do see report that during the years that they attempted to live in the male role they were continuously uncomfortable and felt relaxed only when they permitted themselves to appear in public in feminine attire.

Characteristically, transsexuals who are attempting to live in their assigned gender role manifest their inner turmoil in depression. Other patterns of emotional distress, including what may appear to be character disorders, can be observed in some patients. And just as typically, when the transsexual begins to live in his desired gender role these personality distortions diminish or disappear. One very unhappy adolescent transsexual male, for example, before he began to live as a girl appeared to have a borderline personality. Without provocation and often inappropriately he would burst into agonized, soundless sobs. His behavior was often silly and peculiar, reflecting bizarre lapses in judgment. After he began to live as a young lady, the affective disturbance disappeared and the slightly silly quality that persisted in his personality seemed not at all inappropriate to the pretty "dumb blond" young woman he had become. He simulated perfectly, in this respect, certain television and movie actresses we admire. This improvement in psycho-

---

* This case report is continued in the section headed *Treatment,* see p. 152.

logical state with the assumption of the gender role desired by the patient has been described elsewhere (Benjamin, 1966; Pauly, 1968) but deserves emphasis. Occasionally one comes across reports of feminine young men in great emotional distress who are desirous of becoming women. Their emotional distress is cited as a reason to oppose their wish to change, when in fact the opposite conclusion—to permit them to experimentally live in the desired role in order to evaluate possible improvement in their psychological functioning—would seem more defensible.

Differential Diagnosis

The therapist's first task, as in the case just reported, is to establish with the adolescent a relationship of trust in which the cross-gender aspirations can be explored. The second task is to make a correct diagnosis. Transsexualism can be differentiated from three conditions in which cross-gender behavior is found: transvestism, effeminate homosexuality (or "butch" lesbianism in the case of the female), and biological intersex states.

The transvestite differs from the transsexual in that he lives and works as a man, has a heterosexual orientation in relationship to women, and does not seek to be changed into a woman. He cross-dresses only occasionally, and usually because dressing is sexually exciting and enhances his pleasure in masturbation or heterosexual intercourse. That is, it is for him fetishistic in contrast to the transsexual who does not get genital pleasure from cross-dressing. As an example, a fourteen-year-old transvestite boy I am presently seeing cross-dressed secretly as part of a masturbatory ritual. He is masculine in appearance and mannerism, loves athletics and surfing, and is accepted as a peer by the young men who are his friends.

Effeminate male homosexuals, known as "drag queens," dress and pass on occasion as women. But they consider themselves homosexual men, not women, and recognize that their male genitalia enhance their attractiveness as sexual objects for the homosexual men that they seek as partners. Their effeminate gestures represent an exaggerated mocking imitation of women, characterized by limp wrists and "swishiness," in contrast to the transsexual's behavior, which perfectly simulates that of the normal woman. Drag queens do not seek sex-transformation procedures. A male transsexual patient I have treated, who was friendly with several drag queens, reported on the horror with which they received the news that the patient had decided to seek sex-reassignment surgery.

This distinction can be made: Transvestites and homosexuals prize their male genitalia and do not seek to change their male status. Transsexuals wish to be rid of their male genitalia and to permanently give up their male status.

Transsexualism, transvestism, and effeminate homosexuality share some features in common, and the distinction may appear blurred in any individual case. Where doubt exists prolonged evaluation in psychotherapy is indicated to clarify the picture.

Transsexualism may occur in certain intersex states. Conditions associated with hypogonadism, such as Klinefelter's syndrome, may increase the likelihood in males of a feminine orientation (Baker and Stoller, 1968; Money and Pollitt, 1964). All transsexuals deserve a thorough medical examination to rule out possible chromosomal, hormonal, or gonadal abnormalities. One aspect of such a finding is of special importance to transsexuals: If such abnormalities are discovered the patient will probably be able to obtain sex-reassignment procedures more easily since these are then viewed as "correcting a mistake of nature." This practical consideration has not been overlooked by an occasional biologically normal transsexual. To illustrate: Several years ago there appeared at the UCLA medical center a beautiful young "woman" requesting sex-reassignment surgery. She had well-developed breasts, rounded curves, and was entirely feminine in personality and in her hair style and dress. But she also had a large penis, testicles, and an XY chromosome pattern. She always felt herself to be a girl, she stated, and except for her genitalia, considered herself one. She denied ever taking female hormones. She had been considered a boy in childhood. At puberty, she reported, her breasts began mysteriously to develop. Evaluation indicated that her testicles were the probable source of estrogens, and a diagnosis of testicular feminization syndrome was made. This being an intersex condition, sex-reassignment surgery was performed— the male genitalia removed and an artificial vagina constructed. After several happy years as a girl the patient returned to correct a portion of her original history. She reported that she had indeed been taking estrogens orally prior to surgery and that, in fact, she had been taking them secretly since her early teens. The original prescription was her mother's, which she had surreptitiously refilled over the years. By self-medication she had transformed herself physically into the woman she inwardly felt herself to be and by not revealing this subterfuge she had completed the project by obtaining sex-reassignment surgery as an intersex patient. (See Stoller, 1968, for a more extensive discussion of this case.)

Not all transsexual adolescents make their way to a female role as smoothly as this. Some, encountering the opposition of family and school to their cross-gender aspirations, become depressed, withdrawn, or show other psychological symptomatology. Such adolescents may be referred for treatment.

Treatment

Once we have concluded that the adolescent we are seeing is unquestionably a transsexual, what can we do for him? A rational decision as to management will depend on familiarity with the treatment strategies that have been employed with transsexuals and knowledge of their effectiveness. If we define a successful treatment of transsexualism as one that would make the transsexual give up his cross-gender orientation and become comfortable with his physical sex, a treatment, for example, that would replace the male transsexual's femininity with masculinity, we must acknowledge that nothing approaching this exists (Pauly, 1968; Stoller, 1966).

If profound cross-gender orientation is detected early in life, no later than by age five or six, and intensive individual therapy for the child and counseling for the family instituted on a regular basis, reversal of gender orientation is possible. With feminine boys the treatment is based on interfering with the child's feminine fantasies, reassuring him that he is a boy and will not grow up to be a girl, while at the same time helping him to see that being a male has many rewards. As the treatment progresses, fears of being masculine and fear of his own aggressiveness must be anticipated and interpreted. Such therapy requires the constant participation and cooperation of the parents and therapy for them so that they do not unconsciously work against treatment by permitting or covertly encouraging feminine behavior to take place at home. The therapist must be a person of the same sex as the child so that identification with the therapist can be encouraged to take place and reinforced when it appears. The psychological absence of the parents of the same sex, as noted previously, is a crucial aspect of the etiology of the disorder. I am presently engaged in the treatment of three male childhood transsexuals and have noted significant improvement in two. They are gradually developing masculine interests and becoming less feminine. The third, despite three years of treatment, continues to be completely feminine in orientation. Greenson (1966) describes the successful treatment of one male childhood transsexual and several other successes in treatment of feminine boys have been reported. (See Stoller, 1968, the chapter on childhood transsexualism, for a review of the case reports of feminine boys.) One profoundly masculine little girl treated at UCLA, who prayed that she would grow up to be a man, received psychoanalytic treatment from a male therapist without improvement. On the other hand, a second female childhood transsexual, presently in treatment with a female therapist, is showing significant improvement. It must be emphasized, however, that none of the children under treatment has reached adolescence, and we cannot be sure therefore that the improvements noted will persist.

There are no reports of older children responding to psychological treatment aimed at reversing their cross-gender orientation.

Beyond childhood, psychotherapy, including psychoanalysis as well as other treatment modalities (faradic aversion deconditioning, hypnosis, chemotherapy) have not proven effective in correcting the cross-gender identification of transsexuals (Pauly, 1968; Stoller, 1966; Marks and Gelder, 1967; Baker, 1969). The ideal treatment of transsexualism would appear to depend on prevention, that is, diagnosing and treating gender-identity aberrations in childhood.

In the absence of an effective treatment capable of reversing a transsexual orientation, it is evident that eventually the transsexual will live in the gender role of the opposite sex. The histories of transsexuals indicate that initial attempts to live in the cross-gender role are often made surreptitiously at great risk to the patient, and often require an abandonment of their families. This need not be necessary if the patient is permitted to assume the new gender role on an experimental basis while under therapeutic management. This means that the therapist, after thoroughly exploring the possibility of reversing the patient's cross-gender orientation and concluding that this is not possible, no longer opposes the patient's wish to live as a member of the opposite sex but permits this to occur on an experimental basis.

But when should the patient be permitted to try out the new gender role? This requires a clinical assessment of the amount of distress the patient is experiencing in his assigned gender role. If the discomfort is minimal, therapy should be directed toward assisting the patient in adjusting to his assigned gender role. At the very least the advantages of this approach must be explored with him. The route the patient must follow if he seeks to change his sex is, after all, very difficult and should if at all possible, be avoided. At the other extreme, however, are patients like George, who were profoundly feminine since early childhood, lack any trace of masculinity in behavior or interest, and are intensely uncomfortable in their assigned gender role. These are situations in which an assessment of irreversibility of the cross-gender identification can be made and in which the advisability of a trial in the new gender role, under clinical supervision, is indicated.

Living in the opposite gender role at home on an experimental basis means that the family must be involved in the decision-making and planning. A series of family therapy sessions in which the patient shares his feelings with his family in regard to the new role are an excellent way to begin. During this difficult period the therapist must educate the family about the nature of the patient's condition and provide counseling to individual family members. The feelings of individual members of the family about the patient and what he hopes to do must be explored and worked with. Brothers and sisters of the patient, especially if they, too, are adolescents, may experience great anxiety about the idea. Fears about their own sexual identity may be mobilized, and they will need individual reassurance that they are normal and that their sibling's disorder is not catching or inheritable. Guilt feelings on the part of the parents must be worked with. It is pointless to dwell on what might have been done at an earlier period. It is much more useful to enlist the parents' energies in planning for the difficult problems they will face if the new role proves successful for the patient, for example, in thinking about possibilities for new school arrangements.

After emotional preparation of the family has been completed, the trial period in the new gender role can begin. Characteristically, the patient is able to make the transition effortlessly and immediately seems completely natural and feels at home in the attire of the opposite sex. The happiness and naturalness of the patient in this new role, in contrast to his former awkwardness, isolation, and depression, is profoundly reassuring to the family.

If the trial in the new gender role has been successful for a period of several months, and the patient has shown no evidence of doubts or second thoughts, estrogen therapy should be instituted. Preferably this is done under the direction of an endocrinologist familiar with the treatment of transsexuals. This therapy halts masculinization and begins the development of secondary female characteristics. Early estrogen administration greatly facilitates the possibility of the patient living without detection in the female role thereafter.

The issue of genital surgery is a more difficult one, primarily because such treatment is highly controversial even for adults. Despite the emotionalism that surrounds sex-reassignment surgery (Green, Stoller, and MacAndrews, 1966), we should keep in mind the fact that the postoperative results of such surgery, in regard to the patient's psychological condition, have been extremely good. In a review of the postoperative results of surgery performed on 121 male transsexuals, a satisfactory outcome, as indicated by improved social and emotional adjustment, was found to be ten times more likely than an unsatisfactory result (Pauly, 1968). Still, such surgery is irreversible. Therefore, it is my feeling that such surgery should not even be contemplated for the transsexual adolescent until he has lived successfully and uninterruptedly in the gender role of the opposite sex for at least one year. It is essential also that the family and patient be aware of the fact, from the outset, that sex-reassignment surgery for transsexuals is difficult to obtain in the United States. The medical center at UCLA, for example, where our gender-identity clinic is located, does not perform such surgery for transsexuals.

The case of George illustrates these principles of management.

Long-term psychotherapeutic evaluation indicated that the patient's wish to live as a girl reflected a profound, lifelong, and now irreversible feminine orientation. Then, in family therapy sessions George explained his feelings to his family. Other members of his family expressed relief at being able to talk with him about something that they had in a way suspected but had been ashamed to bring up. It is of interest to note that they were all reassured to discover that George was not a homosexual. The diagnosis of transsexual provided an explanation for his feminine behavior and was, especially for the parents, psychologically relieving. The family decided to permit the patient to carry out his wishes and to begin to live as a girl on an experimental basis in the privacy of the home.

During the following week the mother and the older sister purchased a dress, cosmetics, and shoes for the patient. The next session, George arrived in the company of his mother, fully dressed and made up as a young woman, with his short hair covered by a kerchief. The patient's graceful, feminine manner, which had seemed so out of place when he was dressed as a boy, now seemed completely natural and unaffected. She (I will refer to her now in the more appropriate feminine form of the pronoun) had chosen a feminine form of her name, which I will refer to as Georgina. She was excited and happy, in contrast to her previous miserable and withdrawn state, and described with exuberant pleasure the first shopping expedition she had gone on as a girl with her mother. She was already completely at home in the new social role.

The patient had missed a semester of school because of the psychiatric hospitalization. She moved to a relative's home in another school district. Conferences were held with the school principal, who, after meeting the patient, agreed to keep the matter secret and to permit Georgina to register in school as a girl. (In my experience principals have been understanding and humane in these matters.)

Georgina's ability to make friends and to plunge eagerly into school activities now was in marked contrast to the isolation of her earlier years. She became involved in a number of school activities, maintained her grades, and even was accepted to the school's cheerleader squad. A socially acceptable medical reason was provided so that she could be excused from gym classes.

Though she was accepted socially in school without question as a girl, the idea that her secret might accidentally be disclosed was a continuous source of worry for her. In her individual sessions, which continued throughout this period, she would frequently conjure up images of the humiliation she would experience if her new school friends should somehow find out the truth. She wore a heavy girdle under her dress to conceal any evidence of her male genitalia. I suggested that she might carry a letter explaining her condition in the event of disclosure, but she refused this, accurately deciding, in my judgment, that the likelihood of somebody finding the letter in her purse was greater than that of her accidental physical disclosure. Other than this fear, she did very well in all respects. Once estrogen treatment was instituted, breast development was rapid and gave her a sense of confidence in her appearance she had not known until then. A legal change of name to Georgina was obtained and all other documentation she carried was changed indicating that she was a female. The family destroyed all photographs of Georgina as a boy.

During a several-year follow-up, the patient continued to be content, outgoing, and at home in her female gender role. She found the idea of her ever returning to a male role preposterous and inconceivable. She had crushes on several boys, but avoided intimacies for fear of discovery. She confined her social outings to parties.

Much later the family assisted the patient in obtaining sex-reassignment surgery. The technical result was excellent and provided the patient with a functional, artificial vagina. About the surgery the patient said: It was like a weight being taken off of me, being rid of the male parts. I feel as complete now as I can be as a girl. I'll never be able to bear children, but, then, a lot of naturally born girls can't either. Before the surgery that part, the penis, was always there as a reminder that I wasn't complete. Now I am.

The smoothness with which this family accepted the patient's transformation and provided support for it may not always be found. In another case, that of a fourteen-year-old male transsexual adolescent, the older brother could not tolerate the patient in the new role and brutally assaulted him on several occasions. In the most serious of these episodes he held the patient down and shaved the patient's long hair off to the scalp. This precipitated a crisis in which the patient was acutely suicidal and required emergency psychiatric treatment.

Older transsexual adolescents, especially if they have already abandoned or been abandoned by their families, visit psychiatrists primarily to get help in obtaining sex-reassignment procedures. They deserve a careful diagnostic evaluation, a realistic assessment by the clinician of the limitations of such treatment, of the difficulties they will have obtaining it, and of the problems they may face in regard to employment, socially and otherwise, in the new role (Green, 1969).

Conclusions

In a general way our approach to transsexualism is this: If the mistaken gender identity is reversible, as it may be in childhood, let us make every effort to correct the problem and provide the child with a gender orientation suitable to his physical sex. However, if it is irreversible and the patient finds it impossible to continue in his assigned gender role, let us do what we can to assist him in his adjustment to the gender role he finds most appropriate.

The model for an objective, nonjudgmental approach to the transsexual is provided for us by Freud in his famous letter to the mother of a homosexual (Freud, 1951):

By asking me if I can help, you mean, I suppose, if I can abolish homosexuality and make normal heterosexuality take its place. The answer is, in a general way, we cannot promise to achieve it . . . in the majority of cases it is no more possible. . . . What analysis can do for your son runs in a different line. If he is unhappy, neurotic, torn by conflicts, inhibited in his social life, analysis may bring him harmony, peace of mind, full efficiency, whether he remains a homosexual or gets changed.

Freud, recognizing that it is likely that the patient's homosexuality cannot be reversed, emphasizes alternate goals of peace of mind, harmony, and full efficiency. Our attitude toward the transsexual, irreversible in his cross-gender orientation, is similar. It is no treatment to force the youthful transsexual to remain in a gender role he finds detestable and impossible for him, or to delay indefinitely his transition into the new gender role by prolonging indefinitely the period of evaluation. Nor is it treatment to provide the patient with a psychiatric diagnosis and dispense with him. Clinics or private psychotherapists, sensing the irreversibility of the patient's commitment to the opposite gender role, may tell the parents that there is nothing they can do for the patient or may simply stop giving him appointments. This is unfortunate, because a great deal can be done. In accepting the possibility of the patient's transformation to the new gender role we accept the obligation of helping him and his family in the subsequent problems of adjustment. But such cases are also very gratifying because of the striking improvement in psychological and social adjustment that usually is possible.

Summary

The transsexual is an individual who wishes to live and be accepted as a member of the sex opposite to his biological sex. In consequence of certain crucial relationships in his early life he develops a profound cross-gender orientation that, beyond childhood, is irreversible by any known technique. The transsexual in adolescence experiences an identity crisis that is a product of fast developing but unwanted pubertal changes, the pressure society exerts against his cross-gender aspirations, and his own increasing unhappiness with his assigned gender role. The patient yearns to be allowed to live in the opposite gender role and may secretly experiment with this by cross-dressing.

The therapist must establish a working relationship with the patient in which his cross-gender feelings and aspirations can be explored and the possibility of reversing them, by psychotherapy or other treatment, assessed. The therapist must rule out alternative diagnoses of transvestism, effeminate homosexuality (or butch lesbianism in the case of the female), and biological intersexuality. If the diagnosis of transsexualism can be unequivocally made and the cross-gender orientation appears to be irreversible, an experimental trial in the new gender role is indicated. This will require exploration with the family as a group and with individual members of the family where indicated.

Once the trial in the cross-gender role begins, the patient and members of the family will be able to assess the patient's comfort and happiness in the new role. The transsexual should be as comfortable and natural in the cross-gender role as a fish is in water. Hormonal therapy should be delayed until there is evidence of good adjustment in the new role. A minimum of one year of continuous and successful living in the new gender role is indicated, with continuous professional evaluation, before the possibility of sex-reassignment surgery is entertained.

NOTE

1. I want to express my appreciation to Dr. Robert Stoller for referring the cases discussed in this chapter and in consulting on their management. Without his help and support this chapter could not have been written.

REFERENCES

Baker, H., and Stoller, R. (1968). Can a biological force influence gender identity? *American Journal of Psychiatry,* 124:1653–1658.

Baker, J. J. (1969). Transsexualism: Problems in treatment. *American Journal of Psychiatry,* 125:1412–1418.

Benjamin, H., ed. (1966). *The Transsexual Phenomenon.* New York: Julian Press.

Freud, S. (1951). A letter to the mother of a homosexual. *American Journal of Psychiatry,* 107:786–787.

Goy, R. (1968). Organizing effects of androgen in the behavior of rhesus monkeys. In: *Proceedings of the London Conference: Endocrines and Human Behavior,* ed. R. P. Michael. Oxford: Oxford University Press.

Green, R. (1966). Transsexualism: Mythological, historical and cross-cultural aspects. In: *The Transsexual Phenomenon,* ed. H. Benjamin. New York: Julian Press, pp. 173–186.

———. (1967). Physician emotionalism in the treatment of the transsexual. *Transactions of the New York Academy of Science,* 29:440–443.

———. (1969). Persons seeking sex change: Psychiatric management of special problems. In: *Transsexualism and Sex Reassignment,* ed. R. Green and J. Money. Baltimore: Johns Hopkins Press.

———, Stoller, R., and MacAndrews, C. (1966). Attitudes toward sex transformation procedures. *Archives of General Psychiatry,* 15:178.

Greenson, R. (1966). A transvestite boy and a hypothesis. *International Journal of Psychoanalysis,* 47:396–403.

Hamburger, C. (1953). Desire for change of sex as shown by personal letters from 465 men and women. *Acta Endocrinologica,* 14:361–375.

———, Sturrup, G., and Dahl-Iversen, E. (1953). Transvestism. *Journal of the American Medical Association,* 152:391–396.

Harris, G. (1948). Sex hormones, brain development and brain function. *Endocrinology,* 75:627–648.

Jorgenson, C. (1967). *A Personal Autobiography.* New York: Bantam Books.

Marks, I., and Gelder, N. (1967). Transvestism and fetishism: Clinical and psychological changes during faradic aversion. *British Journal of Psychiatry,* 113:711–729.

Money, J., Hampson, J. C., and Hampson, J. L. (1955). An examination of some basic concepts: The evidence of human hermaphroditism. *Bulletin of the Johns Hopkins Hospital,* 97:284–310.

———. (1957). Imprinting and establishing of gender role. *Archives of Neurological Psychiatry,* 77:333–336.

Money, J., and Pollitt, E. (1964). Cytogenic and psychosexual ambiguity. *Archives of General Psychiatry,* 11:589–595.

Pauly, I. (1968). The current status of the change of sex operation. *Journal of Nervous and Mental Diseases,* 147:471.

Stoller, R. (1966). The treatment of transvestism and transsexualism. *Current Psychiatric Therapy,* 6:92–104.

———. (1968). *Sex and Gender: On the Development of Masculinity and Femininity.* New York: Science House.

11] THE ADOLESCENT

SEXUAL REVOLUTION

MALVINA W. KREMER, FRANK S. WILLIAMS,
DANIEL OFFER, ROBERT S. BERNS,
JAMES F. MASTERSON, HAROLD I. LIEF,
AND SHERMAN C. FEINSTEIN

Malvina W. Kremer: Introduction

The sexual revolution began with Sigmund Freud at the turn of the century. This was a time of intense interest in sex, which focused mainly on deviations and pathology. Freud brought sex and sexual development into the sphere of normality. During subsequent decades, it gradually became not only permissible but even fashionable to speak and write about sexual matters. The pace of change was accelerated in the aftermath of the two world wars. There seems to be general agreement that we are now in the midst of even more rapid changes.

Are we witnessing a revolutionary leap or merely the process of evolution? In the perspective of human history the ultimate judgment will probably not be made on the basis of speed of change, but on whether there will be a basic alteration in the institutionalized regulation of relationships between the sexes.

Institutionalized change is difficult to evaluate. Institutionalized values, whether expressed in literature, in art forms, in the mass media, or in response to questionnaires, do not necessarily reflect the true state of affairs. James F. Masterson and Daniel Offer believe that there is more change in attitude than in behavior, whereas Harold I. Lief believes that a significant change in behavior occurred after World War I, and that attitudes are only now catching up.

There are many indications that Victorian standards were honored more in the breach than in the observance. Perhaps the same will be

160

said of some aspects of the current sexual revolution. For example, Lief, Masterson, and Frank S. Williams stress the egalitarian trend with women demanding the same rights to sexual gratification accorded to men. As Masterson points out, the trend is to liberate women, not to restrict men. Other trends are noted: earlier sexual relations with an emotionally significant partner (Lief and Masterson), and the desire for gratification apart from emotional involvement (Williams). We may speculate about what kind of equality may be achieved in the light of these trends. There is a serious possibility, a danger as I see it, that what will emerge will be only equality in irresponsibility.

The issue is particularly relevant for adolescents, engaged as they are in the search for identity and security. Several authors direct attention to the possibility of enhancing affectionate and stable relationships through the newly emerging opportunities for experimentation. At the same time all the authors point out uncertainties inherent in premature experimentation. It remains to be established that potential benefits outweigh potential dangers. It has been argued that the trend is toward unbridled hedonism and permanent instability rather than toward stable and responsible affection. Changes in society's attitudes and values may eliminate hypocritical constraints and inhibitions, but, as Sherman C. Feinstein points out, these changes offer no protection against narcissistic exploitation. As practitioners, we are already seeing examples of the latter. The long-term effects on family structure and child rearing can only be guessed at. Technology has relieved the participants in sexual relations of the responsibility for pregnancy and diminished the risks of venereal disease. To borrow a phrase, sex is now for recreation, not procreation. But this development leaves the way open for new forms of hypocrisy and exploitation. That both sexes may now have equal opportunity in these directions is a dubious advantage to society.

All our authors express some misgivings about the sexual revolution, especially in relation to premature involvements. Feinstein states the matter most incisively: "the sexual revolution may be based on rather spurious assumptions that freedom will lead to maturity." I can see at least two components of prematurity in the present context. One has to do with the already mentioned issue of responsibility. Responsibility is twofold: toward oneself in terms of growth and development in the direction of optimal long-term relationships and emotional health and toward one's partner in terms of avoiding unrealizable expectations or misleading promises. Implicit in the concept of experimentation is the notion of trial and error leading toward a better final adjustment of mutual compatibilities. This notion underlies the traditional concept of stepwise sexual involvement during adolescence. It is assumed that the depth and intensity of emotional involvement parallels the sexual involvement. Surely the new levels of involvement under the new freedom to experiment will leave many young experimenters vulnerable when the temporary nature of the liaison becomes clear. There is no assurance that this kind of experimentation will increase the likelihood of ultimate mutually satisfying and meaningful relationships. Indeed, it is just as likely that experimentation will produce disappointment and cynicism, which will interfere with the hoped-for satisfactory outcome.

The second component of premature involvement has to do with displacement of unresolved neurotic problems into the sexual area. Here we would have to list the entire catalog of neurotic behaviors and maneuvers: aggression, self-aggrandizement, control, dependency, and many others. Williams emphasizes contradictory value orientations and changing family dynamics as obstacles to the development of intimacy.

The sexual revolution presents problems for mental health professionals as well as for adolescents; these problems manifest themselves in treatment in terms of transference and countertransference. The therapist's own beliefs and values are constantly called into question. He must be clear about and comfortable with his own values and yet at the same time flexible enough to comprehend other viewpoints.

To sum up, no one doubts that changes are occurring even if it is not clear whether the pace is evolutionary or revolutionary. Mental health professionals have a responsibility in these matters. Granted that they are not the final arbiters of the manners and morals of society, their opinions exert considerable influence. A similar responsibility devolves on college personnel who deal with young people, as discussed by Robert S. Berns. This responsibility, as I see it, is to recognize both the potential benefits and the potential pitfalls and not shrink from setting forth both aspects even if the tide of opinion runs only one way at any given moment. Based on a joint session of the American Society for Adolescent Psychiatry and the American Orthopsychiatric Association, these essays provide an overview of a significant aspect of the contemporary scene.

Frank S. Williams: Sociocultural and Familial Conflicts Over Identity and Intimacy

The adolescent sexual revolution reflects certain trends in sociocultural and familial forces related to identity and intimacy. This revolution, or evolution, presents itself in many ways, including younger adolescent

162

girls involved in extensive sexual experimentation (including intercourse), increase in overt homosexual experiences among older adolescent boys and young men, and increased freedom in verbal and physical expressions of sexuality (including nudity). I should like to discuss certain sociocultural and familial forces affecting these changing sexual patterns and trends. These forces include (1) sociocultural double-bind communications regarding sex and intimacy; (2) familial and social stress on ego identity at the expense of experiences with human intimacy; (3) the changing role of womanhood in relation to more assertive expression of rights to sexual gratification and experimentation.

DESCRIPTION OF THE REVOLUTION

In clinical practice, as well as from observations within the community, my colleagues and I have noted an increase in the number of girls between the ages of fifteen and seventeen involved in sexual intercourse, often with subsequent pregnancies. These girls primarily stress their right to gratification and sexual equality in terms of experimentation. In contrast to previous generations, they do not emphasize love and romantic fantasies as having pressured them into early sexual intercourse; nor do they experience the same type of depression seen previously in young pregnant girls who became aware of unrequited love. The Victorian ethic and the related masochistic plight of the young girl seem to have been modified by a sense of freedom to experience sexual gratification.

There seems to be a growing rise in overt homosexual experiences of older adolescent males and young men between the ages of sixteen and twenty-two. This is different from the common mutual masturbation of preadolescent boys in the eleven- to thirteen-year-old age range. An interesting qualitative change in overt homosexual expression is the apparent lack of related conflict over masculinity. In our clinical experiences with past generations of adolescents, homosexual panic was a frequent contributing factor to a male adolescent's first psychotic break. This seems to appear less today. In fact, some of the young men and older adolescents I have seen describe both their homosexual experiences and the lack of distinction between the sexes in regard to clothing and hair styles in ways that include the following: "It makes me a stronger man to be aware of my love for men" "Why not try anything once?" "If girls can be close, why can't boys?" This increase in homosexual activity seems to occur more frequently outside of hippie and drug-using groups. It seems to me that many of these young men use active homosexual experiences as a defense against a deeper homosexual threat, against passivity, and against castration anxiety.

Regarding nakedness, one sees a growing trend toward less apparent inhibition and self-consciousness. This can be seen in male and female clothing, movies, plays, the miniskirt trend, marathon nude group therapies, as well as in the growing production of children's dolls that include genitals.

SOCIOCULTURAL AND FAMILIAL CONFLICTS WITH IDENTITY AND INTIMACY

Our society and culture today presents double-bind communications about sexuality and intimacy. Society's messages confuse physical sexuality with intimacy. Though our movies and plays encourage freer physical intimacy, very little experience of real empathy and real mutuality, major ingredients for intimate involvement and communication, is encouraged during the oedipal, latency, and early adolescent years. Instead, the sociocultural as well as familial emphasis in growing up has been on reinforcing ego identity based upon achievement, performance, grades, and excelling in group activities. A competitive, narcissistic type of ego identity is encouraged. A child has very little further experience with real intimacy following the initial mother-child symbiosis. At age eighteen, he or she is suddenly expected to dip back into that early intimacy experience with mother, and somehow to apply that experience to late adolescent love relationships.

Intimacy in families has decreased during the past forty or fifty years. Instead of one to one meaningful interactions and communication between family members, the emphasis is on group sharing, doing things together, watching things together. The adolescent, faced with a recrudescence of early oedipal feelings, finds it difficult to sublimate these with other types of familial intimacy experiences simply because he has not learned how. The adolescent is trapped. He either leaves the home and looks for intimacy outside or remains within the home and suffers the threat of massive regression to those types of oral and anal intimacy experiences he knew earlier in life with his parents. Should he choose to leave home in an effort to seek love and intimacy, he has had very little experience with intimate communication to sustain him. He winds up, I feel, substituting physical-sexual intimacy as well as the pseudointimacy of the hippie and drug scene for human closeness.

There has been a decided change in the role of women during the past few decades. With this change, there has been subsequent identification by young girls with their mothers' more assertive and liberal attitudes toward sexuality. This not only includes more responsive, active attitudes toward sex, but growing acceptance of older women seeking out young men for relationships.

War, the threat of the bomb, and actual and potential social eruptions also affect the adolescent's fear of castration and of total annihilation. The adolescent not only projects his own guilt onto an ambivalent society but rationalizes acting out of conflicts with the reality-tinged justification of "Why not live and love while one still is alive and has a chance to do so?"

Daniel Offer: Sex and the Normal Adolescent

The aim of the Modal Adolescent Project was to examine the relative influences of internal psychological and external environmental factors on the functioning of adolescents. We were interested in studying the behavior of a specially selected group of middle-class adolescents in order to assess their relative strengths and weaknesses, what kinds of psychological problems they have, how they cope with them, and if not successful, the reasons for their failures.

In this study of the psychological world of normal teenagers (Offer, 1969), we have been interested in the nature of the adolescent's sexual experience, his attitude toward sex and his sexual feelings and impulses. What kinds of problems does the adolescent have when he attempts to cope with sexuality, and how successful is he? If he fails in his attempts to cope with sexual feelings and impulses, what are the reasons behind his failure? We began working with a group of adolescents entering high school. They are currently three years out of high school. We have examined the development of sexuality in a specially selected group of middle-class suburban adolescents, from the age of fourteen to twenty-one.

METHOD

Our aim was to select a normal, typical, or average group of adolescents from a sample of high school students. We constructed a self-image questionnaire in order to tap significant areas in the psychological world of the adolescent. A typical student was defined as one whose answers fell within one standard deviation from the mean in at least nine out of ten scales. Utilizing our questionnaire as a screening device, we selected, in the fall of 1962, 103 typical boys from a total sample of 326 freshman boys in two local suburban high schools. In addition, we selected ten girls from thirty freshman girls in one of the schools. We have been able to follow seventy-three of the boys and the ten girls through the high school years.

All subjects were studied in the same way during the four years of high school:

1. Each subject was interviewed eight times during the high school years. All interviews were conducted in the school by an associate and myself. Both interviewers were psychiatrists, and each saw the same subject throughout this study.

2. Each subject was given a complete battery of psychological testing (Rorschach, Thematic Apperception Test, and Wechsler Verbal IQ) administered by a clinical psychologist during the junior year.

3. All mothers, and 70 percent of the fathers, were interviewed once during their child's junior year to obtain additional information.

4. The subjects' school records were available to us. This included the extensive behavior grading by the teachers in the high schools.

5. In the follow-up study after high school, we were able to study 85 percent of the subjects. We interviewed them yearly and obtained follow-up information by mail (Offer and Offer, 1969).

6. Obviously, our data concerning the boys are more complete and lend themselves to statistical analysis. The data from the ten girls are limited and will be utilized only occasionally for comparison. The data are discussed more fully in Offer and Offer (1968).

RESULTS

Dating Behavior

The dating history of our boys is as follows: A significant number of our subjects (45 percent) had not gone out with girls by the end of the freshman year. The number of adolescents who dated increased slowly during the next two years so that by the end of the junior year, 77 percent of our subjects were dating. It is important to note, however, that most teenagers dated irregularly and did not seem either to relish the experience or to think it important for teenagers to date. Those who did not date by junior year (23 percent) did not feel abnormal or self-conscious because they had not gone out with girls. According to our subjects, if anyone felt that teenagers should date, it was the parents, especially the mothers.

Typical in his attitude toward girls was a student on the football team who, by the end of the sophomore year, had never dated and felt he had not missed anything. As far as he was concerned he would have plenty of time for "this sort of thing" in college. But even while he was expressing his indifference, his level of anxiety went up; when this was pointed out to him, he stated that he simply did not understand girls and wanted to be left alone by them.

We noticed a striking difference in our subjects when we interviewed

166

them toward the end of their senior year. By then 95 percent were dating, and girls had begun to occupy a much more prominent place in the adolescent's life. The change was dramatic. It was not limited to social pressure because other teenagers were dating. More significantly, almost all our subjects, including the above-mentioned football player, looked forward to their dates and enjoyed the relationship with the girls. At this point the few teenagers who did not date stated openly that they wanted to date but lacked the courage.

The dating experience is not a critical one for the adolescent during the first two years of high school. Though many teenagers do not "think much about girls" during the first two years of high school, they were very conscious of them. "I stay away from girls because I am too young, and we do not understand each other." If the interviewer presses the teenager and asks: "How do you know that you do not understand one another?" the reply will be a quick and definite "I know." It was striking to the interviewer to note how often after talking about not dating and giving a rational explanation for it, they unconsciously brought their mothers into the picture. The teenagers might tell us about their conflicts with their mothers or how much they liked their mothers.

Many of the teenagers complained that their mothers (and at times also their fathers) teased them about their anxiety concerning girls. It was almost as if the more embarrassed the adolescent was about girls, the more he was teased by his parents. For example, one subject told us that he liked his mother much more than his father. Next he said that he thought he probably would not marry; he never thought about sex and never daydreamed about girls. He was the only subject to say that he probably would not marry. Other of his comments indicated that his negative responses were owing to a fear of his inexperience. He feared growing older and the possibilities of failure in new experiences. His mother, he reported, enjoyed joking about his lack of interest in girls. Her jokes made him uncomfortable. His parents may have tried too rapidly to turn a serious problem for the boy into something that could be handled by laughter.

As the teenager grows and matures, his interest in girls increases. Toward the latter half of the high school years the involvement became meaningful emotionally to the majority of our subjects. It was as though the curiosity about girls enabled them to overcome their fear of girls. Though the anxiety that they described while learning how to ask a girl out was considerable, according to their own evaluation, the satisfaction that they received was worth it. In the beginning, a major reason for dating was a social one. They shared their experiences with their peers almost immediately after they brought the girl home. The minute dissection that goes on among the boys telling one another what they did, right or wrong, is extremely helpful. They try to do better next time, not so much because they enjoy kissing or petting, but so they can tell their boyfriends. As their anxiety diminishes in their relations with girls, they begin to enjoy the encounter more, and eventually can look forward to a date simply because they like the girl and want to share their experiences with her and her alone.

By comparison to the boys, the girls started to date much earlier. They were dating by the end of the freshman year, and all but one were actively dating by their junior year. They were more preoccupied with sexuality and often asked us what we thought of sex and how far they should go.

Sexual Behavior

Almost all our subjects (more than 94 percent) reached puberty by the end of the freshman year in high school, as measured by the fact that their voices had already changed. The sexual behavior of our group of teenagers was, in general, limited.

During the freshman year, among the small group that dated actively, kissing and necking were the prominent ways of expressing affection. Our data agree with Reiss's (1961); he reported that the majority of teenagers are conservative and restrained in their sexual behavior. During the junior year 30 percent of the subjects were active daters, defined here as those who were going steady or had gone on more than one single date. Half of the active daters had experienced heavy petting. Ten percent of the total group had sexual intercourse by the end of the junior year. No subject admitted participating in overt homosexual behavior. The subjects did state that they masturbated and denied having any problems associated with it. We did not collect any data concerning fantasies during masturbation.

Finally, we would like to add that 80 percent of the subjects approved of premarital sexual intercourse but only after high school. The main reason the teenagers gave for not engaging in sexual intercourse in high school was the fear that the girl might get pregnant. Most thought "anything goes" except intercourse; not intercourse because it was wrong, but because it was dangerous. The students, if sufficiently at ease, would be pressed by the interviewer for more specific responses. This often precipitated confusion. When challenged the student would retract whatever statement he had just made.

Almost all the subjects (more than 90 percent) said that they daydreamed about girls, but only a small group (25 percent) stated that daydreaming included girls they knew personally. When a known woman was included, she was often an older woman. Incidentally, almost all the subjects thought that their mothers were very attractive. The interviewer often did not agree with this when he saw the parents in follow-up interviews. The teenagers who did not date by the junior year daydreamed about girls who were relatively remote: movie stars, heroines from fiction, or even young and attractive teachers. The object of their fantasies was almost never a teenage girl they knew personally.

THE FOLLOW-UP STUDY

The frequency of dating increased significantly after high school. More than half (58 percent) of the subjects were dating once or twice a week. Many of the boys had steady girlfriends. Among this group of active daters were the boys (30 percent of the total group) who had had sexual intercourse at least once.

The other subjects (42 percent), who dated less often, went out an average of once or twice a month. These boys could in turn be divided into two groups. There were the students who were lonely and regretted not having a girlfriend. There were also boys who claimed that dating once or twice a month was as often as they wished. They spoke of other interests, believing that there was time in the future to find a girlfriend.

Phil, who had told us that if he left home it would break his mother's heart, dated often and had a steady girlfriend. Nevertheless, he was roused to anger by the question: "Have you ever had intercourse?" Neither he nor his friends had ever had intercourse: "If you hear anything to the contrary about freshmen, the boys are bragging rather than being truthful."

An hour earlier, Jerry had assured us that 90 percent of college students do have sex. Jerry, of course, had had intercourse many times. When the interview was finished he remained to ask: "Do you think I'm oversexed?" Jerry had complained about the restraints his mother tried to place on him. Now he was trying to break down the resistance of every girl he dated.

The development of intimacy with a girlfriend was beginning for a good number of the boys who dated at least once a week, yet in only one case was the interviewer told about the personality or the desirability of a particular girl.

DISCUSSION

How does today's teenager cope with sexuality? Obviously, the seventy-three boys and ten girls we studied cannot be taken as representing the vast teenage population. However, our psychiatric data are consistent with our questionnaire results, which were given to 800 boys and 400 girls. Our results are also consistent with those of Reiss (1961), Douvan and Adelson (1966), and Simon, Berger, and Gagnon (1972). They, therefore, allow us to generalize our findings somewhat and to say that the latter are representative of one segment of to-day's youth, a significant segment in number, though by no means representing the majority of adolescents. Our hunch is that they might describe accurately about one-third of the middle-class population.

The cardinal findings are that the normal adolescent does not experiment much with sexuality. He is slow in getting involved sexually with a girl, and fantasy plays as significant a role as the actual deed. Extrapolating from our total data we would say that about 10 percent of our study population have had sexual intercourse by the end of high school. The rate rises to 30 percent by the end of the freshman year in college. Whether you believe this rate to be high (or low) depends, of course, on your own values.

The area in which we believe that change has occurred is in the teenager's attitude toward sex. Though the teenager (boy or girl) is very uncomfortable when he talks about his own sexual feelings and impulses, he likes to appear liberal when talking about such issues as premarital sex. This particular event is, after all, pretty far in the future for the fourteen- or fifteen-year-old. Nonetheless, his moral stance is not so strict as it might have been thirty years ago. An interesting question might be raised, however, concerning the relationship between attitudes (or values) and behavior. It is very possible that what we have described above are the seeds, which in the next generation will lead to actual changes in sexual behavior in the kind of population we studied. Changes in attitude eventually lead to changes in behavior. Assuming that attitudes do not return to the ways they were before World War II, the question remains as to when we will see the change.

This does not mean that teenagers are not concerned with what to do with sexual feelings now. On the contrary, the area of sex was of prime importance in their lives throughout the high school years. They shared their intimate thoughts and feelings with their friends and kept their parents intensely curious as to their activities on a late date.

The kind of normal adolescent whom we studied expresses more concern about social expectations than about feelings. He wants to do the right thing. This concern with his place in the social field leads him to ask such questions as "Am I popular?" or "Am I attractive?" much more than, for example, "What kind of feelings do I have toward a specific girl or boy?" Though the feelings were not expressed to the interviewer and actions often were limited, whatever does occur attains great significance for the adolescent. Their fantasy life is vivid, and kissing a boy for the first time may be equivalent unconsciously to becoming pregnant. Gratification from fantasy life may help the girl to deal with sexual impulses in early adolescence. She adjusts to them slowly and over a period of years. The adolescent girl, when she does act out, does so most frequently via the sexual route.

The adolescent boy has to learn how to cope with aggression. He is not so concerned with sexuality in early and midadolescence as the girl. For him, learning to curb his aggressive impulses is more important than learning to handle his sexual impulses. When the adolescent boy acts out, it is most often aggressively, in delinquent or violent behavior.

Our subjects, as well as those studied by Simon, Berger, and Gagnon (1972), did not start experimenting with manifest sexuality early in life. We are reminded of the statement made by Freud (quoted in Deutsch, 1967, p. 24) that: "the postponement of gratification is an important element in the process of sublimation and therefore essential to development." In other words, early sexual experiences can be harmful. This would be especially true for those students who shunned intimacy (Erikson, 1968) and utilized the sexual route to express unresolved conflicts.

In conclusion: Some of us may be surprised that the sexual revolution is not yet with us. Another investigator, Karl Menninger, reported that the degree of sexual activities among our adolescent population as reported in the lay press is highly exaggerated. We are in agreement with him. It might be of interest to note that he made these remarks in 1926. The findings presented here indicate that the majority of our normal adolescent subjects move slowly in the direction of heterosexuality.

Robert S. Berns: Attitudes of College Personnel Relating to Sexual Conduct of College Students

There is no general agreement that an actual sexual revolution has occurred among college students. However, the advent of the pill, the greater freedom with which sex is discussed, its portrayal on the screen, and the vastly increased divorce rate suggest some changes. These changes are taking place despite our Puritan background. It is my opinion that students engage in intercourse with fewer guilt feelings than occurred one or more generations ago. There is also a rise in the dissociation between the sex act and anything corresponding to love and intimacy. College contributes to this dissociation; in the drug culture, couples have intercourse before exchanging names.

Whereas college personnel normally serve as models for students in other respects, they fail to do so in respect to sexual mores, regardless of their suitability. This situation stems from two main sources: (1) It is difficult to counsel students of widely divergent backgrounds in matters as personal and delicate as sex; (2) college personnel adopt conservative sexual attitudes so as to offend no one. Thus, regardless of their own sexual development or maturity, college personnel perceive themselves as asexual objects in their dealings with students.

Most administrators are familiar with the incestuous parent who makes false accusations against an instructor or dean who might be discussing sexual freedom. Recently I saw a case of folie à deux in which a female student thought a science instructor was making allusions to her sexual behavior in his lectures. The girl's father entered into the paranoid delusional system; both brought allegations that the teacher imparted sexual information about the girl. In fact, the instructor was not even aware of the girl's presence in his large class.

All does not go well when sex is a classroom topic, either. A young instructor had very large audiences because he advocated that students learn about their own sexual anatomy, physiology, and psychology. When he thought he was attracting too many hippies to his classes, he modified his teaching. The last I heard, he was advocating the importance of discipline. Perhaps these two illustrations indicate that sex is a dangerous area, whether it is fantasized by a student or discussed by an instructor.

It is my impression that college personnel tend to deny their sexuality or to see themselves as asexual objects. Even among student health service personnel, which includes doctors and nurses, sex is a taboo subject. Exceptions may be found in cases where students have venereal diseases, or when psychiatrists are consulted specifically on sexual matters. Improvement has occurred in student health services since 1969 regarding teaching contraceptive methods, arranging for abortions, and increased teaching of venereal disease prevention.

In the past, college personnel have often been sons of ministers, or persons concerned with upward mobility within the academic context. Some had the "ivory tower syndrome" permitting them to remain detached from both students and society. Often they have a rigid obsessive-compulsive personality or extreme oral proclivity, so that any interpersonal communication is impossible.

Accordingly, at the age when students most need sex information and guidance, it is almost entirely withheld. The explicit message of the administrator is that cohabitation is conditionally condoned, but the implicit message is that sex is a barracks subject, both dirty and dangerous.

Students are dependent on peer pressures and attitudes, not only in respect to sexual development, but to a lesser extent in most other areas. Vastly increased student populations partially account for this phenomenon. However, counseling about one's sexual development has never been an easy subject. College personnel in the past were no more prepared for this than in the present. What has changed, however, is that students talk much more freely about sex, and the opportunities for sexual practice are greater. Thus, college personnel need to have more openness in helping students achieve a sexual identity.

Nevitt Sanford (1967, p. 143) said, "The college assumes the task of helping its students develop their personalities. All its resources and practices, including its actions and policies with respect to sex, should be directed to this end."

James F. Masterson: Adolescence and the Sexual Evolution

We are living in an era of social change that is as vast, sweeping, and dramatic as that of the Renaissance. The core of this change seems to consist of the restructuring of the relationship of the individual to authority, a dismantling of the residual fragments of medieval thinking from the minds of men. It stresses not only the needs and rights of the individual but also the necessity for authority figures to rely more on reason and flexibility than on rules and rigidity. People are demanding not only adequate consideration of their rights but participation in those decisions affecting their own destiny.

This restructuring begins in the home, in the parents' relationships with the child, and extends to the students' relationship with the school. It goes beyond this to the relationship of the employer to employees and to the relationship of the citizen to his government. Finally it also affects the relationship of the laity to the hierarchy in religion. These changes augur well for a future where mankind employs reason and flexibility in his response to human needs.

It is not surprising, then, that sexual values are also involved in these sweeping changes. The evidence is everywhere: Newspapers report that Columbia University, yielding to students' demands that sex is a private matter, turned over to the student council the decision as to when girls

173

can be entertained in the students' rooms. The pill is more widely used. The abortion rate is rising while the percentage of those who believe sexual intercourse prior to marriage to be improper is falling.

Are these changes only in attitude or are they also manifested in behavior? Are they the views and actions of the majority, of a prophetic minority, or of a rebellious fringe group? Is this revolution or evolution? Will it lead to a decline in social morality or to greater human happiness? Is it only among the young, or does the older generation also participate? Why is it happening now? This chapter, presenting some reflections on these questions, also describes some of the implications of these changes for adolescent sexual conflicts.

REVOLUTION OR EVOLUTION?

Many of the older generation viewing these changes from the perspective of their own development—one based for the most part on Judeo-Christian ethics and strict concepts of sexual morality—have tended to see them as sexual revolution and have ascribed them primarily to youth. It seems to me that this may err on both counts, for not only is this ferment taking place among adults but also what the older generation calls revolution—the overthrow of an established system of morals—may actually be an evolution, a process of growth and development toward a new system of morals.

Change has been occurring so rapidly in the adult world that writing this chapter has been much like trying to write the review of a play in the middle of the first act. Illustrations from three social institutions— religion, law, and medicine—will have to suffice.

The furor in the Roman Catholic Church, following the Pope's failure to support his advisory commission's recommendation that the use of birth control pills be permitted, seems to amount almost to a schism. Many American clergy are strongly advocating dramatic reversals of the church's ancient views on sex. This titanic struggle clearly points toward a liberalizing of traditional views.

There is great agitation throughout the country to liberalize abortion laws. A recent survey of psychiatrists indicated that 95 percent felt the laws should be liberalized. Efforts to achieve this have succeeded in Colorado, New York, and other states. To cite another example, a bill was recently submitted to the English Parliament making homosexual acts between consenting adults not a crime. Such laws are in effect in two of our states.

In medicine, the light of reason in the form of experimental scientific study was introduced by Masters and Johnson (1966) into the darkness, superstition, and mystery that have surrounded human sexuality. These

174

changes in the Catholic Church, in the law, and in medicine cannot be ascribed to youth. Clearly the older generation, those charged with preserving, protecting, and transmitting the values of our culture are actively involved in modifying these very same values.

EFFECT ON YOUTH

What is happening among younger people? While their elders, being under less immediate pressure from sexual feelings, cope with these issues in a sober and intellectual fashion, the young people of today, under more urgent pressure, have leapfrogged their parents to apply these newer concepts to their own lives.

How extensive is this change? Though I read much in the press about the increased sexual freedom of the younger generation, I see less of this in my office and read even less about it in professional publications. My guess is that the advance guard of the younger generation is indeed exhibiting a great deal more freedom in sexual behavior, but the majority, though holding to traditional patterns in their behavior even as their parents did, are at the same time submitting their concepts, which were previously taken for granted, to serious and searching scrutiny. In other words, there is more change in attitude than in behavior.

Let us examine the evidence first among high school students (eighteen and under) and then among college students. Kinsey, Pomeroy, and Martin (1948) reported that approximately 30 percent of boys eighteen and under and 3 percent of girls fifteen and under had had sexual intercourse. The recent study by the Sex Research Institute at Indiana did not include teenagers, but there are two other studies whose findings, though admittedly from quite dissimilar groups, are remarkably similar. Schofield (1965) in England studied a random sample of 1,200 teenagers, and Offer and Offer (1969) in the United States reported on 100 normal adolescents. They found that approximately 30 percent of boys and 5 to 15 percent of girls had had intercourse by age nineteen. This hardly represents a dramatic shift in behavior over a twenty-year period.

QUESTIONS TEENAGERS ASK ABOUT SEX

The change in teenagers' attitude toward sex is evidenced by questions, some of which are listed below, which I received from 100 high school students to whom I gave a talk on sex.

1. Do you feel an unmarried girl should have an unwanted child? What emotional factors are there in having a child before marriage?
2. What's wrong with premarital sex? I need better reasons than I have heard so far (I have heard all the usual reasons). What if you have been

going out with a boy for about two years? You really like each other. You go out with other people so you don't limit yourself too much, but you still really like only him (he likes only you). You have even talked of marriage after you finish college. How far should you go? What is wrong with pre-marital sex while you are juniors and seniors in college if your relationship has lasted that long but you don't want to marry until after college?

3. Why does a boy become so emotional when he is having intercourse, and what actually happens to the boy? Do girls have the problem of becoming too emotional when having sexual intercourse with a boy? If so, how can she prevent this? If a boy starts to become too involved in sex (during the "lovemaking"), how can a girl make him stop yet still be on friendly terms as before without sex? What happens when a girl loses her virginity? At the time she actually loses it? Can a boy tell if she has it or not later on?

4. Sex is for having children, but there is something else. How much now? Can we go all the way to everything except offspring?

5. Sex is dirty when it's done out of pure passion. Why is it considered dirty and condemned when done out of love? Why is it defined by other people in terms of good and evil for relationships in which they hold no concern?

6. What does cunnilingus have to do with your relationship with the opposite sex? Is it practiced by sensible married couples?

7. What is the emotional effect when you go through sexual intercourse with a person you're in love with, in relation to the effect of going through sexual intercourse with someone you don't love?

These questions reveal an intense, urgent and earnest quest for a realistic understanding of the role of sex in these young peoples' lives.

When we turn to college students we find marked changes in attitude and moderate changes in behavior. The recent report of the Sex Research Institute at Indiana suggests that more college students are having sexual intercourse than twenty years ago; sexual intercourse occurs not in a casual or promiscuous setting but when they are emotionally involved; more girls enjoy their first sexual intercourse, a triumph in itself. Though most girls have their first sexual intercourse with a boy they plan to marry, a higher percentage than twenty years ago are having sexual intercourse in a relationship that does not imply marriage though the parties are emotionally involved. Boys were found to still be more opportunistic about sex, but there was a trend toward having the first sexual intercourse with a girl with whom they were emotionally involved. Finally there was a dramatic drop in the percentage (25 percent to 7 percent) who visited a prostitute for their first sex experience.

Though these findings (gathered from newspaper reports and from personal talks with researchers) must be viewed as tentative until the full report is published, they suggest a heartening trend away from the dehumanized, exploitative, and manipulative attitudes about sex shown by our generation. This concept views sex as an integral and important part of the total personality, a unique vehicle for the attainment of pleasure and for the expression of tenderness and caring.

To those who would be alarmed that this sort of change may lead to a decline in morality, I would suggest that we are not seeing orgies or lack of control, but rather a different kind of control: self-control based not on guilt or fear of disapproval but on a concept of human relations, human worth, and human dignity.

SOURCES OF EXISTING STANDARDS

What are the reasons for this change? Perhaps we might get some insight by considering how the standards that are undergoing change arose in the first place. Let us journey back in time for a moment to that critical period for the development of Western civilization, Rome around the first century A.D. Prior to that time, during the expansion of the Roman empire, sexual standards had been strict and social morality was quite high and conducive to the strength of the society and the growth of the Roman republic. However, Rome's new found affluence, power, and leisure led to a deterioration of sexual standards.

The emperor, worried about the future of the realm, between 18 and 9 B.C. promulgated a series of laws that have been called the most important social legislation of antiquity. A crucial law forbade a husband to kill an adulterous wife, and ordered him under threat of severe fines to bring her to court and accuse her. For the first time, that which had been a private wrong became the state's business.

A whole series of laws were promulgated in an effort to prop up the birthrate of the upper classes. Bachelors, spinsters, and childless wives were ineligible to inherit; mothers of three or more children were given special legal privileges. Political preference between equal candidates was given to the man with more children.

However, to a greater or lesser degree each of these laws was a failure. Roman philosophers began to argue in favor of sexual restraint and even asceticism. Where legislation and law had failed, religion succeeded. Christian morality allied itself to these latter forces and effectively displaced the traditional Greco-Roman patterns of sexuality and began a new concept of sexual morality that survives till this day. It emphasized chastity, virginity, and the merit of denying the flesh.

Religion supplied the principal motivation for sexual control. Chastity was good; premarital sex, bad. Though this rule may have solved some immediate problems, the underlying issue of the relationship of sexual expression to personality development as well as to human happiness remained uninvestigated. Human nature attempting to follow the rule inevitably seemed to run into trouble, as evidenced by illegitimacy

177

and divorce statistics. It does not seem surprising that at last motivations for sexual control are beginning to be studied through the light of reason.

The profound discoveries of modern sciences have lessened our dependence both on moral dictums and intuitive judgments, leading to an emphasis on reason. This has caused modern adolescents, more than in earlier times, to demand logical reasons for ethical standards. It no longer suffices to speak to them of natural moral laws determining what is right and wrong.

The pervasive influence of the Kinsey findings, as well as the psychoanalytic view that the failure to integrate sexual impulses and feelings into the personality in a healthy way impairs personality growth and produces emotional conflict, has caused us to examine traditional views.

The increasingly strong demands of women for equality at all levels have also lead to changes in attitudes. They perceive the double standard as keeping them from enjoying the pleasures of lovemaking, which men enjoy without serious social condemnation. This rebellion is not designed to curb men, but rather to release women. Finally, the development of the pill has freed womankind from its ancient servitude to pregnancy, while the efficacy of penicillin has minimized the danger of infection, removing two common sources of both sexual anxiety and control.

One might ask what all this has to do with adolescent sexual problems. While his older brother and sister are carrying out the revolution, the adolescent must come to grips with its effects, for he develops his sexual identity through interaction with his peers and with the sexual mores of his culture. Therefore, he is confronted with the shifting sands of a changing sexual morality in the social sphere at a time in his life when, lacking a personal sense of sexual identity, he must wade through the changing social climate. This immeasurably complicates his task, since it gives him fewer certainties on which to rest; yet at the same time it may offer him a greater potential by giving him more freedom to experiment to find that identity.

BENEFITS AND HAZARDS

What are some of the implications of this evolution? Let us consider first some benefits and then some hazards. There are many adolescents who, immature or excessively inhibited, come to a dangerously late period of their development before fully realizing the extent of their sexual problems. The evolution may impel them to seek help earlier.

For example: A twenty-two-year-old senior at an Eastern girls' college sat in my office and hesitantly and tearfully told the following story. She had always been popular with boys since she began dating at fourteen. Initially, she had reveled in her success as proof of her femininity, but when she first became involved with a boy at sixteen she developed such severe anxiety, nausea, and vomiting on each date that her only recourse was to end the relationship.

She allayed her doubts with the thought that she would grow out of this difficulty, but time was to prove her wrong. The pattern was already set, and it continued unabated through the next six years. She felt she must have dated at least 100 boys in college, and every time one became close the symptoms would resume and she would have to break it off.

She had to settle for an endless round of superficial dating without daring a close relationship with a boy. I could not help wondering as I listened to this attractive but immature girl that more pressure of the kind implied by the sex evolution might have brought her for help sooner.

Another example: A nineteen-year-old college sophomore had been having emotional difficulties since the onset of puberty when she became anxious, depressed, withdrew from her friends, and spent all of her time on schoolwork. It was necessary for her parents to send her to a special school for treatment. Gradually she improved and went on to finish high school and enter college, where she again became anxious and depressed and came to my office for treatment.

Though she maintained an active social life with an average amount of dating, she had never had a close relationship with a boy or any sexual activity, neither of which was a source of concern to her. After a year of intensive treatment and much working through of her anxiety and depression, it became clear that she was so terrified of sexual feelings and impulses that she avoided any occasion with boys that might provoke them. She had always been dimly aware, without facing up to the fact that something was wrong with her, that she would grow up to be an old maid.

She took a cross-country trip with some girl friends the summer of her freshman year, and was amazed to find on visiting a number of campuses throughout the Midwest and the West that girls her age were living with boys. This led her to an impulsive but successful effort at sexual intercourse with an older man with whom she was not emotionally involved. Her femininity thus reassured, she began in her interviews to investigate the sources of her sexual conflicts. The confrontation with changing sex standards brought home to her in a profound way her own sexual immaturity and motivated her to work on her sexual problems in treatment. Twenty years ago this girl's sexual difficulty may have escaped notice.

What about the hazards? A parent may be impelled by what he hears about changing sexual standards to act out his own unconscious promiscuous impulses by unduly encouraging his teenager toward sex experiences for which the teenager is not emotionally ready. Or the adolescent himself may attempt sexual relations prematurely.

Some immature adolescents are not ready for sexual intercourse, and others cannot either enjoy the experience or deal with the emotional consequences of their actions. Their efforts then become abortive and can have disastrous consequences for their emotional life. For example, an eighteen-year-old freshman from a well-to-do Puerto Rican family was raised as a strict Catholic, and attended private Catholic schools. His father, feeling no further religious guidance was necessary, encouraged him to attend an Ivy League school. For the first time he was faced with differing views about sexual behavior, and when he fell in love with a girl from another Eastern college he would rendezvous with her in a New York hotel room, spending the afternoon together lying in bed, necking. Driven by his impulses, but unable to consummate them because of his conscience, he developed intolerable sexual tension, which he later relieved by masturbation, and which led to depression and feelings of inadequacy. In these depressions he would roam the streets of New York all night seeking solace. Overwhelmed by these feelings he finally was unable to do his schoolwork, dropped out of college, and was referred for treatment. It took many months for him to understand the conflict between his sexual impulses and his standards.

A second case indicates a different problem. A young girl in her early twenties had always dated actively, had many relations with boys and indulged in a good deal of necking and heavy petting, but through what in retrospect seems unconscious wisdom she had always avoided sexual intercourse. Under the pressure of a particularly intense love relationship she cast aside this heretofore lifelong caution and began having intercourse. This served to remove the last barrier to total emotional involvement on which she became so dependent that she was literally unable to extricate herself from a relationship that compelled her to undergo numerous humiliating experiences with her now reluctant and distant lover. Only with intensive psychotherapy was she able to resolve this attachment.

The sexual evolution has brought to the surface once more some of mankind's most ancient and perplexing questions about the relationship of sexual behavior to emotional health. For example, is it not possible that full growth and development of the personality may involve several or more close relationships or intimate encounters that necessarily involve sexual intercourse and end in separation? This may teach one to deal not only with the emotional potential for a close relationship, but also the emotional problems involved in separation, two important keys to life adjustment.

As we struggle to resolve these questions I think we should be careful to remember that emotional health does not itself become just the latest rationalization for old Puritan standards.

Harold I. Lief: The Sex Revolution and the Adolescent's Search for Identity

Conflicts in gender identity in adolescence are not unique to this generation. They are, however more visible. As Erikson (1968) puts it, young people wear their identity conflicts on their sleeves, Edwardian or leather: "sometimes when we see them walking down the street it is impossible for us to tell, without indelicate scrutiny, who is a boy and who is a girl." In the words of Winick (1968, p. 21) one might see the girl

in hip length boots, "basic black" leather coat, a helmet, and a pants suit or straight line dress of heavy fabric. Her male companion might be wearing a soft pastel sack suit, mauve hat, and a frilled and cuff-linked pink shirt. He could sport a delicate tie and jewelry, exude fragrance and wear tapered shoes with stacked heels. Both could have shoulder length hair, and their silhouettes would be quite indistinguishable.

Gender identity is a very important dimension of ego identity, often the most significant. Ego identity cannot be defined precisely; actually Erikson prefers to have it remain vague and he has added or changed aspects of his thinking about it over the past twenty years. Even if the term identity has been popularized to the point of irritation or tedium, we know that adolescents and young people, displaying a greater or lesser degree of awareness or articulateness, are concerned with the perennial question of "Who am I?"

One's identity depends on a set of factors (see Table 11–1). Among them are social roles, such as student, worker, girl or boyfriend, lover, wife, husband, hippie, gang member, athlete, ethnic club or political group member, rebel, or all-American boy. One's social role must be sanctioned by others, so social roles are always relative and often shifting from one situation to another, from one time to another. A stable pattern of identity is dependent on the achievement of one or at most several primary role identifications continuous over time, an almost im-

181

possible attainment for most late adolescents and difficult for most young adults. This is why an identity crisis is a normative aspect of adolescence.

TABLE 11–1

Ego Identity and Tasks of Adolescence and Young Adulthood

DIMENSIONS OF EGO IDENTITY	QUESTIONS PUT TO SELF	TASKS: TO DEVELOP
Social roles	Where do I belong?	Primary role identifications
Values and standards	What do I stand for or believe in?	Ethical capacity
Personality characteristics	What sort of person am I?	Stable sense of self and self-respect
Goals and expectations	Where am I heading? What will I become?	Occupational identification
Interpersonal attitudes and behavior	How do I get along with others, especially those of the opposite sex?	Capacity for intimacy
Ego (self) boundaries	Am I able to take care of myself?	Capacity for autonomy and self-reliance

A second feature of ego identity relates to the values and standards adopted by the young person. The question "What do I stand for?" has to be answered before one can know oneself. The inability to answer this affirmatively lies behind much of the exuberant Dionysian sensuality and episodic attempts at consciousness expansion of today's youth. The rebellion, however, against the values of the Establishment in response to the question "What am I against?" is hopefully a step in the direction of positive and affirmative value-seeking. At any rate, much of the turmoil and even violence of our student culture is the consequence of the failure to resolve this aspect of identity conflict.

Certain personality perceptions, consisting of polarized pairs of attributes, make up another dimension of ego identity. Some examples are strong-weak, good-bad, active-passive, dirty-clean, ugly-beautiful, rich-poor, couth-uncouth, rough-gentle, and, of course, masculine-feminine. Negative identifications create perceptions often as important as positive identifications. Gender identity, or one's feelings about his masculinity and femininity, and related perceptions such as activity and passivity, dominance and submission, play a central role in answering the question "What sort of person am I?"

A fourth parameter of ego identity relates to one's goals and expectations. "In what direction am I going?" and "What will I become?" are essential queries one addresses to oneself at this period of life. The young person who is definite about his career aspirations has a much more stable and secure identity than the youth who lacks such clear direction.

A fifth dimension of ego identity is the interpersonal one. "How do I get along with others?" and, especially, "How do I relate to the opposite sex?" are questions that assume overriding importance in the thoughts and feelings of young people. The capacity to develop intimacy is the task that creates so many problems for the late adolescent and young adult.

Finally, the ultimate question (short of the creative, generative capacities mature people are able to develop usually somewhat later in life) is "Am I able to take care of myself?" The ability to separate from one's parents and other nurturing adults and to become autonomous, independent, and self-reliant is fundamental to healthy personality development. Surely one's perception of self or one's ego identity is critically affected by the degree to which this capacity is developed. Parenthetically, though this attribute is so highly prized in Western society, it is culture bound. According to Susan Sontag (1969) the Vietnamese do not have this degree of separateness or isolation from others or from society. In their language there is no word for the Western first person singular, "I," "je," "ich." When they speak of themselves, it is always in terms of a social relationship, "your younger cousin," or "your comrade." Their use of personal identity comes from the possibility of identifying with and participating in their society.

SEXUAL REVOLUTION AND GENDER IDENTITY

Before we turn to a discussion of the changes that are taking place in our sexual attitudes and behavior, the so-called sexual revolution, it would be well to direct our attention to the sexual system and its subsystem, see Table 11–2.

TABLE 11–2
Sexual System (Sexuality)

1. Biological sex: chromosomes, hormones, primary and secondary sex characteristics, etc.
2. Sexual identity: sense of maleness and femaleness (sometimes called core gender identity)
3. Gender identity: sense of masculinity and femininity
4. Sexual role behavior:
   a. Sex behavior: behavior motivated by desire for orgasm (physical sex)
   b. Gender behavior: behavior with masculine and feminine connotations

In this discussion we are mainly interested in gender identity and sexual role behavior. Of course these are, in turn, dependent on biological sex characteristics and sexual identity, but the latter (one's sense of maleness and femaleness) is, with rare exception, fully formed by the age of three. The development of gender identity and the sexual role behavior associated with it has a long ontogenetic history, which is more fully described elsewhere (Clausen, 1965; Gagnon 1965; Kagan, 1964; Lynn, 1966), but is in any case profoundly affected, not only by psychological factors within a specific family but by cultural influences, such as the changing sexual mores. Gender identity is the intervening variable between the sexual changes taking place in society and ego identity.

IS THERE A SEXUAL REVOLUTION?

Most behavioral scientists engaged in sex research believe that contemporary sexual mores are the result of a gradual change starting after World War I, and because it is gradual rather than sudden, it does not deserve to be called a revolution. The major change in sexual behavior, according to Kinsey, Pomeroy, and Martin (1948), occurred during the 1920s. What seems revolutionary is a consequence of public attitudes and behavior catching up with private behavior that changed rather drastically more than forty years ago. These changes have created: (1) an increase in the manifestations of sex and gender behavior, witness television, films, advertising of all sorts in all media, avant-garde theater, modern fashion, topless waitresses, some sensitivity groups, and the like; (2) a general preoccupation with sex that, at times, reaches obsessive proportions; (3) on the positive side, a refreshing openness and candor about sex and the human body; (4) some moderate increase in premarital and extramarital coitus during the last decade; (5) a marked increase in sexual permissiveness among some segments of society; (6) an increased desire among young people to achieve sex with affection or love. In this sense we are getting closer to the Scandinavian sexual norms (Christensen, 1966) with more open and accepted premarital coitus but with fewer casual, promiscuous matings. Reiss (1967b) stated:

It is interesting to note that many Scandinavians view our females as *more* promiscuous than Swedish females. They feel that the American female defines "sex" too much in terms of just coitus and therefore pets intimately with many boys while remaining virginal. The Swedish female is more discriminate about petting, but when she is affectionately involved she is more likely to have coitus.

184

SEXUAL BEHAVIOR AND SOCIAL FORCES

Sexual behavior cannot be viewed in isolation from political and social behavior in general. Young people, or at least their rebel leaders, are protesting against the Vietnam War, the threat of nuclear war, discrimination against black and other disadvantaged groups, the hypocrisy of the older generation, and the passive stance of the lone individual in an increasingly technological and dehumanized world. For some, sex becomes an affirmation of love and intimacy, and a reaffirmation of the worth of the individual; for others, even if it is an escape to a masturbatory sort of sensuality, it at least gives them reassurance that some sort of pleasure is possible in a threatening, insecure world, and at most gives them a moratorium before they struggle to achieve the dimensions of ego identity.

Sex always has been used for nonsexual purposes—for mastery, reassurance, power, self-punishment, and so on. These individual variations, however, do not concern us here. We are concerned about changes in sexual normative patterns and the implications of these changes for gender identity.

Though students demand a greater voice in decision-making and hence greater responsibility, they do not always wish to give up the protection society, including universities, gives them. Still, sexual emancipation plus student activism pushes the late adolescent toward early decision-making. Though, with each succeeding generation, the time between puberty and the assumption of adult responsibilities has lengthened, student demands for responsible participation in his milieu create an internal demand for responsible decisions in his personal life. During the 1950s there was considerable emphasis even in high school on going steady, a kind of pseudoautonomy and pseudomutuality otherwise known as puppy love, that unfortunately led to thousands of teenage marriages, a 50 percent divorce rate, and an unknown percentage of intact unhappy marriages. Though, to a considerable extent, this trend is still with us, it is diminishing as the age of marriage slowly rises. Young people are putting off marriage—though shacking up, a formula for instant and reversible marriage, is increasing—until they are more certain of their feelings about their own sexuality and about the type of person they wish for a partner. I see this as a healthy tendency, for, in conjunction with the pill, it may reduce the number of unwanted children and broken marriages.

Social forces, whatever their nature, such as discrimination against ethnic or minority groups, the struggle for political or economic power,

185

student revolt, or the changes in sexual mores, do not fall with equal weight on everyone. Individual life styles are affected by the events peculiar to that person's life as well as by his social roles and his degree of commitment to the groups with which he identifies. Generalizations, then, about the effect of the sexual revolution or renaissance or evolution (other terms that have been used to describe what is happening sexually in our society) on gender identity and sexual behavior must be made hesitantly and cautiously.

1. The greater freedom of sexual expression increases the number of alternatives for young people. For those ready to grow emotionally this may provide opportunities for experimentation in the selection of sexual behavior patterns and partners and in the degree of intimacy or in the quality of emotional investment associated with sex. Given reasonable life circumstances and luck this should speed up and make more secure the development of the adolescent's gender identity. For those whose previous processes of identification have left them confused about their masculinity or femininity, the freedom of choice promoted by our culture may easily increase their anxiety and doubts. When values and standards for sexual behavior are internal matters rather than external impositions, the way is left open for excessive reaction, too great an inhibition or premature or impulsive or stereotyped and ritualistic behavior. In adolescence this may lead to a downgrading of sex in favor of artistic, intellectual, or technical pursuits, to genital activity of all sorts without much intimacy or a narcissistic preoccupation with sexual fantasies and compulsive masturbation. Cultural changes may increase gender confusion and difficulties in achieving the capacity for intimacy. Instead of sexual mutuality there is a self-seeking, identity-hungry kind of sex life.

2. In adolescence there is generally a conflict, in Erikson's terms, between tentativeness and fidelity. In times of rapid social change, when the values of the older generation are suspect anyway, negative identifications are even more frequent. Fidelity becomes fidelity to opposition to the values of the elders and hence interferes with free choice and free experimentation. Under the banner of freedom, new rigidities and rituals emerge. Much of our new sexual freedom is of this sort and accounts for premature foreclosure on alternatives and an early freezing of a partially constructed sense of identity. In an era when greater tentativeness and flexibility are a mandatory aspect of healthy adaptation to rapid change, many exhibit a paradoxical inability to respond other than in stereotyped, albeit rebellious, forms.

3. The essence of the sexual revolution is the final separation of sex from reproduction. Not meant for reproduction, sex has become a pro-

duction. When one realizes that, in the average female, very few of the 40,000 eggs in her ovaries during the reproductive stage in her life will be involved in childbearing, our new knowledge is akin to the insight into the emperor's clothes. However, the notion that almost every act of sex is really connected with reproduction is a highly significant piece of psychic reality. That the long-range impact of the separation of sex from reproduction may be psychologically damaging in some aspects has been suggested by Erikson, though the separation is absolutely vital to population control and family planning. In any case, two factors seem to be responsible for this revolutionary idea: the pill and the woman's struggle for sexual equality to match the political and economic equality that is almost in her grasp. Her achievement of sexual equality depends on her ability to overthrow the double standard of morality, a value system tenaciously held by most males. The revolt against the double standard is just beginning, is quickly gathering momentum, and, I believe, will be complete in the next generation. As a result there is increased insecurity in the male, already accounting (probably) for a rise in male homosexuality and more passive heterosexuals. The adolescent girl, on the other hand, may be torn between an older self-image based on identification with her mother and grandmother and the values of previous generations, and the gender identity of her own emerging generation. As sexual norms change but still fail to keep up with changing sexual practices, these create problems in social as well as sexual intercourse and make doubly difficult the tricky problem of differentiating between healthy self-assertion and "unladylike" aggression. Though no one can prove it, the confusion in dress and style mentioned in the beginning of the chapter is probably an adaptation to the conflict in gender self-image. For in decreasing or eliminating the obvious differentiation between the sexes, the pressures to be either male or female are lessened. (The other explanation is that it is a manifestation of the revolt against the double standard.)

4. Though the percentage of boys who believe in the double standard is decreasing, most boys continue to adhere to that ancient sexual norm. Nonetheless, a marked shift in behavior has occurred. Masturbation is seen to be natural and normal, recourse to prostitutes is rarer, coitus with a girl one loves is permissible, and petting to climax with girls of one's social class is clearly the dominant behavior pattern. This seems to be reducing the amount of guilt associated with sex. If sex is no longer regarded as evil or dirty, it should have a marked effect on modifying the male's self-image and regard. In turn, this should enable him to love others more fully and competently.

5. As Rainwater (1966a, 1966b) has reported, there are considerable

differences in husband-wife relations in different social classes. At the upper-class level there are more feelings of companionship and marital love, whereas at the working-class level there is less communication between spouses with each spending more time with those of the same sex. At this level marital relations involve an exchange of services more than of affection. Sexual dissatisfaction is much greater among lower-class wives than among those in other social classes. The different processes of socialization in these different families affect the entire process of identification and so must have a marked effect on how children perceive themselves and those of the opposite sex. Coital sex is encountered earlier, and sex is more often used as a means of exploiting another person. The damaging effects on attitudes toward one's masculinity and femininity can be seen by the excessive bragging about sexual exploits, the rejection of anything regarded as sissified by males, and the self-punishing pattern of females, or at least the acceptance of the risk of pregnancy in order to gain a feeling of acceptance. Of particular interest is how these perceptions of self and others affect attitudes toward contraception.

6. It has been assumed by most professionals that, in regard to sex and family life behavior, class is more important than race; hence the outcry of resentment that greeted the Moynihan report (1965). Data, however, tend to confirm the findings of that report (Brown, 1968; Reiss, 1967a). At the bottom rung of the social-class ladder, black males and females are far more permissive in regard to premarital intercourse than are their white counterparts. Parenthetically, it should be pointed out that, of all groups, the upper-class blacks were the least likely to accept premarital intercourse. When black children are exposed to coital or other sexual practices going on all around them, as one study of the St. Louis housing project demonstrated (Hammond and Ladner, 1969), they are initiated into very early coital efforts, even during the so-called latency period, a period that is nonexistent for them. The effects of this type of pressure on their gender identities still awaits further study. But one thing is clear: Neither the black lower-class male or female looks for a lasting relationship; rather, premarital intercourse is related to a need to be sought after, and thus to confirm one's worth.

SEXUAL NORMS AND SOCIETY

Where are we heading? Will increased sexual freedom lead to social disorganization, as some prophesy? Is it already a manifestation of social disorganization? Packard (1968) believes there is a relationship between sexual license and the breakdown of society. He quotes Unwin's *Sex and Culture:* "Any human society is free to choose either to display great energy or to enjoy sexual freedom; the evidence is that it cannot do both for more than one generation." Packard cites Toynbee, Sorkin, and others in presenting the case for the danger to society from too great a sexual permissiveness. In this regard a quotation from Toynbee is interesting:

While we are lowering the age of sexual awareness, we are prolonging the length of education. How can the young be expected to give their minds to study during these sex haunted years. . . . I admire the 19th Century West's success in postponing the age of sexual awakening, sexual experience, and sexual infatuation far beyond the age of physical puberty. You may tell me that this is against nature; but to be human consists precisely of transcending nature—in overcoming the biological limitations that we have inherited from our prehuman ancestors.

Apparently this is an ancient argument. In his *Bacchae,* Euripides expressed the opposite notion, namely, that when sexual repression is extreme, society will be destroyed. Actually, Euripides seemed to advocate a balance between sexual expression and restraint.

To state the issue more topically: Does immersion in sensuality, sex, and drugs mean the impending failure to deal with political realities of overwhelming perplexity (nuclear warfare, overpopulation, urban blight) or must we be released from the straitjacket of artificially imposed sensations against feeling and sensing before we can turn our attention as more complete persons to the threats against society?

Sherman C. Feinstein: Effects of Pregnancy on Adolescent Sexual Development

Our current preoccupation with the sexual revolution and the flowering of permissive sexual attitudes in many quarters raises serious questions. Perhaps, from a theoretical viewpoint, there should be freedom to express oneself and satisfy basic drives in order to avoid conflict, but is the adolescent ready and able to handle this drive expression in an interpersonal way that enhances ego synthesis? As Thurber and White (1929) pointed out some forty years ago:

Two factors in our civilization have been greatly overemphasized. One is aviation, the other is sex. Looked at calmly, neither diversion is entitled to the space it has been accorded. . . . In the case of aviation, persons interested in the sport saw that the problem was to simplify it and make it seem safer. They introduced stabilizers and emergency landing fields. Even so, the plain fact remained that very few people were fitted for flying.

189

By allowing new freedoms including contraceptive safety devices and easy access to bedrooms in fraternity houses and dormitories, young people are put into a situation where sexuality becomes a natural part of their relationships. Are these youth fitted for the responsibilities of their actions? What happens to them when the realistic complications of sexuality enter the picture? How do they handle pregnancy, venereal disease, and the pressures of the increased intensity of their relationships?

Adolescence has been conceptualized as a phase of life when a number of ego tasks must be concluded so as to free the developing adult for a future that allows him to express himself in meaningful occupations and to develop gratifying interpersonal relationships. Among these tasks are the modification of one's unconscious concepts of parental figures from idealized imagoes to realistic ones, the assumption of adequate standards of morality, identification with one's biological sexual role, and the selection and stabilization of educational and vocational roles (Gardner, 1959).

The psychic work required to accomplish these tasks is considerable and what had previously been seen as a time of chaos has now been more clearly charted as a definite process, comparable to the infantile period of development.

The achievement of sexual maturity is one of the major tasks of adolescence, and the energies of the child are deeply involved in working through the essential shift from a dependent, infantile sexuality to a genital sexuality manifested by independence, responsibility, autonomy, and empathy. Experimental object relationships create stress on the adolescent ego; mastery over these stresses results in growth. Geleerd (1961) described the vicissitudes of the ego in adolescence when under stress. It regresses to the symbiotic position and then, finding this unsatisfactory, chooses more adequate defenses to deal with both internal and external demands. When the stress is overwhelming, reversion to old fixation-points occur and may lead to disorganization as occurs in the identity diffusion described by Erikson (1956).

Unplanned pregnancy, a complication of adolescent sexuality, is a severe stress for the unmarried mother and the putative father. It places reality demands on the couple which demand immediate action. Some quickly abandon adolescence, marry and begin their adult lives. Many adolescents are unable to undertake this course of action because they are not prepared as yet for these responsibilities. These youths may be struggling with what Blos (1962) described as a prolonged adolescence. Unable to accept the limitations imposed on their instinctual demands, they avoid the binding nature of commitment and attempt to remain indefinitely in a transitional phase of development.

In working with pregnant girls in the unmarried mother's service of a social agency, the emotional needs of the putative fathers become part of the overall approach to the service situation. Caseworkers, and in several instances the author (psychiatric consultant), used a questionnaire to study the fathers' attitudes. We made the following observations during the period of confinement.

The average age of the unmarried mother was nineteen, with a range of fifteen to twenty-three years. These were predominantly Jewish, white, middle-class, college-oriented girls. They were referred to the agency either by their physician or faculty. Communication was usually poor between the unmarried mother and her mother. Dependent, clinging relationships quickly were established between the caseworker and the unmarried mother, and with the setting up of a plan to handle the pregnancy, the putative father felt relieved of responsibility and obligation. Then, he frequently withdrew from the relationship.

The average age of the putative fathers was twenty-one years, more than 50 percent were two years older than the girl. Many had dropped out of high school. About one-third attended college, with three being in their senior year. Many were deeply concerned about the pregnancy but were either not interested in marriage or were not considered marriageable by the girls' mothers. As the pregnancy proceeded a rather typical pattern of behavior developed, which is illustrated by the following case study.

A twenty-year-old white male dropped out of an Ivy League school in his freshman year. After long experimentation with drugs and drifting around the country he entered treatment, depressed and suffering from a brain syndrone following extensive LSD ingestion. He was deeply confused over his identity and preoccupied with political and social issues. Early in his treatment he became involved with a nineteen-year-old girl who was bright, talented, and in deep conflict with her family. He prided himself with the accepting, understanding way he "helped" this girl who was depressed and unable to keep a job. He saw himself as eventually marrying her and felt thrilled because he had "feelings" with her which were otherwise absent. Their relationship was inseparable and they lived together for long periods, but either he or she would return home from time to time for various reasons. His parents were very unhappy with the relationship. They believed that the young lady was immature and exploitative, and feared that their severely disturbed son would get too deeply involved. The two youths, however, clung together and made plans.

He changed considerably when she discovered she was pregnant. He admitted being overwhelmed and he stopped seeing her for several weeks. He

191

regressed and stayed at home, spending time with his family. He could not decide if he were responsible for the pregnancy and whether he should offer her money. He now believed she was not a suitable marital partner. She, however, became more responsible, started dressing appropriately, found a job, and arranged for an abortion. He, in contrast, became more aloof and alienated from his girlfriend. He talked less and less about her and finally admitted that he was avoiding her. He seemed to have little interest or pride in the fact that he impregnated her. He was greatly relieved when she broke off all contact and made it clear he no longer had any obligation to continue the relationship.

DISCUSSION

Working with the youths struggling with problems of adolescent sexuality shows with painful clarity the experimental and tentative level of object relationships during this stage of life. The inability of children to communicate with their parents about sexuality, the incredible ignorance of basic sexual information, and the immature and regressive reactions to the stress of complications such as pregnancy emphasize the burden adolescent sexuality imposes on the still-developing ego.

Prepregnancy relationships, with their emphasis on closeness and dependency, are primarily pregenital. Intercourse satisfies physical needs, but frequently is typified by jealousy, possessiveness, and narcissistic exploitation. Pregnancy causes panic and then a superficial attempt at mastery, but finally the boy withdraws once the girl realizes she has to take responsibility for her condition. The loss of the putative father's self-esteem results in depressive withdrawal or depressive sadomasochistic acting out, and he eventually abandons the unmarried mother altogether.

This study indicates that the sexual revolution may be based on rather spurious assumptions that freedom will lead to maturity. The development of sexual maturation, an aspect of adolescent resolution, is a consequence of adequate ego developmental experiences. The tasks of adolescence can be resolved only after a great deal of ego work is accomplished, and the final synthesis of character is an outgrowth of the mastery of separation and individuation. Too early demands for mature solutions do not result in growth, but rather produce identity diffusion and regression.

REFERENCES

Blos, P. (1962). *On Adolescence: A Psychoanalytic Interpretation.* New York: The Free Press.

Brown, T. E. (1968). Sex education and life in the Negro ghetto. *Pastoral Psychology,* 19: 45–51.

Christensen, H. T. (1966). Scandinavian and American sex norms. *Journal of Social Issues,* 22(2):60–75.

Clausen, J., ed. (1965). *Socialization and Society.* Boston: Little, Brown.

Deutsch, H. (1967). *Selected Problems of Adolescence.* New York: International Universities Press.

Douvan, E., and Adelson, J. (1966). *The Adolescent Experience.* New York: Wiley.

Erikson, E. H. (1950). *Childhood and Society.* New York: Norton.

———. (1956). The problem of ego identity. *Journal of the American Psychoanalytic Association,* 4:56–121.

———. (1968). *Identity: Youth and Crisis.* New York: Norton.

Gagnon, J. H. (1965). Sexuality and sexual learning in the child. *Psychiatry,* 28:212–228.

Gardner, G. E. (1959). Psychiatric problems of adolescence. In: *American Handbook of Psychiatry,* Vol. 1, ed. S. Arieti. New York: Basic Books, pp. 870–892.

Geleerd, E. R. (1961). Some aspects of ego vicissitudes in adolescence. *Journal of the American Psychoanalytic Association,* 9:394–405.

Hammond, B. and Ladner, J. (1969). Sexual socialization in a Negro ghetto. In: *The Individual, Sex and Society,* SIECUS Handbook for Teachers and Counselors. Baltimore: Johns Hopkins Press.

Josselyn, I. M. (1968). Personal communication.

Kagan, J. (1964). Acquisition and significance of sex typing and sex role identity. In: *Review of Child Development and Research,* ed. M. L. Hoffman and L. W. Hoffman. New York: Russell Sage Foundation. Vol. 1, pp. 137–167.

Kinsey, A. C., Pomeroy, W. B., and Martin, C. C. (1948). *Sexual Behavior in the Human Male.* Philadelphia: Saunders.

Lynn, D. B. (1966). The process of learning parental and sex-role identification. *Journal of Marriage and the Family,* 28:466–470.

Masters, W. H., and Johnson, V. E. (1966). *Human Sexual Response.* Boston: Little, Brown.

Menninger, K. (1927). Adaptation difficulties in college students. *Mental Hygiene,* 11:519–535.

Moynihan, D. (1965). *The Negro Family: The Case for National Action.* Washington, D. C.: Office of Planning and Research, U. S. Department of Labor, Government Printing Office.

Offer, D. (1969). *The Psychological World of the Teen-ager: A Study of Normal Adolescent Boys.* New York: Basic Books.

Offer, D., and Offer, J. L. (1968). Profiles of normal adolescent girls. *Archives of General Psychiatry,* 19:513–522.

———. (1969). Normal adolescents mature. *Seminars in Psychiatry,* 1(1):46–56.

———. (1969). Growing up: A follow-up study of normal adolescents. *Seminars in Psychiatry,* 1:1.

Packard, V. (1968). *The Sexual Wilderness.* New York: McKay.

Rainwater, L. (1966a). Crucible of identity: The Negro lower-class family. *Daedalus,* 95(1):172–216.

———. (1966b). Some aspects of lower-class sex behavior. *Journal of Social Issues,* 22(2):96–108.

Reiss, D. L. (1961). Sexual codes in teen-age culture. *Annals of the American Academy of Political and Social Sciences,* 87:53–63.

———. (1967a). *The Social Context of Premarital Sexual Permissiveness.* New York: Holt, Rinehart and Winston.

———. (1967b). *Premarital Sexual Standards.* SIECUS Discussion Guide, No. 5.

Sanford, N. (1967). The integration of sexuality in the personality. In: *Where Colleges Fail.* San Francisco: Jossey-Bass.

Schofield, M. (1965). *Sexual Behavior of Young People.* Boston: Little, Brown.

Simon, W., Berger, A. S., and Gagnon, J. H. (1972). Beyond anxiety and fantasy: The coital experiences of college youth. *Journal of Youth and Adolescence,* 1(3):203–222.

Sontag, S. (1969). *Trip to Hanoi.* New York: Farrar, Straus & Giroux.

Thurber, J., and White, E. B. (1929). *Is Sex Necessary?* New York: Harper & Row.

193

Williams, F. S. (1968). Alienation of youth as reflected in the hippie movement. Paper presented to the American Academy of Child Psychiatry, Philadelphia, October 12.

———. (1968). Erik Erikson's concepts of identity and intimacy: Reviewed in light of present day youth alienation. Paper prepared for presentation at Southern California Society for Adolescent Psychiatry.

Winick, C. (1968). The beige epoch: Depolarization of sex roles in America. *Annals of the American Academy of Political and Social Sciences*, 376:18–24.

PART III

PSYCHOPATHOLOGICAL ASPECTS OF STAGES OF ADOLESCENT DEVELOPMENT

INTRODUCTION

The adolescent patient has impelled us to expand our theoretical focus in order to better understand the nature of his psychopathology. All patients today, but especially the adolescent, emphasize characterological factors. Formulations based primarily upon id-ego conflicts are no longer useful.

Psychic development, in this part, is often described in terms of ego structure and object relations instead of the usual formulations describing psychosexual stages. Not that the two are mutually exclusive; psychosexual stages are included in most developmental formulations but patients suffering from characterological psychopathology enable the investigator to broaden previous concepts and to focus more intensively on relationships with the outer world.

Arthur A. Miller examines the process of identification and describes the psychic restructuring and its intrapsychic and interpersonal aspects during adolescence as well as throughout life. Helm Stierlin, L. David Levi, and Robert J. Savard describe separation patterns in families of adolescents and have identified forces in the family that are either outward (centrifugal) or inward (centripetal). These patterns in their extreme form give rise to family psychopathology.

James F. Masterson studies the borderline syndrome in adolescents and postulates that the basic source of this large group of patients is an abandonment depression created by defective mothering at the separation-individuation stage of development, resulting in a developmental arrest. Peter L. Giovacchini, discussing Dr. Masterson's chapter, concludes that the adolescent period has similar significance for the development of psychopathology as infancy, which is then manifested in adult character structure.

Peter Barglow, Isis Istiphan, Jean E. Bedger, and Claudia Welbourne study the mourning process in unmarried mothers who have suffered an infant or fetal loss. Mourning is described as being either successfully or unsuccessfully concluded, and the psychopathology of the latter is defined.

12] IDENTIFICATION AND
ADOLESCENT DEVELOPMENT

ARTHUR A. MILLER

The process of adolescent development ultimately results in psychic restructuring. The elements of this process involve loosening of ties between existing structural elements, acquisition of new structural features, and reorganization of these components. Identifying is an important factor in this dynamic process, which may have both transient and permanent effects and proceeds with both intrapsychic and interpersonal aspects. This chapter is concerned with these three related matters: psychic restructuring during the process of adolescent development, identifying as it affects this restructuring, and the relationship between intrapsychic and interpersonal operations.

The process of identification operates throughout life and serves various purposes. It is prominent during adolescence. It evokes and shapes the maturing innate psychic apparatus, adding lasting memory traces of transactions with objects. The resulting structures are both systemic and representational. The systemic refers to groups of functions: the ego, superego, and ego ideal. The representational refers to self-representations and object representations and the supraordinate organization, the self.

During adolescence, there is a reorganization of both functional systems and mental representations. Internalizing and identifying play an important, though not exclusive, part in these developmental transformations. Consequently, following the discussion of the role of identification in the adolescent process, other nonidentifying means of psychic restructuring will also be noted.

During adolescence, as in the transference neurosis of analytic therapy, there is an increased externalization of an essentially internalized process. Later, these transactions are once again more fully internalized. Changes in internal regulations and structure occur with intensification of interpersonal transactions. Blos (1962) stated:

The extensive exploration of defenses during the adolescent period seems to be giving way to an investigation of the self in its genetic and pathologic aspects, and the study of psychic organization and psychic restructuring is complementing the concentration on instinctual conflicts as the paramount feature of the adolescent process.

During adolescence, biological changes and altered interpersonal conditions and expectations generate changes in psychic structure and organization. From such structural and organizational dislocations, there ensues a combination of progression, regression, and holding actions (Blos, 1962, 1967, 1968). Intrapsychically, there is an altered relationship to outmoded aspects of existing object representations (Freud, 1958) and the self-representation. This altered relationship consists of a redistribution of emotional investments among these representations. Along with such loosening of emotional investments, there is an acquisition of new representations (objects and self). In addition, there develops a new configuration, a supraordinate organization of the structural components that have been altered by the adolescent process. This supraordinate organization has been discussed in terms of ego identity (Erikson, 1956), self (Jacobson, 1964), and character (Blos, 1962, 1968).

The process of alteration of existing object representations and the emotional relationship to such representations is generated largely by conflict, because the aims and intensity of the drives change. The genital aims, acquired and intensified in adolescence, produce conflict because of their incestuous qualities. Thus, there is a need to develop standards and ideals commensurate with the changed biology and interpersonal context. This leads to changes in the superego and the ego ideal and their corresponding introjects. The adolescent's disillusionment about the omnipotence of idealized parental representations is another important aspect of structural change requiring object representations to be reassessed and altered.

The adolescent needs to overcome or avoid a sense of helplessness and inadequacy. He is vulnerable for several reasons. He has not developed the necessary ego functions to deal with libidinal and aggressive drives, differing in quality and intensity from earlier stages. He is prone to experience loss of self-esteem because of the anachronistic features of his superego. Similarly, he is struggling to maintain self-esteem in relation to ego ideals that are in the process of revision. An altered and expanded interpersonal context requires an adaptation he has not yet achieved. He experiences a sense of inadequacy about the self-representations with which he entered adolescence. Further, he has lost the inner support from previously useful idealized parent representations. The ad-

200

olescent struggles to cope with these various demands. Concomitantly, he is involved in the process of structural change and reorganization. He is getting rid of old structures and emotional investments while acquiring new representational components and organization. At the same time, he tries to avoid premature progression, disorganizing degrees of regression, and stagnating holding actions.

Maturation and development of perception and cognition add to the adolescent's awareness of a developmental lag. Changing internal standards and ideals along with new interpersonal demands are additional factors giving rise to the adolescent's feeling of psychological incompleteness and inadequacy. Further, there is a perception of body changes and a need for revision of the body image. The latter is an important part of the change in the self-representation that will have to be achieved during adolescence.

Our interest here is in how the process of identification is involved in these developmental transformations. Identifying, in a broad and inclusive sense, plays a part in regressive manifestations, in progressive development, and in the holding actions. This process covers a spectrum from transient imitations of an observable object to modification of the self-representation modeled after an external object, the modification persisting in the absence of the object. The aforementioned changes in the adolescent's psychic structure are elements of the identifying process. The adolescent employs one or another part of the total range of identifying operations as he regresses to what he once was, struggles to be what he feels he needs to be now, and strives to become what he feels he should and wants to be.

Anna Freud (1936) discussed identification in relation to the adolescent defensive struggle. Blos (1962) listed various forms of identification during adolescence: defensive, primitive, transient, and adaptive. Identification may be a defensive response to an internal dynamic structural conflict. Primitive identification refers to a regressive revival of an early form of object relations, a blurring of boundaries between the self-representation and the object representation. The transient form refers to a quality of purpose, namely, experimentation, the search for and trying on of necessary and relevant models available in the environment. The adaptive designation points to a reality orientation. It refers to an involvement in the task of coping with the external environment, the contextual aspect of psychic integration. This classification is a noteworthy attempt to differentiate among the identifying processes in adolescence. It provides a point of departure for further refinement of such a classification. Classification of forms of identifying is necessary in order to have a basis for differentiating the clinically observable phenomena. Such a classification will have to include consideration of purpose, duration, intrapsychic effect, and permanence of identifying operations.

Laufer (1965) stated that identifications in adolescence are used for several purposes. They are used to control regression, to maintain repression of ego dystonic thoughts and wishes, to achieve detachment from oedipal objects, to overcome awareness that earlier identifications are now inadequate, to deal with activity-passivity conflicts, and to cope with demands of the superego. He pointed out that they are used defensively or assist in structural rearrangement and that the role of identifications diminishes as the adolescent approaches adulthood.

Erikson (1956) stated that identity formation finally begins when the usefulness of identification ends. Identity, he said, arises from the selective repudiation and mutual assimilation of childhood identifications and their absorption into a new configuration. Adolescence is conclusively complete only when the individual has subordinated his childhood identifications to a new kind of identification. The childhood identifications are resynthesized in some unique way, yet in accordance with the roles offered by a wider section of society.

The effects of identifying in adolescence include (1) defense against drives, anxiety-provoking object relations, superego structures, and ego-ideal demands, (2) a form of relatedness to objects, (3) filling in gaps in undeveloped, unstable structure and a needfulness created by the decathexis of internal representations, (4) replacing, enriching, and reorganizing childhood structures, (5) contributing to the process of identity formation by helping delineate gender identity and contributing to a supraordinate psychic organization of self.

Difficulties arise when one discusses the process of identification, because one or another part of a total complex process is emphasized. In addition, such discussions are burdened by a lack of terminological clarity (Miller, Pollock, Bernstein, and Robbins, 1968). I conceptualize identification as a total process with various partial, intermediate stages. The full result of the total process is a lasting change in the self-representation made in accordance with a model. This model is an object with whom the subject has engaged in an interpersonal transaction. The subject becomes similar to the object model in some respect, for example, in manner of thinking, feeling, or acting. When the process is complete, the alteration of the self-representation endures in the absence of the object.

The process of identifying may have varying effects on psychic structure. There may be behavioral changes, which are reflections of temporary internal structural adjustments. These internal adjustments may have no lasting effect on ego organization. There may be an internalization of an object representation. Behavioral changes may reflect the internal transaction between this object representation and the unaltered self-representation. The identifying process, going beyond imitation or internalizing of object representations, results in alteration of the self-representation, which may lead to temporary or enduring alteration of structure.

The concepts of self-representations, object representations (Hartmann, 1950; Jacobson, 1964), and the representational world (Sandler and Rosenblatt, 1962) are pertinent to the discussion of changes in ego structure owing to identification. These structures also involve function insofar as internalized representations are distributed within the ego, superego, and ego ideal. There is no clear integration at this stage of our theory of representational and systemic concepts. Both need to be considered.

Decathexis of childhood object representations is part of the adolescent process. This may involve a decathexis or cathectic shifts among them. If there is to be a true, enduring identification, there must be a change in the self-representation. This means a process beyond change in structure and cathexis of the component object representations within the representational world. Consequently, the infantile self-representation must undergo drastic changes. Whether any structured elements are entirely lost is unclear, but cathectic changes occur in the organization of the self-representation as well as among object representations. Changes in object representations and self-representations are complementary and reciprocal. An alteration of the self-representations may require changes in object representations. The latter occurs partly by cathectic redistribution. In addition, internalizations of new object representations occur during adolescence. Such internalizations are not yet identifications. However, they may contribute to an alteration of the self-representation by identification with an external object. Identifications that served well at earlier stages may prove inadequate for the needs of the adolescent or emerging adult. The adolescent's developmental task is complicated by the necessity to turn away from anachronistic aspects of his self-representation as well as from anachronistic object representations.

Adolescent regression is not only a defense against conflicts but also a necessary condition for psychic restructuring and subsequent progressive development (Blos, 1967). As existing object representations are decathected, there is an increase in narcissistic cathexis. Regression also revives early forms of object relationships. Rather than clear boundaries between the self-representation and the object representation, there is now a confluence of these representations, phenomenologically manifested as an identification.

Identification, therefore, can be a manifestation of regression or a defense against regression. It can also represent recovery from regression. It may provide a means of experimentation in transactions with object models and may lead to replacement of outmoded structures.

We have noted the difference between total and partial identifications (Miller *et al.,* 1968). The former designates an internal merging of self- and object representations. Total identification operates not only in pathologically regressed states but may occur with ego control, as seen in experimentation with object models. Transitory merging may result in an empathic appreciation of the feelings of the external object. Partial identification, on the other hand, results in limited structural change.

It is important to differentiate between external objects and internal representations, and to consider the relationship between them. Some transactions with external objects may lead to an absorption of behavioral characteristics. This may occur without firm or lasting internalization of the object representation or alteration of the self-representation. Such a mechanism may be, in fact, an avoidance of lasting internalization and structural change. The attachment may be kept loose to avoid conflict with an object that is reminiscent of an incestuous object. In addition, it may be kept loose to avoid choice and premature closure of delineation of the internal world and self. Identification may then be a mode of perceiving and experiencing an object (or its characteristics) in order to determine whether it can be integrated in the emerging self-representation and thus lead to enduring structural change.

There are identifications that persist beyond their functional necessity and thereby become obstacles to further development. Internal restructuring necessary for individuation and character development does not occur (Blos, 1967, 1968). Consequently, though the various forms of identification are important for structural progression, there are also dangers in their excessive or prolonged use.

There may be an incomplete internal transformation of what has been internalized. Or there may be excessive or prolonged reliance on external models, that is, on interpersonal transactions. This can impede the delineation and organization of the self. In an anaclitic fashion there is a dependence on external objects or not fully integrated internal object representations. In the fixed anaclitic type there is a forfeiture of autonomy and a failure of individuation. In some instances, there is a chameleon-like reliance on the external object. Such clinical states occur more frequently than their exaggerated version, the "as if" phenomena (Deutsch, 1934; Ross, 1967).

Identification during childhood differs from identification during adolescence. During adolescence identification occurs in relation to existing structure, whereas in early childhood structure is being established. During infancy, separation individuation is based on internalization of interpersonal dependencies. In adolescence, individuation proceeds toward internal restructuring (Blos, 1967). This involves an intrapsychic reorientation and reorganization of the transactions between object representations and self-representation. Individuation and autonomy are achieved to a greater degree when archaic identifications are abandoned and new ones acquired.

The development of psychic structure is only partly based on internalizations and ensuing alterations of object representations and the self-representation. The fact that development occurs in the context of object relationships does not justify the assumption that identification is always the chief mechanism responsible for change. Other activities may be operative, such as the exploratory exercise of functions and experiential consolidation of existing structures and functions. Other means of achieving structural change will be dealt with only briefly since they are tangential to the thesis of this study.

Transactions between interpersonal and intrapsychic operations appear to be intensified during adolescence. Similar to what transpires in the transference neurosis of analytic therapy, there is an externalization of internal processes. These transactions are once again more fully internalized during adolescent development. I propose that changes in internal regulations and structure occur more readily when there is an intensification of interpersonal transactions. In adolescence, externalizing and more intense relationships with external objects are a consequence of internal structural changes and dislocations. This provides a context in which changes in structure can occur most effectively. Transactions with external objects lead to memory traces of the relationship, which increase the psyche's functional range as these memories can be adaptively utilized by systemic and representational structures. There is a further reorganization of altered structure into new schemata, a synthesis and integration into an emerging self (ego identity, character).

Imitation may be an early step in the identification process. It can, however, lead to other forms of learning, for example, conditioning or insight, rather than changes in the self-representation, as occurs with progression of the identifying process. The interpersonal transaction, with or without imitating or partial transitory identifying, can provide

205

an opportunity for exploratory exercising of functions. These exercises lead to the consolidation of existing structures and functions. Such exploratory exercise and experiential consolidation can be viewed as similar to the process of working through in psychoanalysis. It has been proposed that the terminal phase of psychoanalysis could be considered as a therapeutic adolescence with special reference to the working through of separation anxiety (I. Miller, 1965).

There may be a definition of oneself in the course of trial and error exploration and experimentation. Furthermore, one can divest oneself of defenses that are no longer necessary.

Another nonidentificatory mode of development is the resonance phenomenon (Weiss, 1950; Blos, 1962). This is a mechanism whereby the individual defines his biologically appropriate sexual characteristics, contributing to the resolution of bisexual tendencies. This is done by shifting to a suitable heterosexual object the characteristics appropriate to the object's gender. By divesting himself of the sex-alien component of his bisexual functional and identity orientation, the individual achieves an appropriate definition of himself.

To briefly summarize, internalizing and identifying alter the psyche by acquisition. The mechanisms discussed in the foregoing paragraphs operate by divesting oneself of and renouncing certain features and releasing other existing propensities. The adolescent has to enrich, refine, and reorganize his psychic structure in response to biological and social changes that cause dislocations within that structure. This is done by a combination of identifying, extrusion, and delineating and shaping of inherent maturing capacities in response to complementary object relationships.

Both identifying and nonidentifying operations involve actions occurring in a heightened interpersonal context. This fact makes it necessary to distinguish between acting out and action. Acting out is based on the externalization of internal conflicts and representations. Acting out does not alter structure; it is a reflection of the persistence of structural relationships.

Action, on the other hand, is an important aspect of structural change. It provides a means for exploration, experimentation, and rehearsal of new modes and patterns of behavior. It can implement identifications. Furthermore, it can lead to structural change by evoking existing propensities through exploratory exercise of functions, and refinement of existing structure by extrusion of fixating and constructive elements.

Specific object representations that have to be altered during adolescence are those that emphasize the parent's omnipotence. The adolescent has to view his parents in a new, more realistic light. Adolescence is characterized by disillusionment with the parent's strength.

In prepubertal development there is an identification with the fantasy of omnipotence of the idealized representation of parents. This is not really an identification, but rather an internalization of the object-representation of the idealized parent. This omnipotence is not smoothly integrated into the self-representation. In fact, the self-representation can remain relatively weak, being supported by internal transactions with the parental representations. The disillusionment occurs, predicated largely on an increased discernment of the reality of self and others. A striving for substitutions for the idealized representations follows. The adolescent seeks support through interpersonal affiliations (adolescent groups, ideologies). In addition, he strives for a feeling of strength through the acquisition of actual abilities. Acquisition of functions is in part shaped according to internalized models, models that may be perceived more realistically than were the parents of childhood. These internalized representations not only remain as object representations but also alter (enrich, strengthen) the self-representation by identification. Capacities and characteristics can also be developed in transactions with objects, not being modeled according to these objects but rather evoked and refined by the relationship.

In earlier development, not all omnipotence remains with the idealized object. The residual of omnipotence that remains within the self-representation has to be reassessed in adolescence. One needs to replace fantasy with actual achievement. This is often only approximated, and in prolonged adolescence (Blos, 1962) it is not done effectively. The individual can resist further development in order to maintain the illusion of omnipotence or the continued possibility of achieving it. It is characteristic of the adolescent to try on behavioral modes, which may contribute to development by identification. Some adolescents, however, remain fixed at trying on, thus continuing in an incompleted adolescence. In such cases interpersonal operations retain prominence at the expense of the development of intrapsychic regulations and structures.

The adolescent struggles to achieve narcissistic equilibrium (Laufer, 1964). Such an equilibrium is related to the state of the self-representation. It is derived from external, internalized, and inherent sources. External regard and recognition in the contemporary interpersonal contest enhances self-esteem. Internally, transactions with object representations offer measures for self-regard. Another source of self-esteem is an inherent sense of competence (White, 1963), which decreases feelings of vulnerability and helplessness. This refers to characteristics of the self-representation, based on actual capacities and characteristics rather than omnipotent illusory remnants of childhood self-representation.

Identifying is involved in all three sources of self-esteem: the external, internalized, and inherent. The external is affected by imitations of individuals and belonging to groups. The internalized is not yet a true identification but rather the establishment of an object representation. Inherent capacities are enriched and shaped by identifications (Hendrick, 1951).

Narcissistic balance depends on feeling good rather than bad, successful rather than a failure, and strong rather than weak. These are related to structural conditions: those object representations that form the superego and ego ideal, and the state of the self-representation. These structural conditions, as have been discussed, are affected by the process of identifying.

Adolescent group phenomena reflect the attempt to deal with the problem of self-esteem in the face of internal structural flux. Transactions with the group can bolster one's self-esteem. The group presents gratifying interpersonal contacts, recognition and acceptance, an identity delineation arising from such recognition and acceptance, and a manageable set of ego-ideal standards. Along with such immediate effects, the group can provide interpersonal transactions that implement psychic restructuring by identifying and other operations.

If, however, such transactions with an adolescent group are too successful, they can limit progressive development. By buttressing self-esteem, such experiences can help one avoid the perception of one's undeveloped state and a clear awareness of unaccomplished developmental tasks.

There are various reactions to the loss of self-esteem arising from sensing one's relative ineptitude. There can be a regression to earlier modes of mastery. This may involve a recrudescence of a symbiotic form of relatedness and primary identification. There may be narcissistic withdrawal and self-inflation. Alternatively, the individual might seek object models or allies for emotional support and progressive development. Transitory or persisting participation in the omnipotence of a group or an ideology is another type of response. Sometimes there is a commitment to an occupational choice or a marriage. Either of these can be based on reality possibilities for actual doing and progressive development. They offer, however, possibilities for an illusory substitute for progressive development.

Friendships, on an individual basis as well as within a group setting, are intimately involved in identifying, specifically, and processes of psychic restructuring, generally. This is a subject deserving full exploration in connection with the subject of object relations and character development (Rangell, 1963). Though such an effort is beyond the scope of this chapter, it is worthwhile to note here what friendships can offer that is relevant to the adolescent's developmental state and transformations. Libidinal gratification and aggressive discharge are implemented. Friendships offer relief from and support for superego functions, for example, by shared guilt, complicity. Ego-ideal functions are provided transiently (Laufer, 1964), and they are developed into an enduring form through friendships. There may be a support of defenses by the meshing of characters. Contributions are made to the formation of identity and self. There are opportunities for trial actions, exploration, and experimentations regarding developing functions and structure. Friends may be transference figures with whom transferred conflicts are acted out in contrast to the restructuring actions described. Regarding the latter, transactions among friends provide an opportunity for alloplastic actions, which affect autoplastic transformations. Friends serve as object models that can be internalized, initiating the identifying process toward enduring psychic restructuring. They may also serve as a scaffolding for restitution from, or protection against, narcissistic regression during the fluid state of adolescent developmental transformations.

Summary

Psychic restructuring during adolescence is considered especially from the viewpoint of the identifying process and its characteristics during progression, regression, and holding actions.

Identifying as involved in these developmental transformations is contingent on the models, roles, and transactions available in the interpersonal world. Its effects are seen as contributing to defenses against drives, anxiety-provoking object relations, superego structures, and ego-ideal demands. It functions as a form of relatedness, fills in gaps in needed structure, participates in reorganization of childhood structures, and contributes to the process of identity formation.

REFERENCES

Blos, P. (1962). *On Adolescence: A Psychoanalytic Interpretation.* New York: The Free Press.

————. (1967). The second individuation process of adolescence. *Psychoanalytic Study of the Child*, 22:162–186.

————. (1968). Character formation in adolescence. *Psychoanalytic Study of the Child*, 23:245–263.

Deutsch, H. (1934). Some forms of emotional disturbances and their relationship to schizophrenia. In: *Neuroses and Character Types*. New York: International Universities Press, 1965, pp. 262–281.

Erikson, E. H. (1956). The problem of ego identity. *Journal of the American Psychoanalytic Association*, 4:56–121.

Freud, A. (1936). *The Ego and the Mechanisms of Defence*. New York: International Universities Press, 1946.

————. (1958). Adolescence. *Psychoanalytic Study of the Child*, 13:255–278.

Hartmann, H. (1950). Comments on the psychoanalytic theory of the ego. *Psychoanalytic Study of the Child*, 5:74–96.

Hendrick, I. (1951). Early development of the ego: Identification in infancy. *Psychoanalytic Quarterly*, 20:44–61.

Jacobson, E. (1964). *The Self and the Object World*. New York: International Universities Press.

Laufer, M. (1964). Ego ideal and pseudo ego ideal in adolescence. *Psychoanalytic Study of the Child*, 19:196–221.

————. (1965). Assessment of adolescent disturbances: The application of Anna Freud's diagnostic profile. *Psychoanalytic Study of the Child*, 20:99–123.

Miller, A. A., Pollock, G. H., Bernstein, H. E., and Robbins, F. F. (1968). An approach to the concept of identification. *Bulletin of the Menninger Clinic*, 32:239–252.

Miller, I. (1965). On the return of symptoms in the terminal phase of psychoanalysis. *International Journal of Psychoanalysis*, 46:487–501.

Rangell, L. (1963). On friendship. *Journal of the American Psychoanalytic Association*, 11:3–54.

Ross, N. (1967). The "as if" concept. *Journal of the American Psychoanalytic Association*, 15:59–82.

Sandler, J., and Rosenblatt, B. (1962). The concept of the representational world. *Psychoanalytic Study of the Child*, 17:128–145.

Weiss, E. (1950). *Principles of Psychodynamics*. New York: Grune & Stratton.

White, R. W. (1963). Ego and reality in psychoanalytic theory: A proposal regarding independent ego energies. *Psychological Issues*, No. 11.

13] CENTRIFUGAL VERSUS CENTRIPETAL SEPARATION IN ADOLESCENCE: TWO PATTERNS AND SOME OF THEIR IMPLICATIONS

HELM STIERLIN, L. DAVID LEVI,
AND ROBERT J. SAVARD

In this chapter we outline two patterns of separation that emerged in a study of separating adolescents. One pattern we shall call "centrifugal" and the other "centripetal." These patterns reflect forces in the family that are either outward (centrifugal) or inward (centripetal) directed. We consider these patterns extreme variants of the separation course of adolescence. These separation patterns, we try to show, can illuminate those sequences and configurations which in adolescents give rise to various forms of psychopathology, particularly certain forms of schizophrenia and sociopathy. Also, we shall try to show how other patterns can be conceived within the proposed framework.

The separation patterns can be cast into relief by relating them to a conceptual model of separation that need not necessarily occur in reality. We have in mind what Max Weber (1966) called "ideal types." This ideal typical pattern reflects a developmental process wherein the adolescent can reconcile parental values and characteristics with those derived from his peers and alternate adults. As the process of conflict between parent and adolescent gets under way, there emerges, on ever newer levels, a new synthesis in which the adolescent is differentiated from his parents and enriched by the outside influences of his culture. But he also maintains common values and certain solid features of identification with the parents.

We deal thus with an expanding spiral of separation and differentiation on various levels: emotional, intellectual, and moral. The steps on this spiral are small enough so that the pain and depression involved in the increasing differentiation of parent from adolescent can be worked through without tumultuous disruption or complete rupture of the relationship. Yet neither is the pain so intense and intolerable that the differentiation process is brought to a standstill. This dialectical process of conflict and reconciliation is more thoroughly described in Helm Stierlin's *Conflict and Reconciliation* (1969). It unfolds in all phases of human development and relatedness, yet seems to become most acute during the oedipal period and adolescence.

During the oedipal period the child, as a way of establishing distance from his incestuously tempting and threatening parents, erects these parents as introjects in himself. He thereby separates from them and yet remains tied to them in important respects. While he separates from his parents, he invests himself in persons outside his family, such as friends or teachers. Thus he attenuates and further modifies his ties to his parents in a positively expanding separation circle.

The period of adolescence reactivates oedipal conflicts and, hopefully, permits their final resolution. In order for this to happen, the dialectical process of separation, as here outlined, must gain a new momentum and complexity. Once more the adolescent is drawn into the orbit of his parents and in the process suffers ambivalence, incestuous temptations, and threats. At the same time, he can invest himself in a wider range of peers, alternate adults, and potential sex partners than was possible before.

With this model in mind, we can distinguish between two extreme vicissitudes of separation. In one of these, the orbit of the family and parents exerts an unusual attraction for the adolescent: Centripetal forces are here predominant. These forces tend to delay or abort the adolescent's endeavors at separation. They may nonetheless facilitate certain enriching experiences, conflictive and painful though these may be.

In the other extreme configuration suggested by this model, the adolescent evades or attenuates the attraction of the parental orbit. At the same time he maximizes the importance of peers or alternate adults. Here we find centrifugal forces strongly at work: Instead of delaying his separation, the adolescent is rushing it. In so doing, he subjects himself to experiences and problems different from those found in the first-mentioned configuration.

These two different separation patterns imply thus different vicissitudes in relationships and different potentials for growth.

The separation patterns here outlined are constituted by the family and the separating adolescent. We may therefore speak of contributing[1] family factors and individual factors. Altogether we arrive at four

FIGURE 13–1.

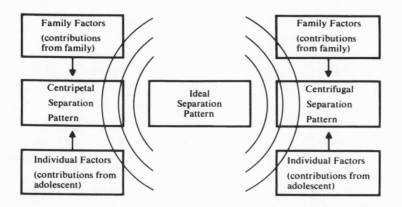

groups of factors (or contributions) that need to be considered (see Figure 13–1).

In elucidating these groups of factors we drew on approximately thirteen families with adolescents seen at the National Institute of Mental Health (NIMH) initially for family therapy of three months' duration. After approximately two to three years, these families were followed up with detailed interviews. The interviews focused chiefly on items on which predictions had been made earlier. Also, we made use of another twenty families whom we have seen in family treatment over the last four years and with whom we have kept informal contact or who are still in therapy at NIMH. We shall, first, describe those family factors that enter into a centripetal separation pattern.

Family Factors in the Centripetal Pattern

In the centripetal pattern the family holds greater promise for the fulfillment of crucial relationship needs than does the outside world. This seems to be a basic family assumption. As such, it is comparable to the basic assumptions Bion (1961) described for groups.[2] The antennae of the family members, while trying to spot possible sources of gratification and security, seem more or less rigidly geared to each other; they only pick up what seems available within the family boundaries. What lies outside these boundaries is only perceived dimly or not at all. This outside world appears dark and threatening. To the extent that within-family gratifications (and expectations for such gratifications) become important, the actual contact with the outside world tends to lessen. At closer inspection many of these families turn out to be socially isolated, despite often seemingly harmonious, nice professional relationships and an occasional flurry of club or church activities carried out by (as a rule) one parent.

Though remaining fixated on one another, the antennae in the family seem to have a peculiar selective sensitivity. In order to grasp important features of such sensitivity, we can make use of a concept David Reiss (1970) experimentally derived: Reiss spoke of consensus-sensitive families in cases where it seemed more important for the members to establish (an often unacknowledged and emotional) consensus among themselves than to face disagreement over their pursuit of a superordinated task. The term "consensus-sensitive," though derived from an experimental context, seems also to describe these families clinically. We appear to deal with some of the phenomena that Wynne, Ryckoff, Day, and Hirsch (1958) described under such headings as "pseudomutuality" and "pseudohostility," and to which, Lidz, Fleck, and Cornelison (1965) partly seem to refer under the label of "family skew": All these families seem to present an imbalance in favor of those forces that make for an often sticky and squelching family togetherness as against those forces that allow for a developmentally appropriate differentiation and separation of the family members from one another. Clinically, such consensus sensitivity often seems to imply an excessive sensitivity of the members to certain unacknowledged and dissociated needs of other members. Of these needs, disowned erotic and masochistic needs often stand out.

Further, in many such families we notice a network of parental perceptions and expectations that seem specifically designed to tie the adolescent to the family orbit. Elsewhere (Stierlin, Levi, and Savard, 1971) we described some of these perceptions and expectations. In one way or the other they make it difficult for the adolescent to conceive of himself as a legitimate and successful separator. Instead, he is seen, and comes to see himself, as unfit to separate, that is, as too sick, too inept, too dependent, too weak, and so on to do so, or as too selfish, too cruel, and too destructive should he actively seek his independence. The parents threaten the adolescent with sanctions, produce guilt in him, and tend to lessen his confidence in himself, but also often hold out rewards, such as special attention and gratification, should he stay in the family orbit. The parental messages are often covert and contradictory on the intra- as well as interparental levels. They thus often mystify the adolescent, as this has been described by Laing (1960, 1961), Wynne and Singer (1963, 1965), and others. In so doing, the parents tend to exploit their children psychologically: They recruit these children persistently for the

214

purpose of making them (the children) into undifferentiated and unseparated lifetime complements to their own uncorrected defects, unmastered conflicts, and unmet needs.

Finally, these families seem often grossly imbalanced with respect to how the two parents invest themselves in an adolescent at the time when the latter's oedipal conflict is reactivated. One parent appears here overinvested in the adolescent in the binding, mystifying ways just mentioned, and the other appears to step back and withdraw. Mostly, but not always, it is the opposite-sexed parent who overinvests himself (or herself) in the adolescent, while the same-sexed parent retreats. Such reactivated oedipal stalemate seems to further amplify the binding, centripetal forces that operate in the family: An overinvested, regressively tinged dyadic relationship seems to mire the adolescent ever more deeply in the parental orbit.

Individual Factors in the Centripetal Pattern

Individual factors seem to complement logically the family factors just described. In order to become vulnerable to centripetal family forces, an individual adolescent can be expected to have certain typical character traits, defenses, and motivations. He can be expected to be the kind of person who lets himself be conditioned into seeking his main gratification and security within the family and not in the outside world. He can be expected to specialize himself for symbiotic survival in the manner described by Stierlin (1969). He can be expected to find his way, more or less, in a jungle of mystifying and binding parental perceptions and expectations. Thus he will learn to latch onto at least some precious sources of gratification and security hidden in this jungle. In fact, he can be expected to make these sources of gratification and security so precious to himself that any sources the outside world can offer must pale in comparison. In succumbing to his parents' separation-blocking strategies and perceptions, he can be expected to more or less lose the will to separate. These parental strategies can be expected to ensnare him, to fill him with sufficient terror and guilt so as to make separation for him the number one unforgivable crime. We expect him to be more of an ocnophil than a philobat (in the sense in which Balint [1959] coined these terms), possibly to be more field dependent than field independent, to be rather less than more stimulus seeking, and to be more basically passive than active.

Further, this adolescent can be expected to restructure his reality while he adheres to the family orbit and its squelching entanglements. He can be expected to establish a private niche and fantasy world amid a generally consensus-sensitive yet agonizing family field. The more his personality make-up predisposes him for this course, the more likely will he succeed in establishing such a private niche and world. This means he will distance himself from his parents without *really* distancing himself: He will separate by a withdrawal from parental objects that is not counterbalanced by a commensurate investment in new real-life objects.

These expectable individual and family factors we found more or less clearly demonstrated in certain typical families and adolescents. In the following we shall present two such families, whom we shall call the Fenwalds and the Kowalskis.

THE FENWALD FAMILY

This family consisted of Mr. Sigmund Fenwald, an electronics data engineer in his midforties, his wife Martha of about the same age, the sixteen-year-old index patient Kurt, and fourteen-year-old brother Marvin. One older sister had moved away and was not available for therapy or interviews. The Fenwalds attended either family or couple therapy for approximately eight months and were followed up about two and one half years later.

On the whole, the Fenwalds appeared socially isolated, though not inordinately so. Mr. Fenwald, at the time of our contacts with him, was shy and retiring. He had no real friends, and associated mainly with a few business colleagues whom he met at lunch time. He tended to spend his evenings at home either reading or watching television. On his weekends he worked in the garden or went fishing.

Mrs. Fenwald, intense and elaborately dressed, was socially more active. She joined several housewives in a few afternoon coffee klatches and seemingly tried to win other couples for joint outings in the evenings. She was particularly fond of French movies. Few of these outings materialized, though, because her husband was not interested. For this reason she berated him incessantly. Again and again she dwelt on his lack of social enterprise which she saw at the root of her own emptiness and frustration. When Mr. Fenwald asked her to go out with her friends and leave him alone, she refused to do so, however. In the family and couple therapy it became evident that she was actually afraid to socialize because she was not sure of her friends and feared rebuff and neglect. She had been a salesgirl at the time of her marriage and had had high hopes of becoming an actress or singer. But none of her ambitions had materialized, essentially owing to her lack of talent. (To her credit she had mainly a pleasing face and voice.)

She had married Mr. Fenwald mainly to be relieved of an unglamorous routine job and existence. Because of her husband's more prominent social position, she gained through her marriage a potential foothold on what seemed to her the "big world." Yet in trying to take advantage of the big world (even though this big world comprised little more than avant-garde movie houses, boulevard restaurants, and the like), she could not help reactivating old ambivalences: On the one side, she wanted to become a glamorous figure and, on the other, she feared her downfall because of lack of talent. She tried to resolve this conflict essentially by disowning her fears of social contacts and, in the process, by berating her husband for his social insecurity. Yet the upshot of these psychological maneuvers was that she had only tenuous investments in the outside world. In her actual quest for satisfaction and security she was even more (as became clear in the family and couple therapies) mired in her family than her husband. And in investing herself within the family, she concentrated almost exclusively on her son Kurt.

To the extent that the Fenwalds had only tenuous relational investments in the outside world, they appeared bound and sensitized to one another. Yet, though almost constantly sniping at one another, they avoided open or sharp arguments that could have served a distancing and self-defining function. The poisonous arrows of blame, innuendo, and provocative bickering seemed sugarcoated and, by hurting, seemed to tighten the family cohesion. In sadomasochistic fashion, the members appeared sensitive and receptive to one another's needs. Separation or divorce seemed inconceivable for the parents.

This bittersweet family togetherness seemed to paralyze Kurt's efforts to extricate himself from the family orbit. Increasingly, he seemed to enjoy the erotic element in the sadomasochistic hassles Mrs. Fenwald offered him. These hassles originated often over his not getting up in the morning and not going to school on time. Though remaining tied to his mother in an erotized hostile dependency, Kurt seemed to see less and less need for going to school and for thereby grounding himself in the outside world.

Further, Mrs. Fenwald, and to a lesser degree Mr. Fenwald, tended to mystify Kurt and to employ stratagems that undermined his confidence and sense of legitimacy over whatever strivings for independence were left in him. For example, Mrs. Fenwald would overtly prod Kurt to invest himself in the construction and repair of high fi sets, his favorite hobby, only to denounce as inept and selfish his efforts at achieving therein some mastery.

Finally, we need to emphasize the parents' unequal investments in Kurt. Whereas the mother clung to Kurt with desperate, engulfing intensity, meddling with and exasperating all persons with whom Kurt promised to relate meaningfully (such as teachers, psychiatrists, and potential buddies), Mr. Fenwald, depressed, passive, yet apparently concerned, seemed to lack the energy to engage himself with Kurt and to protect him from his intrusive mother. (As a result of the family therapy, though, he invited Kurt on some of his fishing trips.)

Kurt Fenwald at the age of sixteen was a handsome, lanky boy. Prior to joining family therapy at the NIMH, he had seen a local psychiatrist for about a year once or twice weekly. This therapy had ended after he had shown up increasingly late at his therapeutic sessions or had missed them altogether. In his preadolescent years he had had some friends, who also had been those of his brother, and had seemed to enjoy roaming and exploring the countryside, but by the time he had joined family therapy, little expansive drive and initiative seemed left. By this time he would read a great deal, tinker in the basement with his high-fi sets, and occasionally visit hamburger stands with his brother Marvin. Only rarely would he deign to go out with a former boy friend. In the family therapy he would either just sullenly and defiantly sit there, not uttering a word, or would teasingly engage himself with his mother; or would, abruptly and only for short periods of time, join the family discussion. At such a point he would frequently offer a particularly perceptive or challenging comment. When he did this, he appeared more interesting and honest than all other family members.

When we met Kurt for the first time, he appeared entangled with his family, particularly so with his mother, yet also seemed already on the way of distancing himself from the family through restructuring his reality and through seeking his private niche. Though hassling with his mother in the above erotized, sadomasochistic manner, he also seemed to entrench himself more deeply in a detached routine of his daily life wherein his books and fantasies were the things that counted. In some way, this routine seemed to fall into place with the ongoing family entanglement. Thus, Kurt seemed to prepare himself for an existence that, on the one side, would allow him to stay in the family orbit, that is, continuously establish him as a focus for parental concern and support, yet, on the other, would assure him an undisturbed niche of his own. Less and less he seemed interested in seeking out either male or female friends. He never tried to have a date with a girl.

The family therapy with the Fenwalds ended prematurely: The mother became dissatisfied with the family therapist and wanted to return to her former individual therapist. After the family therapy had stopped, Kurt's dual existence within the family orbit (where he appeared deeply entangled as well as detached) continued for a while. Then Kurt suddenly had to be hospitalized in a psychiatric institution. In a seemingly bizarre fashion, he had entered a trailer where he had run into an unsuspecting girl. This girl had notified the police who transported Kurt to a psychiatric hospital. When his former family therapists visited him in this hospital, Kurt appeared unperturbed, friendly, and almost relieved. He could give no reason why he had entered the trailer. Subsequently, he was transferred to a residential school in another state where he soon withdrew from almost all human contacts and refused to attend classes. He was then transferred to a private psychiatric hospital where our follow-up interviews took place. At the time of these interviews, he refused to see a hospital therapist, yet talked pleasantly though vaguely about philosophy and the hippie life, which he intended to join. He seemed detached from his parents but appeared also assured that they would take care of him as long as they and he lived. Because he lacked hallucinations, delusions, and other clear-cut evidence of schizophrenia, Kurt was then not diagnosed as schizophrenic. However, even though not yet unequivocally schizophrenic, he seemed headed toward this condition.

In sum, we notice in Kurt a lack of centrifugal expansion and, along therewith, only feeble attempts to actively seek outside relations. Instead, he restructured his interpersonal reality and established for himself a niche in a continuously entangled family field. Though, in a sense, he had successfully detached himself from his family, he seemed unable to perceive for himself a future outside the (extended) family orbit. Whatever may happen, he seems confident that his parents will always rescue or support him.

THE KOWALSKI FAMILY

The Kowalskis emigrated to this country from Eastern Europe. Both parents, at the time of our first contacts with them, were in their mid-forties. Mr. Kowalski worked as an economic advisor in a government agency; Mrs. Kowalski until recently was a housewife. The Kowalskis have two boys and one girl. For the purpose of this study, we want to focus on Alfred who, when we first saw him, was fifteen years old. By the time of our follow-up interviews, he was approaching eighteen. Alfred has a two-years-older brother, Manfred, and a two-years-younger sister, Marla.

The Kowalskis were socially isolated to an uncommon degree. They had not had a social gathering in their house in years, though Mr. Kowalski had repeatedly wanted to arrange one. He blamed his wife for letting the house turn into a pigsty that would abhor guests. Mrs. Kowalski felt her husband exaggerated and criticized her unduly. She admitted, though, that sometimes she neglected her household because her children demanded too much of her. Only once or twice in the last two years had a fellow emigrant from the Kowalskis' native country stepped into the Kowalski home. Such almost total social isolation made the Kowalskis more dependent on one another than seems normal even for first-generation immigrants, but also accentuated the ambivalence and frustration they felt among themselves. As a result, they seemed to vacillate between being close in an entangled, suffocating way and being unduly distant. When they waited in the waiting room for their family sessions, they tended to sit as far apart as possible, yet usually became intensely embroiled after the sessions had started. In these sessions, Alfred could at one moment present himself as an arrogantly detached outsider and then step in as the most sensitive observer, commentator, and debunker of the family. In particular, he seemed to be uncannily gifted at spotting vulnerabilities in his parents. On the surface, he seemed to shift alliances easily. In the hateful stalemate that had arisen in the marriage of his parents, he would either, in evident collusion with his father, triumphantly cut down his mother or in seeming compliance with his mother's covert commands, show up his father as a passive weakling.

Underneath such versatility in the shifting of alliances, however, one could discern a strong tie to his mother. As in the relation between Kurt Fenwald and his mother, mutual sadomasochistic needs and gratifications seemed to cement this tie. There was lacking, however, the erotization we found in the Fenwald mother-son relationship. Mr. Kowalski seemed engaged in a more straightforward power struggle with Alfred. She insisted, for instance, that Alfred show loyalty and respect to his new country by saluting the flag and learning patriotic songs. Alfred would inevitably do the opposite of what she wanted him to do. Instead of saluting the flag, he would spit on it publicly; instead of learning and singing songs at a patriotic ceremony, he made a laughingstock of himself and his parents.

At closer inspection, we find also here the imbalanced oedipal investment described above that, given the overall family configuration, had not the effect of bouncing Alfred out of the family, but impelled him to restructure his interpersonal reality and to create for himself a niche within the (extended) family orbit.

Though Alfred appeared a little more solidly grounded in the peer world than Kurt (he was, for example, temporarily a member of several athletic teams and, for a while, competed vigorously in wrestling events)

his contacts and investments outside the family also were extremely tenuous. By the time of the follow-up interview, he had become alienated
from all his peers. Earlier he had had a close relationship with only one
boy who happened to be black. The problems that seemed built into
this interracial relationship caused him to lose also this only friend.
Like Kurt, to the extent that he withdrew from the world of real people,
Alfred began to invest himself more heavily in books that did not expose him to interpersonal strain and ambivalence.

Alfred, despite the developments just outlined, at the time of the follow-up interview seemed in some ways to function better than we had
expected and predicted. He no longer seemed to give evidence of some
of the school and behavior problems, such as truancy, refusing to do his
homework, or arrogantly defying his teachers, which originally had trig-
gered the family therapy. We concluded nonetheless that Alfred, during
the follow-up period, had consolidated a rather schizoid position. Particularly, the strong paranoid streak made the eventual prognosis appear
guarded.

In reviewing this separation course, we were impressed by what appeared to be a loosening of Alfred's involvement with his mother,
which in this form and relative abruptness we did not expect. We finally
concluded that this was probably an aftereffect of the family therapy,
which in this case had been planned and carried out for only three
months. Probably as a result of this therapy, the mother had (approximately one year after its discontinuation) decided to lead a more active
life outside the family. She took steps to become a barmaid and, in so
doing, defied and upset her husband. Though introducing more turmoil
into her marriage, she also managed to exacerbate if not to break the
hostile stalemate in her relationship with her husband. She thus became
again more intensely engaged with her husband, and she also invested
herself more in the outside world. Her husband responded to all these
relational overtures with several suicidal gestures, as a result of which
he finally sought individual psychotherapy. Given these redirections in
the lives of his parents, Alfred seemed somewhat freed of the previously mentioned pressures and, as a result, seemed in a better position
to carry out his academic studies. Also, it appeared that the mother
could turn more easily away from Alfred because the younger child,
now growing into adolescence, seemed to offer herself as a potential
target for renewed investments. Still, given the overall picture, it remains
to be seen whether Alfred can put to good developmental use the apparent respite from, and relaxation of, centripetal forces operating in
the Kowalski family.

Family Factors in the Centrifugal Pattern

Here the basic family assumption contrasts with the one found in the centripetal constellation: Essential sources of gratification and security cannot be found inside but only outside the family. Therefore, when the parents feel frustrated with each other and with their children (which is bound to occur frequently), they will look beyond the family orbit. Also, they will tend to instill in their children a centrifugal orientation: They will impress them with the idea that things on the outside tend to be better than inside the family. As a part of this orientation, they foster in them the notion that one can solve problems by moving out of the family.

Along with such a centrifugal family assumption, we find lacking or less prominent those forces that seem to foster family cohesiveness: We find less consensus sensitivity and less reliance on stratagems that tend to mystify other members and thereby tend to block the offspring's separation. Instead, we find an open and frequently hostile argumentativeness, seemingly made safe and perhaps enjoyable by the fact that the family members can bounce away from one another, that no unyielding family boundaries prevent them from putting distance between one another.[3]

Given the relative ease with which the adolescent can bounce away from the family field, dyadic incestuous involvements with one parent are bound to affect him differently than those described in the centripetal pattern. They are here more likely to incite him to act out revengefully in the reactivated oedipal battle and, in so doing, to recruit sex mates from the peer group to serve as his pawns. Predictably, these sex relations with peers will tend to end abruptly once they have fulfilled their purpose. Yet nonetheless, as we shall describe later, they can serve as steppingstones for identifications and learning experiences that eventually will help to pull the adolescent out of the parental orbit.

Thus, given the centrifugal valences prevailing in such families, the adolescent can be expected to move (or be expelled) into the outside world early and forcefully. In separating himself from his family, he appears pushed by a *vis à tergo*.

Specifically, we can distinguish several dynamic features operating on the family level that may account for an adolescent's premature and possibly abrupt separation.

An adolescent in this centrifugal constellation may have to serve as the family's delegate to, and experimenter with, the outside world: The parents may eagerly send out a given adolescent in the anticipation that he will satisfy their hunger for the goods they perceive to lie outside the family. In particular, they may expect him to provide them with sexual excitement they cannot find in their own marital relations. Parents seem more likely to delegate to an adolescent the task of bringing in the outside Eden, the more they feel themselves incapable of living out their own centripetal longings (because they are too much bogged down by fears and internalized prohibitions). However, though they expect this adolescent to report back to them like a good retriever dog, he will often stall in so doing since the parental demands have little force over him and since he finds too gratifying the scrounging around outside the family.

Besides the use of an adolescent as delegate to the outside world, other separation inducing family dynamics can come into play. Such dynamics include, above all, the parents' rejection and neglect of their children. Whenever these children encounter rebuff, neglect, hassling, conflictive demands, and other unpleasant experiences that originate with their parents, they will, almost as a reflex, try to get away from the parental orbit and seek support from peers or alternate adults. These adolescents will do so because they need not cope with those separation-blocking family forces we described as typical for centripetal configurations.

It may be difficult to decide what triggers in such families an adolescent's centrifugal tendencies. Such adolescent tendencies may lessen the more parents will try to satisfy such longings through actions. This then seems to decrease their need to use the adolescent as a delegate and outside experimenter as just described. On the other hand, it can be argued that such outside-oriented parents may set also an example for centrifugal action which their adolescent may be tempted to follow. This may, for example, be the case when there is infidelity or when these parents show other ways in which they lack faith in anything that parental and family relationships could offer. Much will therefore depend on the quality of the parents' motivations and of their activities outside the family as to whether these parents will either foster or discourage centrifugal tendencies in their adolescent children.

Individual Factors in the Centrifugal Pattern

Again, the individual factors that operate in this configuration relate logically to the family factors just outlined. Here, too, the adolescent, in order to succumb to the centrifugal pull, must have certain complementing character traits, defenses, and motivations.

This adolescent can be expected to be more motorally expansive than his counterpart in the centripetal constellation, to act out more readily because of defective impulse controls, to be more field independent and actively stimulus seeking, to be more adventurous and philobatic (Balint, 1959). Given these traits and/or defenses, he is in a better position to establish "instant distance" by argumentation and fighting: He can easily "bounce out of the parental orbit." Given the ease with which he can escape from discomforting family stresses, he is under less pressure to restructure his reality by the earlier described psychological maneuvers and to stake out for himself a niche in an embroiled family field.

The relative ease with which he can bounce out of the family orbit seems commensurate with the ease with which he can enter into new relations with peers or alternate adults, transient and exploitative as these relations might be. In particular, he seems to have little difficulty in finding sex mates who conform to his wishes.

Let us now turn to two families who represent the centrifugal configuration.

THE KENWOOD FAMILY

The Kenwoods include Mr. and Mrs. Kenwood, both in their midforties, and their four children: Jack, the index, who at the time of the first family contact was approaching sixteen; his two-years-older sister, Evelyn; one boy two years and another eight years younger than Jack. Only Evelyn and Jack, together with their parents, were seen in family therapy.

Mr. Kenwood, a lean, depressed-looking man with a voice both accusatory and wailing, works as a demolition expert. In his late teens he was thrown out of high school because of truancy and petty thievery and subsequently spent some time in jail. He views this as evidence of his having been an adventurous youth, one who got involved in scrapes but was liked by his peers and finally was able to manage his life. From his early twenties on he drank heavily. Approximately eight years before our first contact with him he had lost control of his drinking and eventually had joined Alcoholics Anonymous (AA). During the last several years, while attending regular AA sessions, he has not touched alcohol.

When his drinking went out of control, family life (according to his wife) became hell. He would arbitrarily beat the children and make feebly disguised advances at the elder girl. The mother was compelled to protect her children, but particularly the two oldest ones from their

224

"brute alcoholic father." In so doing, she could not help establishing an intimate bond with them which had infantalizing as well as parentifying features. After Mr. Kenwood had stopped drinking, the marriage moved along on a more even keel, the parents bickering and fighting only verbally, without physical assault and violence.

The mother, an outwardly soft-spoken and demure housewife, had an alcoholic father and brother. She was attracted by her husband's worldliness and, so she said, never suspected that his social drinking could get out of hand. Though initially she saw herself as obedient and meek, with time she learned to defend herself against her violent and alcoholic husband. At the time of the follow-up interview, she argued sharply with him. Also, she criticized her son Jack who was then absent.

In contrast to the two earlier described families, the Kenwoods had easy social contacts. The father appeared on easy terms with various buddies and colleagues and impressed us as the type who in a bar can instantly start a cozy conversation with a fellow traveler or barmaid. Repeatedly, he was unfaithful to his wife.

The discussions in this family appeared fragmented, animated, and hostile, yet clear. While arguing, the members seemed to bounce away from one another but also easily resumed their argumentation. One of us who participated in the follow-up interviews and was as yet unaware of the separation patterns here under discussion wrote after one interview: "It looks like this family, fragmented in the inside, looks to contacts outside for sustenance."

We noted an unequal balance of oedipal investments: Each parent appeared unduly involved with the opposite-sexed older child. However, here the incestuous bonds, instead of adding a centripetal push, gave rise, as we shall presently see, to Jack's and Evelyn's flight from the parental orbit into outside peer and sex relations.

Jack Kenwood, at the time of the family therapy, presented himself as a lanky, handsome youth with marginal academic grades, but an excellent athlete and swimmer. In the sessions he defended himself well against his father. When the father would decry him as a lazy bum, certain to fail in life, Jack would triumphantly dwell on the father's shortcomings, such as his earlier truancy and thievery and, above all, his later alcoholism. The mother tended to support Jack against what she perceived as the father's brutal and unjustified onslaughts.

While this went on, Jack almost imperceptibly seemed to drift out of the family orbit. He spent much of his time with peers, many of whom belonged to a tough breed of motorcyclists. Following the family therapy, he tried a number of different jobs, such as working as a carpenter's helper or hardware salesman. Each time he was fired after a short period because he was either too unreliable or too defiant. Despite his irregular school attendance and marginal academic work, he graduated from high school. At this point he seemed apprehensive and undecisive. After failing in another attempt at work, he finally joined the army with the blessings and active support of his father. Here he seemed to welcome limits and discipline. However, after at first adapting to military life, he went AWOL. By the time of the follow-up interviews with the family, he was known to roam around in the neighborhood. The parents knew then through indirect sources that he was "shacking up" with a sixteen-year-old girl, that he had been involved in "gangbangs," and that he was associating with his tough delinquent boyfriends. The mother, still feeling close to Jack, seemed to nurture a vindictive grudge against the latter for his having betrayed her confidences. The father, in contrast, seemed strangely unconcerned about what Jack was doing. It was as if by now he had discarded the bad seed from the family.

Such discarding of the bad seed, the parents' relatively easy emotional deinvestment in an adolescent offspring after seemingly bitter and invested arguments with him, seems typical for the centrifugal separation pattern. So seems the resolution of the reactivated oedipal conflict by the adolescent's flight into precocious sexual activities wherein sex partners appear exchangeable and devalued as persons.

Also, the separation course of Evelyn, Jack's two-years-older sister, revealed strong centrifugal features. On the whole, however, Evelyn appeared better integrated than Jack and more likely to succeed in a conventional life career. During the period of Mr. Kenwood's uncontrolled alcoholism, Evelyn, as already noted, had suffered the father's crudely seductive advances. This fact seems to have fostered a strongly sadomasochistic tie between them that seemed difficult to break. In the family sessions, Evelyn, with covert assistance from her mother, attacked the father even more vituperatively than did Jack, but also like him, she turned precociously to heterosexual sex partners in the above-described bounce-away fashion. By one of these she was made pregnant and had to have an abortion. Though her actions seemed to reflect a pathologically incomplete separation from the father in the sense that boys served her as pawns to revengefully antagonize him and that she seemed to vicariously act out some of his (the father's) delinquent sexual propensities, there could be little doubt that the parental orbit was quickly losing its attraction for Evelyn. Evelyn would willfully stay away from home whenever she pleased. She seemed determined to lead her own life outside the family. Whatever ongoing problems and conflicts she, via traumatization and internalization, had inherited from her father, she seemed now prepared to reenact, if not to solve, by transferring them to persons outside the family.

THE PECK FAMILY

This family provides our second example for a centrifugal configuration. The Pecks include the two parents and six children. When the therapy with the Pecks started approximately three years ago, the oldest boy was in his last high school year (after which he left his home town for a distant college). The three youngest children had not yet reached preadolescence. The focus was therefore on Sybil, then about fourteen, and her one and one-half year older brother Tim.

Mr. Peck, a small stocky man, was then in his late fifties, and his wife was eight years his junior. Mr. Peck, who held a middle-echelon desk job in a bank, throughout his life had felt overshadowed by his older, more successful brother. This brother, outgoing and socially expansive, had become a well-known surgeon. Mr. Peck, in contrast, was rather passive and shy, though conscientious in his work. While envying and admiring his older brother, he seemed ambivalently resigned to a niche that allowed him to deal with numbers instead of human beings. He married his wife in his late thirties after the two had worked for a while at neighboring office desks. He liked to tinker around with various schemes and contraptions and, in order to be able to do so more freely, had joined a hobby club, which also came to serve as his major social outlet. He could overcome his social shyness when he drank and did so more and more as the years went by. However, he never clearly qualified for the label of an alcoholic, as had Mr. Kenwood. His friends at the hobby club and elsewhere saw mainly his charming, more extroverted side when he had gulped a few martinis. At home, however, he presented an increasingly pathetic figure, often dozing and slurring in speech, and consequently became despised by his wife and children.

The more Mr. Peck was found wanting as an effective male in the house, the more the burden for the children's care fell on Mrs. Peck. In some ways, the latter seemed better equipped for this role as she had a hard compulsive streak; however, she resented the task of the family organizer and tried to spend as much time as possible working away from home, for this work she loved. Though there were six children in the home, of whom three were still small, Mrs. Peck left the house at approximately 8:30 A.M. and did not return until 5:00 P.M. The children were left to makeshift arrangements and to one another's care. The result was chaos at home and neglect of the children. In the vacuum created by the parents' absences, but also with their covert permission, Tim and Sybil started to have sexual relations with each other. The relations began when Sybil was eleven years old and they lasted for approximately three years. After Sybil and Tim had stopped their incestuous activities, both moved aggressively into peer groups. In so doing, they both became what we might call precocious experimenters with life. Tim prided himself at the age of fifteen and one-half that he had access to all kinds of persons and groups in town, including pimps, motorcycle gangs, Black Panthers, heroin addicts, and the like. He would often be truant from school since he, after spending his evenings with jazz bands or just hanging around, was too tired to get up the following morning. His mother's angry attempts to get him out of bed were usually to no avail, the more so as she was hurried to arrive at her job on time. As he grew older, Tim became more outright delinquent: He dealt with illicit drugs and participated in petty thieveries, possibly in robberies. In one instance, Tim joined his peers in a burglary attempt directed at his parents' home. Tim had then assured himself that his father was drunk so that he would be either unable or too embarrassed to take decisive action. The plan succeeded, and the boys stole a record player and disks that belonged to Tim's older brother Biff.

After he had discontinued his sexual relations with his sister, Tim became involved with a girl slightly younger than himself. He made her pregnant and subsequently tried to abort her by supplying her with an overdose of LSD while at the same time withholding her food. The girl's pregnancy terminated finally through medical and psychiatric intervention. At present, Tim lives separated from his parents on the fringes of respectable society. Though over the years he seemed repeatedly ready to involve himself more intensely with our treatment program, he avoided a lasting commitment.

Sybil, his younger sister, at first participated actively in the family therapy and later involved herself intensely with an individual psychotherapist. After Sybil had stopped her incest with her brother, she began to relate to a string of boys and repeatedly was made pregnant. These pregnancies ended spontaneously after a few months.

Like her brother Tim, Sybil turned to the outside world with a hunger for thrills and adventure. Like Tim, she experimented heavily with illicit drugs. At one point she ran away from home for several weeks, during which time she became heavily promiscuous. Also, she was then almost constantly drugged. She finally passed out on the streets after having lost approximately ten pounds. She was hospitalized and, helped by an intense individual and milieu therapy program, slowly began to find herself. When her individual therapist left town after approximately one year of treatment, she became pregnant once again, and this time carried the pregnancy to full term; the child, after delivery, was placed for adoption. When last seen by one of us, approximately three years after our initial contact with her, Sybil had given up drugs and sexual relations and, instead, was engaged in strenuous backpack trips with a new boyfriend. To the interviewer she appeared overexperienced for her age, but also determined not to make a mess of her life. After having lived for so long in an alienated, hassling relation with her mother, she had recently grown closer to her. In the last year the mother (as a result, we believe, of the family therapy), had finally reduced her outside workload and had begun to devote more time to her children and home.

The Peck parents, as well as the two here-described children, reveal several features that we associate with the centrifugal pattern: The parents were either withdrawn from the family or were unduly invested outside it and were therefore unable to provide their children with the constant caring attention that the latter's character development needed. Instead, they blatantly neglected their children. The father, further, covertly encouraged his children to move out into the exciting outside world and to experience there the thrills and adventures that he himself, mired in his shyness and frequent drunkenness, could not pursue. In our first intake interview with the father, we heard him talk admiringly of Tim's and Sybil's social skills and "maturity," traits he felt lacking in himself, which he envied in his older brother. Further, the father's passive inefficiency, in addition to being held in contempt by the mother, made him particularly unsuitable as a model for identification to his more energetic and expansive children. Hence, the children's drive to find alternate models for identification in the outside world becomes even more understandable.

These two children show typical traits we associate with the centrifugal pattern, such as thrill- and adventure-seeking, a motoric expansiveness, a capacity to relate easily (though often fleetingly) to peers, and to have sex partners available when needed (even though these partners may be used as pawns in the oedipal battles with the parents). (As a special dynamic factor in Tim's and Sybil's centrifugal separation course, we must consider their efforts at breaking up their own incestuous and guilt-ridden relationship by turning with a self-destructive vengeance to peers as sex partners.)

Variations in Separation Patterns

The separation patterns so far outlined represent extremes on our hypo-thetical scale. More frequently than such extremes we can expect mixed patterns, wherein either centripetal or centrifugal elements dominate. Of the many variations of clinical interest, we want to single out two com-binations. These we shall call pseudocentripetal and pseudocentrifugal patterns. The following two cases from our sample reflect these two var-iations.

In one case, the family made great efforts to present to us a picture of absolute family togetherness. The parents and their children—there were four of them—emphasized constantly that they were a happy, united family: They did everything together; they enjoyed family pic-nics, had frequent outings to the zoo, and were all happily chatting away at the breakfast table. The index adolescent, who was at the time of the family therapy fifteen years old, seemed to contribute to the centripetal configuration. He did not want to go to school, spent most of his time in the basement where he collected stamps and toads, and enjoyed being infantilized by his mother. Also, he seemed to prefer the company of his younger siblings to that of peers of his age.

However, the follow-up carried out approximately three years later made the earlier centripetal trends look largely like expressions of his physical and psychological immaturity at that earlier time. At fifteen years of age he looked like a ten-year-old and seemed untouched by the concerns and problems of average fifteen-year-olds. When, for example, a young and ambitious teacher introduced his class to *The Catcher in the Rye,* by Salinger (1951), he found, despite superior intelligence, the book completely incomprehensible. Instead, he continued to think of his toads in the basement. He did not play with his age mates because the discrepancies in physical and mental development seemed too great at that period. At the time of the follow-up, the boy still looked immature, but appeared more related to his peers in an age-appropriate manner. We felt then safe to predict that in time he would separate and embark on a conventional career and marriage. On the family level, the earlier-mentioned togetherness seemed less convincing the more and the longer we saw this family. It appeared at closer inspection that the children were in fact branching out successfully in diverse directions, though they made little ado about this. Probably because of this family's exces-sive conventionality, the members seemed unduly compelled to convey an image of themselves as a happily united American family. In sum, this happened to be a family whose centripetality on closer scrutiny appeared rather weak and transient.

In another family, whom we shall call the Neidermans, centrifugal tendencies seemed at first prominent. This family consisted of the parents and four children, of whom Paul, the third youngest, had become the index. Paul's three sisters were five years older, two years older, and one year younger, respectively. By the time of our first contacts with him, Paul had become truant and had repeatedly run away from home for short periods. In the family sessions Paul tended to be either silent in an explosive sullenness or jabbed angrily at his parents. At home he had proven increasingly uncontrollable to his father. Like the two older girls, Paul indicated frequently that he expected nothing good from his family and that he therefore was turning to outside sources for gratification. When the family therapy started he seemed involved with several girlfriends and seemed to have no unusual difficulties in relating to peers. Neither seemed his sister next to him in age to have such difficulties. This sister presented herself as a popular and attractive girl who in the family sessions chatted eagerly about her boyfriends.

In the years following our short therapy contact with this family Paul continued to be truant, to do poorly in school, and to work only sporadically in various jobs. Finally his father, in seeming exasperation, "expelled" Paul into the army where he subsequently went AWOL.

The Neidermans were thus a family which we initially, without hesitation, would have placed on the centrifugal side of our spectrum. However, when we, prompted by the follow-up interviews, took a new look at them, we became aware of powerful, though hidden, centripetal elements. To be sure, all three older children had seemed intent on moving out of the family orbit abruptly and precociously. However, in each case we noticed how the initial centrifugal momentum had seemed to fizzle out while the attraction of the family orbit seemed to increase correspondingly. As it turned out, the oldest daughter had left the family precipitously for a hastily arranged marriage; but after she had given birth to a child, this marriage quickly, though not unexpectedly, broke up, leaving the young woman no other choice than to return with her baby to her family of origin. The second oldest earlier-mentioned daughter, who at the time of the family therapy presented herself as a popular knockout chased by boys, became subsequently entangled with married older men who seemed poor prospects for stable relationships. This girl subsequently made several suicidal attempts or gestures, which each time necessitated the parents' interventions. All this had the effect of tying her more closely to these parents as she moved on in her adolescence. Also in the first-mentioned index adolescent and his younger sister, we discerned a similar pattern of seeming precocious and abrupt attempts at separation from the family, which soon seemed to lose momentum and then seemed to give way to a counteracting centripetal tendency. It looked as if these children were kept by their parents on a long leash, which made it easy for them to dash into the outside world at first only to feel later its retracting force. A closer look at this family also made us aware of strong mystifying and separation-blocking stratagems and expectations of the parents of the kinds we have mentioned earlier.[4]

The Relevance of Separation Patterns to Schizophrenic and Sociopathic Developments

We do not expect that separation patterns, as here outlined, will differentiate conventional groups of emotional and mental disorders. However, they can help us to see these groups in new perspectives. This probably holds true for such disorders as neuroses or perversions, which we expect to reveal specific combinations of centripetal and centrifugal elements; this holds particularly true for disorders in the schizophrenic and sociopathic groups.

Though some recent studies, among them the Denmark studies of Kety, Rosenthal, Wender, and Schulsinger (1968) and Rosenthal, Wender, Kety, Schulsinger, Welner, and Ostergaard (1968), suggest a blurring of boundaries between schizophrenic and sociopathic groups (the authors include sociopathic traits and personalities in their concept of schizophrenic spectrum disorders), other studies suggest a different view. At least some forms of schizophrenia and sociopathy, according to these studies, reflect distinct personality make-ups and family configurations. Particularly, studies of Reiss (1970), Stabenau, Tupin, Werner, and Pollin (1965), and others make it appear that these two diagnostic groups are linked to different family climates and configurations. In the families of schizophrenics these authors have noted mainly squelching, binding, and mystifying interactions with high degrees of consensus sensitivity or pseudomutuality (as described by Reiss, 1970, and Wynne *et al.,* 1958, respectively); in families with sociopathic offspring, in contrast, they tended to observe a bitter and fragmented, yet articulated argumentativeness and a willful and apparently selfish disregard of the members for one another.

Observations such as these suggest different separation patterns for these two groups of disordered adolescents and their families. Such different separation patterns seem cast into clearest relief when we compare certain extremes in schizophrenic and sociopathic developments.

On the extreme end of the schizophrenic separation spectrum we have in mind those patients who end up as chronically hospitalized "vegetables." These are patients who make themselves at home in their restructured inner reality amid a given psychiatric institution while they seem to have lost all will to seek new relations or new activities outside this second "home." Different authors (Scott and Ashworth, 1969; Nameche and Ricks, 1966; Nameche, Waring, and Ricks, 1964) described such patients in paradoxical terms. These terms suggest, at the same time, extreme states of nonseparation and of separation from the patients' families of origin. Ashworth and Scott, for example, depict these patients as having died and become mere shadows to their parents. Nonetheless, in their very death and shadowiness, these patients remain for their parents a never-ending, consuming source of worry and guilt. These chronic, "dead" patients, on their part, appear forever preoccupied with, and tied to, their parents either as rigidly cathected inner objects or as background persons from whom they can never imagine themselves becoming separated. Nameche and his associates reviewed the longitudinal course of schizophrenic patients who became chronically hospitalized and compared this course with that of schizophrenic patients who remitted and spent various periods of time outside mental institutions. They found the chronic patients to have been much more consistently and symbiotically enmeshed with their parents (particularly their mothers) than had the patients in the remitting group. Though they had remained enmeshed with their parents, these chronic patients had had practically no contacts with peers or alternate adults during their preadolescent and adolescent years. In the remitting group, in contrast, the patients had, as a rule, been able to make some contacts outside the family orbit, fragmented, short and agonizing though these contacts might have been.

If we turn to extremes in the sociopathic separation spectrum, we find comparable outcomes of chronic institutionalization. This time, though, the chronic institutionalization does not occur in a mental hospital but in a jail. Claude Brown (1965), in his *Manchild in the Promised Land,* has movingly described the sequences through which children from our black ghetto culture may inexorably move toward such chronic institutionalization. He depicts these youngsters' disorganized hate and neglectful family milieu, their precocious, brutal experimentation with sex and drugs, their early removal from the family orbit and correspondingly early move into a delinquent peer group. This peer group then confirms their view of the world as a jungle wherein only toughness and cunning promise survival: He depicts further the step by step increases in the seriousness of their crimes which then lead them to the reformatory whence they, labeled as hopeless cases and further confirmed as incorrigible delinquents, eventually move on to the permanent jail.

Can we further specify how certain forms of schizophrenia may develop in accord with a centripetal separation pattern? In order to answer this question we must consider those major sets of factors that may contribute to an eventual schizophrenic outcome. This is not the place to describe these sets of factors in detail. We refer the reader to the latest work of Wynne and Singer (Wynne, 1972; Wynne and Singer, 1972a, 1972b) which provides the most up-to-date outline of this subject. Suffice it to state that an eventual schizophrenic outcome seems to hinge on three interacting sets of factors: (1) an individual genetic component that gives rise to a psychophysiologic response disposition that implies vulnerability for schizophrenia; (2) certain characteristic communication deviances in the family, which affect the preschizophrenic child continuously during the formative years of his emotional, intellectual, and relational development, and which in their totality tend to confuse and mystify him and to make idiosyncratic his orientation toward his inner and outer worlds; (3) the child's separation course in adolescence, which, instead of finding alternate experiences and models of identification than are available in a disturbing family, preclude crucial alternate experiences and identifications. It is at this point where our concept of separation patterns becomes relevant, for it offers a framework that, at this developmental phase, brings into view those factors that may either foster or prevent an eventual schizophrenic outcome in the adolescent. Also, such framework might facilitate tracing those sequences that lead to outcomes not clearly schizophrenic but still lying within a schizophrenic spectrum.

The distinction between genuine and pseudocentrifugal patterns seems useful here. For example, with the possibility of pseudocentrifugal separation courses in mind, we can single out a special type of seemingly precocious and abrupt separator who, his overt centrifugal tendencies notwithstanding, seems to adhere to a basically centripetal pattern.

By the same token, we can look for hidden centripetal elements in the separation courses of actual or potential sociopaths. We can, for example, take a fresh look at the quality and duration of those transient states of pathologically incomplete separation during which many overtly independent and precociously separating delinquents tend to obediently comply with their parents' covert expectations and wishes, as these have been described by A. M. Johnson (1959) and others.

Implications of the Two Separation Patterns for the Adolescent's Growth

These considerations become further meaningful when we specifically consider the adolescent's growth, for each of the described patterns implies dangers as well as opportunities, advantages as well as disadvantages, for such growth.

If we begin with the centripetal pattern, its potential dangers become immediately visible: The adolescent, in sticking too long to the family orbit, becomes subject to a disordered separation timetable. Because he does not invest himself duly in peers and alternate adults, he misses out on new learning experiences and models for identification which could serve as springboards for entering the outside world. Because he remains lastingly tied to his family and parents, he runs the danger of getting stranded in relational dead ends such as we found represented by the fate of the chronically hospitalized schizophrenic. Even when he achieves a separation of sorts by restructuring his reality and establishing a niche in the family field, his parents qua introjects will continue to exert a malignant spell over him. For their influence is not mitigated by real contacts with other people. Stierlin (1970) described how such malignant inner objects become important and alive at the expense of potentially available outer objects. In cases less extreme than the earlier-mentioned chronically hospitalized schizophrenics, we find in this group often lonely schizoid individuals who are tenuously established in the outside world, as these have been described by, among others, Fairbairn (1952) and Guntrip (1961).

However, and herewith we shift our perspective of the centripetal pattern, what may appear as a danger from one angle may, from another, appear as an opportunity. The persistent tie with the parents, agonizing and conflicting as it may be, may foster an introspective depth and strength that often seem unavailable to early and abrupt separators. As much as many of the adolescents in this group may have to cope with nearly unresolvable binds and contradictions, they may nonetheless grow while trying to master them. Particularly Bateson (1969) and Wynne (1969) commented on the pitfalls and challenges inherent in family constellations with schizophrenic offspring where centripetal features tend to dominate. Also, in situations where one sibling pursues a more centripetal and the other a more centrifugal separation course, it is our impression that the first sibling, usually the index, tends to be the emotionally richer and more sensitive person. As far as families with schizophrenic offspring are concerned, such an impression appears confirmed by observations made by Day and Kwiatkowska (1962) on the art productions of schizophrenic index patients as compared with those of their nonschizophrenic (and more centrifugally separating) siblings.[5]

In the centrifugal pattern, in contrast, it is the opportunities for growth that at first sight impress us. Here we find, so it appears, those adolescents who are bent on liberating themselves from a family that threatens to squelch and stifle them. By easily moving into the world of peers and alternate adults, they make available to themselves new learning experiences and new models for identification. They thus create for themselves a springboard for further entering into and growing amid the interpersonal world that exists outside their families. We have, on the basis of observations made by Nameche and Ricks (1966), Nameche *et al.* (1964), Artiss (1962), and others, reason to believe that whenever an adolescent is allowed to branch out into the outside world, the chances for a chronically crippling schizophrenia become remote.

However, and herewith we turn to the dangers and disadvantages of this second separation course, a high price may nonetheless have to be paid. The ease with which many of these adolescents seem to move into the orbit of their peers, join their gang activities, and find their needed sexual partners, often indicates a shallowness and transiency of their human relations. Because of their centrifugal bent, many of these adolescents will enter new (sexual as well as nonsexual) relationships when conflicts and ambivalences deriving from unresolved oedipal problems become reactivated. Certain features of the modern group and communal life, particularly as existing in the hippie culture and the human potential movement, seem tailored to the needs of mainly centrifugally separating adolescents who need warmth from human relations but are ill prepared to cope with the conflicts and ambivalences that intense and lasting dyadic relations inevitably arouse.

Many of these youngsters tend to lack the strength of remaining detached amidst emotional turmoil, which we find in a number of adolescents who follow a centripetal separation course.

Further, centrifugally separating adolescents, in fleeing their actual parents, seem often driven to find in their peers what they failed to obtain from their parents. Therefore, they will often feel compelled to parentify their peers, that is, relate to these peers as if they had important parental attributes. But such parentification of peers can seldom be a one-way process. In order to become accepted by their peers, these youngsters must often, in one way or the other, allow themselves to become parentified in turn. This then introduces into their peer relations some of the very strains and problems they tried to avoid by removing themselves prematurely from the family orbit.

Also, delinquent activities carried out with peers seem often designed to ward off the painful feelings of loss and grief besetting these youngsters as a result of their premature separation from their parents. For, in a sense, their early separation from their parents implies that their parents have died for them.

We are presently looking more closely at what is involved in such overinvested relations with peers. It appears to us that in important respects many centrifugally separating adolescents do only delay, but not achieve, their separation from their families. Instead of remaining stuck in a family orbit, they chose to remain stuck in a peer orbit. Even though this latter orbit seems to offer openings for moving into the adult world, these openings seem of little use. Even where these individuals finally seem to move into the adult world, they seem to bring into this world many of the immaturities, irresponsibilities, and unresolved problems that bedeviled their peer relations. We thus observe many dead ends in human relations and arrests in growth that though qualitatively different from those described in the extremes of the centripetal pattern, seem hardly less serious.

NOTES

1. On the concept of contributions to relationships, see Stierlin (1968, 1969).

2. More recently, Shapiro and Zinner (1971) have taken into account the implications of Bion's work for the study of families.

3. This hostile argumentativeness, creating as well as presupposing distance, must be distinguished from pseudohostility (Wynne et al., 1958). Though phenomenologically similar, pseudohostility is structurally different from the phenomena discussed here in that it implies a rigidly structured and bounded family field. We do not find the bouncing-away phenomenon so typical of the centrifugal family here described.

4. The term "separation pattern," we must here remind ourselves, implies always a longitudinal dimension: Between the family and individual factors described above, we must interpolate certain situational and experiential contingencies. These contingencies, to various degrees, affect the family and individual dynamics and thereby affect the separation course of the given adolescent. These contingencies are either more or less predictable.

Some of the more predictable contingencies tend to occur in conjunction with what we may call *separation landmarks,* such as the adolescent's expected or actual graduation from high school or (in the case of boys) his eligibility for the draft. Another predictable contingency comes into play when the index adolescent is followed by younger siblings relatively close in age who may or may not fill for the parents the interpersonal vacuum created by the separating adolescent. Less predictable contingencies include changes in the parents' or adolescent's interpersonal lives such as might be brought about by individual or family therapy (for example, the relations between the Kowalski parents, described earlier), deaths of family members or close friends, or other unexpected catastrophes, such as illnesses or unemployment of the father, during the adolescent's crucial separation years. These changes may crucially alter the various family or individual factors. Contingencies, as here outlined, were not the focus of this chapter, though they are clearly important. In our ongoing and anticipated studies we intend to pay closer attention to them.

5. We have observed that siblings close in age may occasionally differ substantially in their separation patterns, the one pursuing a rather centripetal, the other a centrifugal, course. We intend to look more closely at the specific configurations underlying this phenomenon.

REFERENCES

Artiss, K. L. (1962). *Milieu Therapy in Schizophrenia.* New York: Grune & Stratton.

Balint, M. (1959). *Thrills and Regression.* London: Tavistock.

Bateson, G. (1969). *Double Bind, 1969.* Paper presented at the symposium on the Double Bind, Annual Meeting of the American Psychological Association, Washington, D. C., September 2.

Bion, W. R. (1961). *Experiences in Groups.* London: Tavistock.

Brown, C. (1965). *Manchild in the Promised Land.* New York: Macmillan.

Day, J., and Kwiatkowska, H. Y. (1962). The psychiatric patient and his "well" sibling. *Bulletin of Art Therapy,* Winter.

Fairbairn, W. R. D. (1952). *An Object-Relations Theory of the Personality.* New York: Basic Books.

Guntrip, H. (1961). *Personality Structure and Human Interaction.* New York: International Universities Press.

Johnson, A. M. (1959). Juvenile delinquency. In: *American Handbook of Psychiatry,* Vol. 1, ed. S. Arieti. New York: Basic Books, pp. 840–856.

Kety, S., Rosenthal, D., Wender, P., and Schulsinger, F. (1968). The types and prevalence of mental illness in the biological and adoptive families of adopted schizophrenics. *Journal of Psychiatric Research,* 6 (suppl. 1): 345–362.

Laing, R. (1960). *The Divided Self: A Study of Sanity and Madness.* London: Tavistock.

———. (1961). *The Self and Others: Further Studies in Sanity and Madness.* London: Tavistock.

Lidz, T., Fleck, S., and Cornelison, A. R. (1965). *Schizophrenia and the Family.* New York: International Universities Press.

Nameche, G., and Ricks, D. F. (1966). *Life Patterns of Children Who Became Adult Schizophrenics.* Paper presented at the Annual Meeting of the American Orthopsychiatric Association, San Francisco, April 16.

Nameche, G., Waring, M., and Ricks, D. F. (1964). Early indicators of outcome in schizophrenia. *Journal of Nervous and Mental Disease,* 136:232–240.

Reiss, D. (1970). Varieties of consensual experience: Contrast between families of normals, delinquents and schizophrenics. *Journal of Nervous and Mental Disease,* 152:73–95.

Rosenthal, D., Wender, P., Kety, S., Schulsinger, F., Welner, J., and Ostergaard, L. (1968). Schizophrenics' offspring reared in adoptive homes. *Journal of Psychiatric Research,* 6 (suppl. 1):377–391.

Salinger, J. D. (1951). *The Catcher in the Rye.* Boston: Little, Brown.

Scott, R. D., and Ashworth, P. L. (1969). The shadow of the ancestor: A historical factor in the transmission of schizophrenia. *British Journal of Medical Psychology,* 42:13–32.

Shapiro, R., and Zinner, J. (1971). *Adolescence and the Family.* Paper presented at the Annual Meeting of the American Psychoanalytic Association, Washington, D. C., April 30.

Stabenau, J., Tupin, J., Werner, M., and Pollin, W. (1965). A comparative study of families of schizophrenics, delinquents, and normals. *Psychiatry,* 28:45–59.

Stierlin, H. (1968). Short-term versus long-term psychotherapy in the light of a general theory of human relationships. *British Journal of Medical Psychology,* 41:357–367.

———. (1969). *Conflict and Reconciliation.* New York: Science House.

———. (1970). The functions of "inner objects." *International Journal of Psycho-Analysis,* 51:321–329.

———, Levi, L. D., and Savard, R. J. (1971). Parental perceptions of separating children. *Family Process,* 10:411–427.

Weber, M. (1966). *The Theory of Social and Economic Organization,* ed. T. Parsons. New York: The Free Press.

Wynne, L. C. (1969). *On the Anguish, and Creative Passions, of Not Escaping Double Binds: A Reformulation.* Paper presented at the Symposium on the Double Bind, Annual Meeting of the American Psychological Association, Washington, D. C., September 2.

———. (1972). Schizophrenics and their families: I. Research redirections. *British Journal of Psychiatry,* in press.

———, Ryckoff, I. M., Day, J., and Hirsch, S. I. (1958). Pseudomutuality in the family relations of schizophrenics. *Psychiatry,* 21:205–220.

Wynne, L. C., and Singer, M. T. (1963). Thought disorder and family relations of schizophrenics: I. A research strategy; II. A classification of forms of thinking. *Archives of General Psychiatry,* 9:191–206.

———. (1965). Thought disorder and family relations of schizophrenics: III. Methodology using projective techniques; IV. Results and implications. *Archives of General Psychiatry,* 12:187–212.

———. (1972a). Schizophrenics and their families: II. Recent research methods. *British Journal of Psychiatry,* in press.

———. (1972b). Schizophrenics and their families: III. Recent Rorschach communication findings. *British Journal of Psychiatry,* in press.

14] THE BORDERLINE ADOLESCENT

JAMES F. MASTERSON

The borderline syndrome emerged on the modern psychiatric scene during the early 1950s as a vague, ill-defined entity comprising symptoms that ranged from the neurotic through the character disorder to the psychotic.[1] Psychiatrists gave it little attention; for example, the sole article on this subject in any psychiatric textbook to this date was by Schmideberg (1959).

During the last ten years the concept of the borderline syndrome has been greatly refined by psychoanalytic study,[2] which found that irrespective of presenting symptoms the basic psychopathology was a specific and stable form of pathologic ego structure, a developmental arrest. Rinsley (1963, 1965, 1967, 1968, 1971; Rinsley and Hall, 1962) described the clinical manifestations, psychodynamics, and intensive treatment of this arrest in adolescents. Grinker, Werble, and Drye (1968) classified the clinical manifestations of this pathologic ego structure in adults. However, the cause of the developmental arrest remained unknown.

The more recent developmental studies of Mahler (1963, 1965, 1968; Mahler and Furer, 1963; Mahler and LaPerriere, 1965; Mahler and McDevitt, 1968; Mahler, Pine, and Bergman, 1970) on the contribution of the stage of separation-individuation to normal ego development and of Bowlby (1969) on the psychopathology of separation at this time of life when applied to the borderline adolescent led me to the theory that the developmental cause of this arrest is a faulty separation-individuation.

This theory laid bare the underlying psychodynamic structure of the borderline syndrome and so enhanced the understanding of transference and resistance that it made intensive psychoanalytic psychotherapy not only possible but the treatment of choice for many of these patients. Properly treated (a combination of support and analysis) they can and do work through much painful regressive affect, which results in a dramatic attenuation of their disorder.

240

This chapter briefly outlines the theory and applies it to the diagnosis, psychodynamics, and treatment of the borderline adolescent. It supports the point of view of Rinsley (1968) and takes issue with the point of view most recently expressed by Zetzel (1971) that the borderline patient is seldom capable of tolerating the painful affect integral to the emergence of regressive transference reactions. As illustrated here, many, though not all, borderline patients can tolerate this painful affect when given the appropriate therapeutic support. These issues are dealt with in more detail elsewhere (Masterson, 1972).

The Borderline Syndrome: A Brief Review

The diagnosis of borderline syndrome has had a long and undeservedly bad reputation in psychiatry. It has been frequently attacked as a misnomer in both the psychiatric and psychoanalytic literature (Rickman, 1928; Zilboorg, 1941).

The term seemed to convey more about the uncertainty and indecision of the psychiatrist than the condition of the patient. Knight (1954) observed that

most often these patients were called severe obsessive-compulsive cases; sometimes an intractable phobia was the outstanding symptom; occasionally an apparent major hysterical symptom or an anorexia nervosa dominated the clinical picture; and at times there was a question of the degree of depression, or of the extent of paranoid trends, or of the severity of the acting out.

A plethora of labels appeared, varying according to the diagnostic style of each psychiatrist, suggesting that the diagnosis might be schizophrenia. Some labels were incipient schizophrenia, latent schizophrenia, ambulatory schizophrenia, transient schizophrenia, pseudoneurotic schizophrenia, chronic undifferentiated schizophrenia. Others favored such labels as chronic severe personality disorder or chronic severe character disorder or narcissistic character disorder. The official American Psychiatric Association nomenclature included these patients under the diagnosis of personality disorder.

This confusion—in retrospect a reflection of the diagnostic emphasis on descriptive symptomatology as opposed to an emphasis on psychodynamics and developmental considerations—persisted, and the ambiguities of the disorder continued to weigh on the psychiatrist as he began to see an increasing number of patients with this clinical picture.

During the last twenty years, as interest in ego psychology grew, this disorder became more of a focus of psychoanalytic study.[3] Much of the confusion cleared, and the consensus felt that the basic psychopathology was not the presenting symptoms but a specific and stable form of pathologic ego structure, that is, a developmental arrest.

Kernberg (1967) emphasized that the presenting symptoms did not differentiate the syndrome. He stated that many symptoms could be present in different combinations, for example,

Anxiety, polymorphic perverse sexuality, schizoid or hypomanic prepsychotic personalities, impulse neuroses and in addition, infantile, narcissistic and antisocial character disorders and many polysymptomatic problems such as phobias, obsessions, conversions, dissociation, hypochondriasis and paranoia.

Speaking of the adult borderline, Knight (1954) made the important point that, despite severe damage to ego functions, the patients' adaptation to the demands of the environment for conventional behavior was adequate. Superficial object relations were intact, and habitual performances were unimpaired; in other words, the patient was sicker than he looked.

However, despite transient psychotic episodes under severe stress and despite such symptoms as depression, withdrawal, and schizoid adjustment, the borderline syndrome was not an incipient or early schizophrenia.

Giovacchini (1964, 1965a, 1965b, 1967a, 1967b) observed that these cases distribute themselves according to the severity and complexity of their disturbances along a spectrum from the more severe psychoneurotic to the most disturbed borderline case, which closely resembles the overt psychotic. At the healthier end of the spectrum are the patients with narcissistic defenses, giving an appearance of more or less normality. In the center of the spectrum are the bulk of the cases; these are less stable, less successful, more erratic, more actively disturbed. They tend to act out, trying to fill up their emptiness with alcohol, excessive sexual indulgence, or with any other kind of excitement. But they do manage to preserve considerable successful adaptation. Closest to the psychotics are the most disturbed patients, who show considerable paranoid ideation, marked feelings of void, very tenuous object relations, and the most marginal adjustment. In spite of their serious pathology, what seems to characterize the bulk of the borderline patients is their resistance to psychotic illness.

Giovacchini stated that the dynamic basis of the clinical picture was a developmental arrest resulting in excessive narcissism and deficiencies in crucial ego functions, such as the perceptual and executive. The ego defects deprive the patients of techniques for mastery that they need to deal with their internal and external world. The narcissistic, magical, omnipotent fantasies erected by these patients to contend with these defects and to protect them from the painful memory traces of a traumatic infancy and childhood are of little help in coping with the realities of the adult world. In spite of their unadaptive value, these fantasies are maintained by the patients, who even live their lives around them, perhaps in an effort at belated mastery.

Kernberg (1967) added that though the borderline as contrasted with the schizophrenic had differentiated ego boundaries and good reality testing, he could not synthesize positive and negative introjects and identifications. As a result he resorted to the defenses of ego and object splitting to preserve the good self- and object images and the external good objects from the bad.

Ekstein and Wallerstein (1954) described their concept of the ego defect in children. They postulated an ego mechanism of control that could be roughly compared in its function to that of a thermostat. A reliable thermostat is capable of maintaining fairly even temperature in a room despite climatic changes, and may be thought of as analogous to the ego state of the neurotic, which fluctuates minimally and is subject to relative control by the individual. An unreliable thermostat, on the other hand, can lead to unpredictable and inappropriate temperature changes and figuratively represents the unpredictable regulatory and controlling devices of the borderline. They wrote:

It seemed characteristic for the borderline that ego-state fluctuations occurred many times throughout their day, occasionally with control, but that a large part of their waking life bore strong similarity to the sleep-dream life of their neurotic contemporaries in the lack of control exerted by the dreamer.

Ekstein and Wallerstein illustrated the intensity of this disorder by saying that the neurotic patient conceives of his problems as leading to dangerous or unhappy consequences but the possible solutions he envisions have some reality anchorage and are less overwhelmingly catastrophic than those of patients in the borderline group who seem to face absolute dilemmas which admit of no solution. If we think of the neurotic dilemma in terms of the excursions of a pendulum, can we say that the excursions of the pendulum in the psychological world of the borderline patient cover an infinitely wider amplitude than in that of the neurotic?

In 1968 Grinker et al. gave clinical verification to the concept of the borderline syndrome through study of the ego functions of fifty-one borderline adults. Behavior was observed, described, and rated through traits extracted from an ego psychology framework. They found the clinical characteristics of the borderline syndrome to be not only consistent when subjected to cluster analysis but also to make sense clinically. They described the essential clinical characteristics as being a defect in affectional relationships, an absence of indications of self-identity, with depressive loneliness and anger as the main or only affect. Within this gestalt the patients could be divided into four groups representing different positions. Members of Group I gave up attempts at relationships but at the same time overtly, in behavior and affect, reacted negatively and angrily toward other people and to their environments. Persons in Group II were inconsistent, with movement toward others for relationships, which was then followed by acted-out repulsion and movement away into isolation where they were lonely. This movement corresponded with the fact that these people were both angry and depressed but at different times. Patients in Group III seemed to have given up their search for identity and defended themselves from their reactions to an empty world. They did not have the angry reactions characteristic of Group I. Instead they passively awaited cues from others and behaved in complementarity—"as if" (Deutsch, 1942). In no other group were the defenses observable as clearly or as consistently as in Group III. Subjects in Group IV searched unsuccessfully for a lost symbiotic relation with a mother figure, and they revealed what may be called anaclitic depression.

All this work has brought the borderline syndrome into clearer focus. The clinical characteristics of the developmental arrest have been described and verified in children, adolescents, and adults. The following pages will describe a theory of the role of separation-individuation in the psychodynamic cause of the borderline syndrome in adolescents and will apply this theory to diagnosis and treatment.

A Developmental Theory

Appropriate diagnosis depends on an understanding of the underlying psychodynamics since the clinical picture is not what it appears to be. The fact that the borderline syndrome is the root of the problem is concealed by the patient's defense mechanisms, which mask his feelings of abandonment, and by his chronologic age, which belies the infantile state of his character.

To understand this syndrome it is first necessary to understand not only the theory of the contribution of symbiosis and separation-individuation to normal ego development, but more importantly the developmental consequences that ensue when separation from the symbiotic partner is burdened by what I have chosen to call an *abandonment depression*. The theory of the former has been creatively worked out by Mahler and her coworkers (Mahler, 1958, 1963, 1965, 1968; Mahler and Furer, 1963; Mahler and LaPerriere, 1965; Mahler and McDevitt, 1968; Mahler *et al.*, 1970) through their developmental studies. The latter evolved from application of the work of Mahler and also Bowlby (1958, 1960a, 1960b, 1961, 1969) to the borderline adolescent.

ROLE OF SEPARATION-INDIVIDUATION IN NORMAL
EGO DEVELOPMENT SYMBIOSIS

The symbiotic relationship can be defined as one in which the functions of both partners are necessary to each. The child's image of himself and that of his mother is of one symbiotic unit. The mother acts as auxiliary ego for the child, performing many functions for him that his own ego will later perform. For example, she sets limits to both external and internal stimuli, and she helps to perceive reality, tolerate frustration, and control impulse.

At approximately eighteen months, under the impetus of the biologically predetermined maturation of ego apparatuses (that is, his own individuation, including a physical development, learning how to walk) the emotional growth task of separation from this relationship begins. The child now undergoes an intrapsychic separation and begins to perceive his own image as being entirely separate and different from the mother's.

This achievement brings with it many dividends for the development and strengthening of the child's ego. Rinsley (1968) stated that separation from the primary maternal object sets in motion the mechanism of reintrojection with whole-object retention; as a result instinctual defusion occurs, making neutralized energy available to the ego's defensive, representational, and synthetic functions. Reintrojection associated with mourning the separated object and the operation of obsessional mechanism have together the effect of bringing back a multiplicity of bad part-objects previously extruded from the territory of the ego through the mechanism of projection. During this stage of ego development, self- and object representations have become progressively and clearly differentiated as the child's perceptual apparatus has matured. These representations, according to Kernberg (1967), have become progressively assimilated to instinctual affect charges of either positive (libidinal) or negative (aggressive) valence, hence have become either positive or negative states. The assimilation of self- and object representations to affect comes about, of course, as a result of the operation of the ego's synthetic function; the latter is energized by deinstinctualized libidinal cathexes, resulting, in turn, from instinctual defusion consequent on whole-object reintrojection. Thus, the territory of the ego is expanded and its "contents" increased.

Three forces—(1) the infant's unfolding individuality, (2) the mother's encouragement and support, and (3) the mastery of new ego functions—press the child forward on his developmental pathway through the stage of separation-individuation toward autonomy.

Mahler stated that the average toddler seems from the end of the first year on to become so preoccupied with practicing the emerging autonomous functions of the ego that he does not seem to mind his mother's casual short departures from the familiar playroom. Some infants behave as though they were drunk with their newly discovered ability to toddle in space and to widen their acquaintance with large segments of reality. The average infant, following the inception of toddling, does not clamor for his mother's attention and bodily closeness during this practicing period. He toddles up to his mother once in a while for "libidinal refueling," but his behavior seems to indicate that for the most part he takes his mother's emotional presence for granted.

Mahler further stated that as soon as free locomotion is mastered the normal toddler seems to need to return to the mother to seek proximal communication with her in a directed way. The phenomenology of this behavior leaves no doubt that the representations of his self and that of the love object are now well on their way to differentiation. After an interlude of greatly varying length, ranging from a few weeks to a period of months, and with various degrees of insistence and impetuousness, the toddler's active approach behavior toward his mother gains pre-eminence. It is interesting to note how, in general, by the time the toddler has mastered the ability to move from and to the mother, the balance dramatically shifts within the bipolar mother-toddler interaction from activity on the part of the mother to activity on the part of the child. Once the toddler has mastered locomotion and begins to learn manipulation, these important partial functions and every new skill becomes elements of a language weighted with a steady accretion of secondary and largely unconscious meaning, a wordless appeal for love and praise from the mother, an expression of longing, a search for meaning, a wish for sharing and expansion.

Mahler concludes that the mother, as the catalyst of the individuation process, must be able to read the toddler's primary-process language. She emphasizes the resiliency with which the child's autonomy unfolds from within his own ego, if he feels a fair degree of emotional acceptance and a fair degree of what she calls "communicative matching" on his mother's part.

In the course of this separation, the child assumes into his immature ego through the mechanism of introjection those ego functions that the mother had performed for him, and his ego structure becomes endowed with essential new functions: secure ego boundaries against both inner and outer stimuli, strengthening of repression, which makes more affect available for sublimation, improved reality perception, frustration tolerance, and impulse control. He begins to substitute the reality principle for the pleasure principle. Object constancy develops, and object splitting as a defense disappears. These two key characteristics will enable the child later in life to cope with loss by mourning.

The child's feelings about his own now separate self-representation as being worthwhile or positive spring in part from the introjection during this phase of the mother's positive attitudes toward him. This new sense of self and these new functions can be viewed as benefits of the achievement of separation and autonomy. Clearly, the mastering of this phase is a key part of the foundation on which the rest of the ego structure is built.

ROLE OF SEPARATION-INDIVIDUATION IN THE BORDERLINE SYNDROME: A DEVELOPMENTAL ARREST

This theory is built upon evidence from our adolescent patients that in the borderline the events described above do not take place. The mother of the borderline adolescent suffers from a borderline syndrome herself.

Having been unable to separate from her own mother she fosters the symbiotic union with her child, thus encouraging the continuance of his dependency to maintain her own emotional equilibrium. She is threatened by and unable to deal with the infant's emerging individuality.[4] She depersonalizes the child, cannot see him as he is but rather projects on him the image of one of her own parents, or of a sibling, or she perceives him as a perpetual infant or an object and uses him to defend herself against her own feelings of abandonment (Rinsley and Hall, 1962). Consequently, even in the symbiotic stage she is unable to respond to his unfolding individuality, and he early learns to disregard certain of his own potentials in order to preserve his source of supplies (approval) from the mother. The mother clings to the child to prevent separation, discouraging moves toward individuation by withdrawing her support.

Emergence of Feelings of Abandonment

Therefore, between the ages of one and one-half and three years a conflict develops in the child between his own developmental push for individuation and autonomy and the withdrawal of the mother's emotional supplies which this growth would entail. He needs her approval to develop ego structure and grow; if he grows the supplies are withdrawn. These are the first seeds of his feelings of abandonment (depression, rage, fear, guilt, passivity and helplessness, emptiness and void), which will have such far-reaching consequences.

Unable to tolerate the awareness of these feelings he handles them by ego splitting (Freud, 1927, 1938) and denial mechanisms and turns his back on his own unfolding individuality, which now threatens his support. Though separated, he continues to cling to the mother to defend himself against the return of feelings of abandonment into awareness. The clinging, splitting, and denial are further reinforced by various defense mechanisms, which later in his life will determine the form of the clinical picture: acting out, reaction formation, obsessive-compulsive mechanisms, projection, denial, isolation, detachment, withdrawal of affect.

The abandonment feelings then recede into the unconscious where they lie submerged like an abscess, their overwhelming but hidden force observable only through the tenacity and strength of the defense mechanisms used to keep them in check. These defenses, however, effectively block the patient's developmental movement through the stages of separation-individuation to autonomy. He suffers from a developmental arrest. He is caught, so to speak, in midstream, en route between two stages of development. Unlike the autistic or infantile psychotic child, the child with the borderline syndrome has separated from the symbiotic stage but has become fixated in one of the subphases of the separation-individuation stage, possibly the rapprochement phase (fifteen to twenty-two months), where the mother's sharing (Mahler, 1965) is so vital to the progress of the child's individuation.

In order to understand the disastrous consequences of these events for the development of the child's ego structure we must shift to another framework, namely, Freud's (1914) psychosexual continuum, which has common meeting points with the one we have been discussing. Freud spoke of two phases, the autoerotic and the narcissistic, that precede the oral phase of development. Symbiosis is a narcissistic phase, and separation-individuation is ushered in by orality. It is likely that the developmental arrest of the borderline occurs either in the narcissistic or early oral phase. The earlier the arrest occurs the more likely the patient's clinical picture will resemble the psychotic, and the later it occurs the more likely the clinical picture will resemble the neurotic. In either case the developmental arrest produces severe defects in ego functioning. There is a persistence of the defenses of ego and object splitting, a failure to achieve object constancy and the development of a negative self-image (Fairbairn, 1952; Klein, 1932, 1946, 1948a, 1948b).

Some of the characteristics of this ego structure referred to by Rinsley (1968) as the weak ego are failure of normal repression; persistence of primitive mechanisms of defense with reliance on projection, introjection, regression, and denial; impairment of ego's synthetic function; lack of basic trust; persistence of object splitting with a consequent impairment of object relations; failure of sublimation of raw instinctual impulses; and serious difficulties with preoedipal and sexual identity. Two key characteristics of this ego structure, so important to an understanding of the patient's reactions to separations are the persistence of object splitting and the failure to develop object constancy. In addition, his own impulses to individuation create such a threat that, rather than enjoy them as does the normal toddler, he attempts to suppress them.

This theory poses a version of the nature-nurture problem. I am postulating that the cause of the borderline syndrome is the abandonment depression created by the mother's withdrawal of supplies at the patient's attempt to separate and individuate. The patient's need to defend himself against his feelings of abandonment produces the developmental arrest and the clinical picture. The evidence for this view comes from two sources: (1) When the patient's defenses are interrupted in psychotherapy he relives the abandonment depression with appropriate affect and appropriate recall of the traumatic separation experiences later in life that revived the feelings of abandonment. (2) Direct observation of the mother's behavior in joint interviews as the patient, under the influence of psychotherapy, attempts to separate and individuate.

Another possibility that must be considered is that the patient has a constitutionally inadequate potential for autonomy. At the moment it is impossible to say which or what combination of these two factors is the root cause of the disorder.

Prepuberty: A Second Separation-Individuation Phase

The child's defenses enable him to function until prepuberty—approximately ages ten to twelve years—when a second marked developmental maturation of the ego occurs. This growth spurt, manifested by a thrust toward activity combined with a turn toward reality, is similar in scope to the maturation of the ego that occurred in the separation-individuation phase (Deutsch, 1944). This maturation, together with the need to further separate from the mother, produces a recapitulation of the separation-individuation phase of development, that is, a second separation-individuation phase.

Deutsch (1944) suggests that prepuberty is a phase in which sexual instincts are the weakest and the development of the ego is most intense. This phase is characterized by a thrust of activity and a turn toward growth and independence, and is an intensive process of adaptation to reality and mastery of the environment as a result of this ego development. The adolescent here is caught between the past and the future, between childhood and adulthood, just like the infant is caught between a symbiotic relationship and autonomy. The struggle for independence in this period strongly reminds us of the processes that take place approximately between the ages of one and one-half and three years, in the course of what we call the preoedipal phase of childhood (the transition from the symbiotic stage to autonomy).

Deutsch (1944) adds that in order to take his first steps in the outside world the infant, after the utter dependence of babyhood, must also disengage himself from his mother who carried and later fed him. Very similar is the behavior of the girl in prepuberty: Full of hatred and rage, she wants to tear herself away from her mother's influence, but at the same time she frequently betrays an intensified, anxious urge to remain under the maternal protection. She concludes that prepuberty repeats the preoedipal phase (separation-individuation phase) not only in the struggle for liberation from the mother that is the central point of the girl's psychological life at this time, but in other respects too.

There is debate in the psychoanalytic literature as to whether this second separation-individuation stage occurs. For example, Peter Blos (1962), disagreeing with Deutsch, explained the same phenomenon as follows: "The girl's 'thrust of activity' constitutes an attempt to master actively what she has experienced passively while in the care of the nurturing mother; instead of taking the preoedipal mother as love object, the girl identifies temporarily with her active phallic image."

Though Blos's view is interesting, he was describing specific dynamic constellations which do not necessarily invalidate Deutsch's formulations. I suspect that the lack of other psychoanalytic corroboration of Deutsch's view may be owing to neglect of this area of study. I stumbled on this report which was written in 1944 while attempting to find out why the borderline syndrome in adolescents makes its clinical appearance at prepuberty. Many begin at the time of the change from local to junior high school.

The first and most obvious answer was that many experienced a physical or emotional separation from the figure to whom they had been clinging. However, when a number appeared who had not had such an experience the problem became more complex. It was not until I ran across this theory of Deutsch's that the pieces of the puzzle finally seemed to fit together.

All adolescents go through a second separation-individuation phase in prepuberty, owing to the maturational spurt of the ego. In some borderline patients this alone is able to precipitate a clinical syndrome; in others this internal event combined with an actual external environmental separation exposes the patient to the experience he has been defending himself against since early childhood, separation from the maternal partner to whom he has been clinging. This, in turn, reactivates with great intensity his defenses against his feelings of abandonment, which wax strongly at this point. The environmental separation precipitates the intrapsychic feelings of abandonment.

These precipitating factors—either the second separation-individuation phase alone or in combination with an actual separation—reinforce the feelings of abandonment and produce a clinical syndrome based on intensification of defenses. The clinical manifestations depend on the patient's unique defenses against his feelings of abandonment. Over and above the defenses, the two diagnostic hallmarks of the borderline syndrome are abandonment depression and narcissistic oral fixation.

It is difficult to convey in words the intensity of the feelings of abandonment and the primacy that these hold over the patient's entire life. His functioning in the world, his relationship with people, even his physiological functions are subordinate to the need to defend against these feelings. Bowlby (1969) called it "attachment behavior" and referred to animal world concepts of ethology and evolution in order to understand what seems to be the most primitive and the most primary "order of business" for the patient.

What gives the feelings of abandonment their awesome dominance? The depression carries with it intense feelings of emptiness, starvation, death, despair, futility, hopelessness, helplessness, inadequacy, which spring from the loss or threat of loss either of part of the self or of supplies that the patient has clung to as vital. This is often expressed by patients in physical terms such as losing an arm or both legs, or of being deprived of such vital substances as oxygen, plasma, or blood.

The word "void," with its connotation of terrifying inner emptiness, describes the feelings aptly. Filling the void becomes a dominant motivation and all sorts of activities are used for this purpose: drugs, drinking, eating, both homosexual and heterosexual affairs, clinging relationships, and so on. The patient clearly experiences unique terrors which are not associated with other kinds of depression, as, for example, a midlife depression.

251

This consideration, that is, filling the void, forms a link with alcoholism and drug addiction and suggests why these disorders have not been amenable to traditional psychotherapeutic methods. Reality considerations become subordinated to the need to fill the void. Psychotherapy cannot be successful. There is no analysis until the defenses against the void are blocked. When they are the patient rejects the therapy because he is unable to tolerate the feelings of abandonment. The depth and source of these feelings as well as the resistance to them must be appreciated.

Defenses Against Separation: The Clinical Picture

In order to illustrate how these patients experience and deal with these abandonment feelings it is most useful to choose an adolescent and follow the lead of Rinsley (1965), who first observed that the adolescent's experience was similar to that of the infants studied by Bowlby who had to undergo a physical separation from their mother by separation at the very developmental period we are concerned with, the first two years of life.

Bowlby (1960a, 1960b) describes these infants as passing through three stages: Protest and wish for reunion, despair, and finally detachment if the mother is not restored. The adolescent is unable to contain the affect associated with the second stage, that of despair.

A physical or emotional separation so reinforces the abandonment feelings that the patient's defense mechanisms intensify to the point that the clinical condition results. These defenses against the depression, however, interfere with the work of mourning so essential to further ego development.

The clinical picture portrays the repetition in adolescence of an infantile drama: the abandonment depression grafted onto the separation-individuation process, the combination effectively halting further ego development. The syndrome itself resembles an iceberg in that only the most superficial part can be clinically detected above the water line, while the rest remains hidden beneath the surface.

To illustrate let us use the acting-out adolescent to describe the five clinical characteristics of this syndrome:

1. Presenting symptomatology—acting out: It may begin with mild boredom, or restlessness, or concentration difficulty in school, or hypochondriasis, or even excessive activity of all kinds (physical and sexual). Finally more flagrant forms of acting out may appear—antisocial

behavior, stealing, drinking, marijuana, LSD, methedrine, heroin, glue-sniffing, promiscuity, running away, car accidents and hippie-like behavior, including long hair, sloppy dress, and unsavory companions.

2. Environment separation experience: The separation experience itself, though sometimes blatant and obvious, is more often quite hidden and must be winnowed out of a great deal of chaff by selective questions. For example, actual separation, such as in death or divorce, are obvious but it can often be such subtle occurrences as an older sibling going away to college, or a grandparent, a governess, or a maid becoming ill, or merely some change in the focus of the symbiotic partner's behavior, for example, a mother who becomes involved in an affair, or is herself too depressed to properly care for the child or one who might have to give most of her attention to a sick sibling. It is important to keep in mind that neither the patient nor the parent have any awareness of the profound significance of the separation experience so that the therapist must ferret this out by himself.

3. Past history—narcissistic orally fixated character structure: The difficulties in obtaining the clinical facts necessary for the diagnosis of the underlying character structure are similar to those encountered for the presenting symptomatic episode. The parents, as character disorders themselves, are most often quite unaware of the fact that the patient has failed to achieve the usual developmental milestones. Therefore, again, the doctor must pursue the patient's developmental history on his own, looking for signs of prolonged dependency and passivity, developmental defects in ego structure, such as poor frustration tolerance, poor impulse control, and impaired reality perception, which give rise to a host of symptomatic expressions from very early in life, ranging from disciplinary problems at home and in school, difficulties in developing social skills with peers, and such symptoms as enuresis and obesity. Once an accurate developmental history has been obtained, the clinician must use the evidence to assess the patient's character structure, keeping in mind the difference between developmental level and chronological age.

4. Parental personalities: As already noted, the parents themselves have borderline syndromes and suffer as much from a lack of parenting as do their adolescents. Consequently, the parents, never having been mothered, cannot mother, and never having been fathered, they cannot father. They perceive their children as parents, peers, or objects and are unable to respond to the child's real needs. Thus the child is subjected to a scapegoating process of the most extreme sort.

The fathers are often passive, inadequate men, dominated by and dependent on but also maintaining great distance from their wives. They assume almost no parental role. The mothers are dependent affect-hungry, aggressive, dominating, demanding and controlling women who need and vigorously maintain the symbiotic tie with their child. They are unable to gratify dependency needs or to set limits appropriate to behavior, and they unconsciously provoke acting out. They discipline inconsistently, being either permissive or punitive.

These parents, weary of the burdens and responsibilities of the job, set their children loose too soon to sink or swim on their own after a continuous series of failures throughout childhood to set the limits so essential for growth. If they cannot say no to their children, how will their children say no to themselves?

When the abandonment occurs and the acting out begins their permissive-punitive response only furthers the adolescent's sense of abandonment and throws him back on the anarchy of his own impulses.

5. Pattern of family—communication: The adolescent expresses his need for help by an act—a plea for help—that expresses as exactly and poignantly as any words, the blind, hopeless, trapped crying out for succor and aid. The final act that brings the patient to treatment usually occurs as the end point of a long series of gradually escalated acts, whose goal is somehow to break through the vacuum of unawareness and/or indifference of the parents to the adolescent's drowning in his own struggle with his feelings, like a child who, struggling in the water and unable to swim, cries out as he is about to go down for the third and perhaps last time "help!"

One experiences a sense of wonder at reviewing the long history of pleas for help in the form of acts on the part of the adolescent. To each the parents respond with unawareness or rejection which then leads to an even more flagrant and dramatic act on the part of the patient, until intervention finally occurs, and even then the intervention often is still not at the behest of the parents but some outside figure, such as a friend, a schoolteacher, or even the police or a wise judge.

A case from my practice illustrates this phenomenon: It was 2:00 A.M. when Mr. Johnson was awakened by a phone call from his former wife from whom he had been divorced for the last four years. He was dismayed to hear from her that their seventeen-year-old son, a senior at a New England preparatory school, had been arrested for entering houses and stealing. He put down the phone, tried to clear the cobwebs of sleep from his brain, and puzzled as to why this had happened and how.

Peter returned from Christmas vacation, bored and apathetic and disinterested in his work, though previously a good student. He gave initial warnings of his future activities in two beautifully written English themes describing breaking into houses and stealing. When this plea was disregarded he unconsciously intensified the plea by proceeding to carry out this plan. Each night when the others in the dorm were asleep, he would slip out and enter a different house just for the satisfaction and thrill of doing it. This was followed by a second phase. He began stealing objects from the houses, usually small objects—jewelry, candlesticks, and the like. This kept up for several months until an alarm was spread about the neighborhood and policemen were posted.

Then, all his previous efforts having failed to obtain the necessary help, one night Peter walked directly past a policeman into a house where he was finally apprehended and brought down to the police station. He freely admitted his guilt and took the officer back to his dormitory where he had carefully wrapped and stored in his footlocker all the things he had stolen.

The source of his distress was later found to be as follows: His mother and father had been divorced the year he went away to prep school at the age of twelve. He usually spent most of his time with his mother, but that year when he had come home for Christmas vacation, he got into a fight with his mother who threw him out and told him to spend the vacation with his father. The father, then living with his current mistress, had no room for Peter, so he put him up in a hotel room for the vacation. Peter, abandoned, alone, and depressed, spent the whole vacation sitting in his room reading and watching television. Little wonder that he later found an inappropriate but effective vehicle to express his plight and to obtain the necessary help.

It is clearly of the utmost importance that the clinician sense and respond to the underlying distress and alarm that the adolescent is not able to verbalize. This response is as much a true rescue operation as the lifeguard who dashes into the water with a life preserver. The doctor's response becomes the life preserver that assists the adolescent to keep afloat long enough for more definitive measures to be taken, in other words, until the therapy begins to help him in his struggles.

The question arises here: Why a soundless act rather than a simple verbal request for help? These families, parent and adolescent alike, have borderline syndromes, and the significant, if not all the meaningful, communication between them occurs in the form of acts and not words. Feelings are communicated by doing and not by saying. It is small wonder that when the adolescent is in danger he turns to this most familiar vehicle to express his distress.

Let us now turn to a characteristic clinical illustration.

PATIENT ANNE

Fate struck Anne, a sixteen-year-old adopted girl, a particularly cruel blow at the age of ten when the maid who had taken care of her died and her mother became chronically ill with acute intermittent porphyria. The mother and father had a very distant relationship, the father spending most of his time at work so that the patient was left alone to care for the mother.

Anne, always a behavior problem, was unable to tolerate the feelings of abandonment and responded with a worsening of her behavior both at home and at school. At home she was rebellious, staying up most of the night and sleeping during the day. In school she resented the teachers and dressed inappropriately.

As she entered her teens, she started to smoke marijuana. At age fourteen, she was taken to see a psychiatrist who said she was hopeless and recommended that she be committed to a state hospital. Her parents refused to do this but took her out of the public school system after clashes with teachers and sent her to a private boarding school. After one year there, at age fifteen, she was suspended for violating a number of rules, including visiting a boy in his room. At this time she had sexual intercourse for the first time, feared she was pregnant, and had fantasies of running away, taking the baby with her and working to support it. Fortunately for her this event did not come to pass. After being suspended she returned to the local high school where she remained for only seven weeks before dropping out. She was taken to see another psychiatrist, started treatment, and again would not talk about herself. The psychiatrist sought more information by means of amytal interviews, which were also unproductive. Several months before admission, her behavior got worse; she began leaving the house to take long walks during the middle of the night and dating boys who were taking heroin. Finally her doctor insisted that she be hospitalized. She was sedated and placed in the hospital against her will.

Anne began life with the handicap of having an unwed mother of whom little was known except that she was fifteen years old. Anne early suffered a second reverse when she was adopted at the age of six weeks by a couple, presumably because they were unable to have a child due to the father's sterility, but more probably in order to preserve an already shaky marriage. Surely, this was an ominous beginning for a new life.

According to her adopted mother, she was a difficult baby, crying constantly and banging her head during the first year of life. A Negro maid, Louise, was hired to care for her. The mother says "the three of us took turns rocking her to sleep. She was a feeding problem. She didn't like anything, she spit everything out unless Louise cooked it for her."

She had difficulties in school beginning in the first grade and disobeyed teachers continually. At five she was told she was adopted and that she was the chosen one for her parents.

Her mother says she had so much difficulty in school that "I would be in school more than she would." The mother tried to discipline her by spanking her or taking things away but, "Anne would scream so that I couldn't stand it." During the first six years Louise was the only one who could handle her. Louise was overindulgent, did everything for her, and took sides with her against the parents. The mother frequently felt angry at the maid, yet acknowledged her inability to manage the patient without her help. When Anne was eight and one-half the maid left. The patient looked forward to her infrequent visits. Then when Anne was ten, fate stepped in again, and suddenly and unexplainably Louise stopped visiting. The die was now cast.

Anne's appearance on admission was striking: shoulder-length black hair partially covering her eyes, pale white skin, her only make-up blue and white eyeliner, giving her an almost ghostlike appearance. She dressed either in bluejeans with a black turtleneck top and black boots, or very short miniskirts. She wore one blouse cut out on the sides almost down to the waist without a brassiere. When visited by her parents (as we had not yet learned to prohibit visits), she would demand that they bring in all sorts of unnecessary items for her—five more shirts than she would need—and she was particularly hostile and contemptuous toward her father.

TREATMENT

Phase 1: Testing [5]

This phase, which extends from the beginning of treatment to the control of acting out and the establishing of a therapeutic alliance, is obviously crucial. If its ingredients are not recognized and properly handled, the remaining hours or even years of therapy may be rendered ineffective. Why is this first phase so important, and what is its significance to the patient? More simply, why does the adolescent attempt, often so ingeniously, to thwart the well-intentioned efforts of the therapist to help him? What are the dynamics of this encounter, and more important, what do we do about it?

The adolescent with a borderline syndrome is usually defending himself against separation and mourning. He has been repeatedly hurt and deeply disappointed by rejections and abandonment by his parents and other significant adults in his world. Nevertheless, he clings to and spends his effort to keep alive the pathologic symbiotic relationship with his mother. His façade of resistance, rebelliousness, lack of concern, though tenaciously clung to, actually masks a feeling of utter hopelessness: his despair and dread of abandonment. His despair stems from the impasse that has evolved in his relationship with his parents. He feels, though usually not consciously aware of the reasons behind it, that their abandonment indicates they do not care, and in his thwarted dependent symbiotic state this is extremely painful, producing rage, depression, feelings of starvation, impending death, hopelessness, and helplessness.

He is fearful and anxious as he enters treatment. Though aware on some level that he needs help he is frightened that if he allows a relationship to develop with the therapist he will risk re-experiencing the abandonment of his earlier relationship. In addition, driven by the wish for reunion with the parent, he feels a need to fight anything that smacks of separation. He wants reunion, not consolation, for his loss. His first unspoken question then will be: "How do I know you, the therapist, are any different? Prove to me that you have the capacity to understand me. Nobody else ever has. Prove to me you will not also abandon me." Thus the testing process aims to answer these questions.

The therapist is put through the same trial by fire the parents experienced, for there is no therapeutic alliance as we understand the term. Words at this point are not used to convey or express feeling, but to manipulate and test. Behavior is the principal means by which the patient expresses his emotions.

He employs acting out not only as a defense against feeling and remembering but also as a vehicle for testing. Though basically ineffective and self-destructive, acting out is perhaps not so painful for him as risking trust and placing his all-embracing symbiotic needs in the hands of a person he, as yet, has no reason to trust.

He must then conceal his need for help and engage in an elaborate game of testing which the doctor must successfully pass before the adolescent will feel enough trust to reveal his painful state. The patient makes a virtue out of a necessity by extolling the benefits of his acting out and of his manipulation, all the while hoping his doctor will have the ability and good sense to see through him. After all, what else can he do? He is grappling with overwhelming primitive conflicts: wishes for fusion, fears of engulfment on the one hand, abandonment on the other.

How does the therapist handle this testing phase of therapy? The patient's acting-out behavior is conceived of as both a defense against mourning and separation and as a means of testing the doctor. The goal of treatment is to pass the test by controlling the acting out (Holmes, 1964), thereby enabling the patient to resume the work of mourning and separation. How does the therapist go about this?

In this first stage the essential vehicle for communication, for therapist as well as for patient, is not words but actions. The patient, communicating mainly by actions, scrutinizes the therapist's actions for feedback. The principal drama takes place outside the usual psychotherapeutic arena of words, in the world of action.

The content of Anne's initial interviews was more or less as follows: She did not want to be here. There was nothing really wrong. Why should she follow the stupid rules? People don't live by rules. She denied depression, but said, "No, it is just a feeling of vagueness, numbness, emptiness. I'm not really unhappy; it is just that I don't care. All I really want is out." She wondered why she didn't feel more depressed in a horrible situation like this. She hoped something would happen so that she could get out of the hospital.

Anne's initial acting out consisted of her exhibitionistic appearance, wearing miniskirts, her negativistic, sarcastic, flippant attitude toward the therapist, writing provocative letters to her friends about hospitalization, procrastinating in school, telephoning friends to make provocative statements and failing to keep her room clean.

We began to limit the acting out by forbidding miniskirts, monitoring her letters, limiting the phone calls, and expecting her to be at school on time and to keep her room clean.

The anger that had previously been dissipated in this defiant behavior now began to come out more directly. For example, "I'm not picking up this room, you can tell the doctor that if I am in Occupational Therapy and she wants an interview, I'm going to refuse to come down. If she comes near me I'll throw something at her face." In short, she is saying the doctor is unreasonable, she doesn't understand her and she is "square."

At this point the patient was totally unaware of the relationship between her acting-out behavior and her emotional state. For example, she did not realize that after an upsetting visit or phone call from her parents she would resume acting out by staying up late and dressing inappropriately.

The first breakthrough in her awareness of the relationship of feeling to behavior occurred about ten weeks later, when the doctor forgot to leave an order giving the patient permission for a visitor. The patient was furious but rather than verbalize it she acted it out, refusing to go to bed on time, wearing heavy eye makeup and perfume, and a shirt borrowed from one of the male patients. She remained in the next interview only five minutes and said: "This interview is a waste of time. You forgot what was important. You demand things of me, but forgot what was important to me." And she stormed out.

In the next interview, it was pointed out to her that she expressed her anger at the doctor in the same destructive acting-out manner as she had with her parents. In addition, it was suggested that verbalization might be more constructive. Still angry she denied any connection: "People are trying to change me. When I get out nothing will change, I will still be the same."

After many interviews dealing with the relationship of feelings to behavior the patient began to control her behavior. She now dressed appropriately and participated well in school. Her acting-out defense thoroughly controlled, the feelings of depression and abandonment against which it had been a defense rose to the surface.

Phase 2: Working Through [6]

Passage of the patient from Phase 1, testing, to Phase 2, working through, is signaled clinically by control of the major part of the acting out, a consequent deepening of the depression, and by spontaneous recall, this time with more appropriate affect and detailed memory, of the history of the separation and abandonment.

The patient has now fulfilled the conditions necessary for the working through of the mourning process and his other emotional conflicts in the interview: (1) The patient is now aware of the relationship between feeling and behavior. (2) He has begun to check the impulses to act out, which allows feeling to rise into consciousness and which also impels him to remember his past.

At the same time that conflicts are brought to the interview for discussion rather than acted out, words are used to express feeling rather than to manipulate the situation. Finally, with the conclusion of the testing process, the patient, assured of the therapist's competence and trustworthiness, allows a therapeutic alliance to develop that makes the first dent in the patient's feeling of despair and hopelessness.

The patient enters into a transference, which later will have to be resolved. But nevertheless, this relationship breeds confidence and allows the patient to work through the rage and depression associated with separation from the mother.

This change in the patient's clinical condition warrants a parallel change in both the therapeutic focus and the therapeutic approach. The focus shifts from the environmental milieu and behavior to expression of the patient's feelings in the interview with consequent recognition and working through of the conflicts. The goal of therapy in Phase 2 is to work through the rage and depression at the abandonment and complete the separation process, which lays the groundwork for the repair of ego defects through new introjections.

To accomplish this the therapeutic techniques shift from those involved in controlling acting out to those dealing with the working through in the interview, that is, from limit setting to interpretation. With the control of acting out there immediately ensues a deepening of the depression. Thereon, the patient institutes a secondary line of defense against the depression, such as withdrawal and evasion and denial of his feeling state, which must be interpreted by the therapist, bringing the patient back to accepting and working through his depression. At the same time, the therapist supports and encourages verbalization as a superior alternative to acting out for relieving the depression and for eventual resolution of the conflict.

"After Louise left I started getting really lonely." The doctor asks: "What did you think about her leaving?" Patient: "I don't know but I felt more acute loneliness. She used to stay with me. I didn't realize she was good for me until long after she had gone. Mother told me she didn't know where she was. I had the feeling that maybe something happened. I felt nostalgic, something that was part of me was taken away." Here Anne literally reports her feeling that the separation involved a loss of part of herself.

Doctor: "Was that about the time you began to have trouble in school?" Patient: "Yes, I started getting called down. I didn't do well in the first part of the seventh grade. In the summer I really got close to Jan and Bill. We used to stay over at each other's house. Jan and I were always freer; we had less of a front with each other than I had with other people. I really was terribly lonesome. Mother started getting sicker then. I'd come home to a different friend's house each night, and father stayed in New York City." Anne then reports her acting out as a defense against the depression. "I think I would have talked to anyone. I didn't know what I felt. I mainly acted. I did whatever I wanted to. I don't think I have ever talked to anyone really deeply. I wasn't aware of feeling lonely, but I thought I really needed somebody. I wasn't aware of feeling lonely until one or two years ago."

As the patient slides further into the trough of her depression she works through her feelings of being abandoned by her mother surrogate and then confronts the basic conflict over separation-individuation with her mother. At this point she begins to near the bottom of her depression wherein lie feelings of homicidal rage and suicidal depression at the mother not caring. "I never remember a mother-daughter relationship, maybe just a bit when I was young. I ended up hating her. I wish

I didn't. Talking to her makes me pissed off at the world. Sometimes I could pound her into the ground. Then she'd get sick and I'd feel bad and I'd take her to the hospital. A couple of times she would come up to slap me and I'd push her away. I felt I could kill her a couple of times. I wound up feeling sorry for her."

"I don't think she ever knew what it would be like to love without convenience." Anne then suddenly recognizes the relationship between her behavior and her anger. "It is funny, I thought I was doing all those things because I wanted to do them.

"I spent a lot of time with Bill—I'd be upset and he would come over to my house, and then when he left I would be upset again. We would watch TV or go to a movie. I'd also go to Jan's house. But when I was thirteen or so, Bill and I broke up and Jan moved away. Things were still groovy in a way, but we were more separated.

"Then I started to smoke pot and go out with Denny. When Jan and I got together we used to look back to when everything was okay, two years before when I wasn't smoking pot. My parents didn't hassle me as much about Bill, and I stayed away from them as much as I could, and I had stuff to look forward to, such as being with Bill or going to Jan's.

"I think that there is a kind of loss that goes with smoking pot. I was kind of happy but I knew that it couldn't go on, but I didn't want things to change so radically. I had to have someone to hang on to. I figured I could focus all my attention on Bill and Jan. I was out of school, nothing to do, just waiting and waiting. My mother expected me to be rotten no matter what happened."

With the expression of the rage and hopelessness the patient begins to improve. In an interview a few days later the patient said, "I don't know why, but I feel more comfortable now, calmer, waiting for something to happen. Up to now I have had no hope. I have thought things would go on just like before. But now things do seem to be getting better, perhaps not completely changing. In fact, I am coming back to when I was comfortable, and I kind of expect things to keep getting better."

At some point in the latter part of Phase 2, when the patient has a working alliance with his therapist, has verbalized his rage, and is well on his way to working through his depression, and when the parents have become aware of their conflicts in the parental role and have, to some extent, learned a more appropriate parental role, it is necessary for parents and patient to be brought together.

These joint interviews have a specific and limited purpose: not to do family therapy as such but (1) to expose the family myth, (2) to restore more appropriate patterns of emotional communication in the family, the patient doing now what he was unable to do originally, that is expressing his rage verbally and working it through with the psychotherapist, thereby relieving the pressure behind the acting out and discovering a new mechanism for dealing with family conflict, and (3) to find more constructive and newer ways of dealing with family conflicts on the part of both patient and parents. This initial confrontation always arouses great anxiety, which immediately leads to regression on the part of both patient and parents. However, after successful confrontation and catharsis of the underlying emotions the family is freed to seek better patterns of adjustment. This crucial operation finally brings a strong shaft of hope to the patient.

Phase 3: Separation [7]

As the patient enters the separation phase he develops great anxiety, since the impending separation from his therapist revives all the old feelings of being abandoned, which then come to dominate the issue of separation. The patient responds to this anxiety as of old by regressing and acting out to impel the therapist to keep him in the comfortable, dependent position and not require him to deal with the frightening reality of becoming independent and autonomous.

A corollary of this anxiety is the patient's feeling that alone he will be unable to handle his problems with his parents, who will draw him back into the old bind of dependency and anger.

Anne talked about experiencing the impending separation from the therapist as abandonment, and at last perceived that she was handling this fear by acting out in an effort to get the therapist to hold her back as her mother always had.

The therapist reinterpreted her fears with a discussion of the difference between separation and abandonment and reassured the patient that she would not have to move away from the security of her relationship with her therapist any faster than she was able. Anne then began to work through her fears of being abandoned in the setting of the impending separation from the therapist.

She recalled the day, at age ten, when Louise left, and her feeling that people could only get so close; much as she loved and needed Louise, she could not hold onto her. She then remembered her loneliness and anger at her mother for not fulfilling her needs when Louise left. Patient: "When Louise left, mother was pretty cold to me. She would be sick and sleep a lot. I would get home from school and go to my room. There was nothing to come home to. My mother wasn't even around to say 'Hello.' She really wasn't a mother at all. As far as I was concerned she was a grown-up living a world apart from me."

As the patient returned to her fear of doing things on her own, the therapist reassured her about her capacity to handle things herself, and of the therapist's support until she was on her own, pointing out that the patient's life had been either overindulgence or abandonment and that there was a middle course until she was able to be independent.

She summarized her treatment: "I have gone through three stages here: First, it was really hard and everything was a drag. Second, then I went back to being a little kid, running to you and mama. Third, now it is okay, I am growing up at last. I hope it will be more like a happy medium between the dependency I hated and the freedom I feared, like you have talked about for a long time now." After this interview, which was in the middle of June, the patient gave no evidence of any regressive tugs, nor any acting out, nor any depression.

A LIBIDINAL REFUELING STATION

Our early unsuccessful experiences attempting to send these patients either home or to a boarding school after discharge have slowly led us to understand that the hospital treatment, effective as it is, is only a beginning for the following reasons: The patient has not resolved his separation anxiety which continues to frustrate any effort at a close heterosexual relationship because of fears of engulfment or abandonment.

The manifold problems associated with the oral fixation, particularly the demand for an exclusive dependent relationship, have not been fully worked through. Discharge from the hospital, the caretaking apparatus, over and above its abandonment significance leaves the patient open to severe oral frustration with consequent rage and depression owing to his continued emotional need for supplies in order to build ego structure.

In addition, though the patient is somewhat freed from the old environmental conflict with the mother, he now engages in an intensive intrapsychic battle between his push for individuation and the anxiety and guilt that spring from his introjected maternal image. Beyond this, the patient's discharge from the hospital again raises the mother's wishes for reunion, which she implements to pressure the patient to regress and return to the old symbiotic union. The patient, for his part suffering severe depression and guilt, is severely tempted to regress and rejoin the mother.

The issue that dominates all others, however, is the patient's continued need for emotional supplies and for relief from anxiety and guilt in order to continue on his developmental way to autonomy. To meet these issues we are now in the process of setting up another caretaking facility, a halfway house, which can be used as a libidinal refueling station until the patient is emotionally ready to go off on his own. Our patients will be able to put the halfway house to a use similar to that of the normal toddler who returns to the mother for libidinal refueling as an aid in his journey. In addition, to minimize some of the separation anxiety we have arranged to have the patient continue with his inpatient therapist for a second outpatient year.

In the meantime, we have been placing our patients with relatives or at boarding schools. Freed from the regressive pull of constant contact with their parents, and supported by a continuing relationship with their therapist, the patients are far better able to cope with their intensive intrapsychic conflicts. The vicissitudes of this therapeutic struggle are described in other publications (Masterson 1971a, 1971b, 1972).

Though the borderline adolescent's problem is severe, and therefore his therapeutic requirements high, there is no reason for discouragement. If we have understood and properly treated the patient's pathology we will have made it possible for him once again to harness the enormous power of his own inherent growth potential to his own ego development.

NOTES

1. See Deutsch (1942), Knight (1954), Rickman (1928), and Zilboorg (1941).
2. See Benedek (1938, 1949, 1956, 1959), Ekstein and Wallerstein (1954), Fairbairn (1952), Fraiberg (1969), Giovacchini (1964, 1965a, 1965b, 1967a, 1967b), Grinker, Werble, and Drye (1968), Guntrip (1964), Jacobson (1964), Knight (1954), and Winnicott (1958, 1960, 1962, 1963a, 1963b, 1963c, 1963d).
3. See Benedek (1938, 1949, 1956, 1959), Deutsch (1944), Ekstein and Wallerstein (1954), Fairbairn (1952), Fraiberg (1969), Giovacchini (1964, 1965a, 1965b, 1967a, 1967b), Grinker et al. (1968), Guntrip (1964), and Jacobson (1964).
4. See Bateson, Mishler, and Waxler (1968), Giovacchini (1965a, 1965b, 1967a, 1967b), and Zentner and Aponte (1970).
5. Rinsley (1965, 1968, 1971) terms this phase the resistance phase of residential treatment.
6. This phase corresponds with Rinsley's definitive or introjective phase.
7. Rinsley's phase of resolution (desymbiotization).

REFERENCES

Bateson, C. F., Mishler, E. G., and Waxler, N. E. (1968). *Family Processes and Schizophrenia.* New York: Science House.
Benedek, T. (1938). Adaptation of reality in early infancy. *Psychoanalytic Quarterly,* 7:200–215.
———. (1949). The psychosomatic implications of the primary unit: Mother-child. *American Journal of Orthopsychiatry,* 19:642–654.
———. (1956). Psychobiological aspects of mothering. *American Journal of Orthopsychiatry,* 26:272–278.

————. (1959). Parenthood as a developmental phase. *Journal of the American Psychoanalytic Association,* 7:389–417.

Blos, P. (1962). *On Adolescence: A Psychoanalytic Interpretation.* New York: The Free Press.

Bowlby, J. (1958). The nature of the child's tie to his mother. *International Journal of Psycho-analysis,* 39:350–371.

————. (1960a). Separation anxiety. *International Journal of Psycho-analysis,* 41:89–113.

————. (1960b). Grief and mourning in infancy and early childhood. *Psychoanalytic Study of the Child,* 15:9–52.

————. (1961). Process of mourning. *International Journal of Psycho-analysis,* 42:317–340.

————. (1969). *Attachment and Loss.* New York: Basic Books.

Deutsch, H. (1942). Some forms of emotional disturbances and their relationship to schizophrenia. *Psychoanalytic Quarterly,* 11:301–321.

————. (1944). *The Psychology of Woman.* New York: Grune & Stratton, Vol. 1, pp. 3–23.

Ekstein, R., and Wallerstein, J. (1954). Observations on the psychology of borderline and psychotic children. *Psychoanalytic Study of the Child,* 9:344–469.

Fairbairn, W. R. D. (1952). *Psychoanalytic Studies of the Personality.* London: Tavistock.

Fraiberg, S. (1969). Libidinal object constancy and mental representation. *Psychoanalytic Study of the Child,* 24:9–47.

Freud, S. (1914). On narcissism: An introduction. *Collected Papers.* London: Hogarth, 1953, Vol. 4, pp. 30–59.

————. (1927). Fetishism. *Collected Papers.* London: Hogarth, 1952, Vol. 5, pp. 198–204.

————. (1938). Splitting of the ego in the defensive process. *Collected Papers.* London: Hogarth, 1952, Vol. 5, pp. 372–375.

Giovacchini, P. L. (1964). The submerged ego. *Journal of the American Academy of Child Psychiatry,* 3(3):430–442.

————. (1965a). Maternal introjection and ego defect. *Journal of the American Academy of Child Psychiatry,* 4(2):279–292.

————. (1965b). Transference, incorporation and synthesis. *International Journal of Psychoanalysis,* 46 (3):287–296.

————. (1967a). Frustration and externalization. *Psychoanalytic Quarterly,* 36:571–583.

————. (1967b). The frozen introject. *International Journal of Psychoanalysis,* 48 (1): 61–68.

————. (1970). Effects of adaptive and disruptive aspects of early object relationships and later parental functioning. In: *Parenthood,* ed. E. J. Anthony and T. Benedek. Boston: Little, Brown, pp. 525–537.

————, et al. (1967). On regression: A workshop. *Psychoanalytic Forum,* 2 (4):293–316.

Glover, E. (1932). A psycho-analytical approach to the classification of mental disorders. *Journal of Mental Science,* 78:819–842.

Grinker, R., Werble, B., and Drye, R. (1968). *The Borderline Syndrome.* New York: Basic Books.

Guntrip, H. (1964). *Personality Structure and Human Interaction.* New York: International Universities Press.

Holmes, D. J. (1964). *The Adolescent in Psychotherapy.* Boston: Little, Brown.

Jacobson, E. (1964). *The Self and the Object World.* New York: International Universities Press.

Kernberg, O. (1967). Borderline personality organization. *Journal of the American Psychoanalytic Association,* 15:641–685.

Klein, M. (1932). *The Psycho-Analysis of Children.* London: Hogarth.

————. (1946). Notes on some schizoid mechanisms. In: *Developments in Psycho-Analysis,* ed. J. Riviere. London: Hogarth.

————. (1948a). Contribution to the psychogenesis of manic depressive states. In: *Contributions to Psycho-Analysis 1921–1945.* London: Hogarth.

———. (1948b). Mourning and its relation to manic depressive states. In: *Contributions to Psycho-Analysis 1921–1945*. London: Hogarth.

Knight, R. P. (1954). Borderline states. In: *Psychoanalytic Psychiatry and Psychology*. New York: International Universities Press.

Mahler, M. S. (1958). Autism and symbiosis: Two extreme disturbances of identity. *International Journal of Psycho-Analysis*, 39:77–83.

———. (1963). Thoughts about development and individuation. *Psychoanalytic Study of the Child*, 18:307–324.

———. (1965). On the significance of the normal separation-individuation phase. In: *Drives, Affects and Behavior*, ed. M. Schur. New York: International Universities Press, Vol. 2, pp. 161–169.

———. (1968). *On Human Symbiosis and the Vicissitudes of Individuation*. New York: International Universities Press.

———, and Furer, M. (1963). Certain aspects of the separation-individuation phase. *Psychoanalytic Quarterly*, 32:1–14.

Mahler, M. S., and LaPerriere, R. (1965). Mother-child interaction during separation-individuation. *Psychoanalytic Quarterly*, 34:483–489.

Mahler, M. S., and McDevitt, J. (1968). Observations on adaptation and defense *in statu nascendi*. *Psychoanalytic Quarterly*, 37:1–21.

Mahler, M. S., Pine, F., and Bergman, A. (1970). The mother's reaction to her toddler's drive for individuation. In: *Parenthood*, ed. E. J. Anthony and T. Benedek. Boston: Little, Brown.

Masterson, J. F. (1971a). Intensive psychotherapy of the adolescent with a borderline syndrome. In: *American Handbook of Psychiatry*, ed. G. Caplan. In press.

———. (1971b). Treatment of the adolescent with borderline syndrome (a problem in separation-individuation). *Bulletin of the Menninger Clinic*, 35:5–18.

———. (1972). *Treatment of the Borderline Adolescent: A Developmental Approach*. New York: Wiley-Interscience.

Rickman, J. (1928). *The Development of the Psycho-Analytic Theory of the Psychoses, 1893–1926*. London: Baillière, Tindall & Cox.

Rinsley, D. B. (1963). Psychiatric hospital treatment with special reference to children. *Archives of General Psychiatry*, 9:489–496.

———. (1965). Intensive psychiatric hospital treatment of adolescents: An object-relations view. *Psychiatric Quarterly*, July.

———. (1967). The adolescent in residential treatment: Some critical reflections. *Adolescence*, 2(5):83–95.

———. (1968). Economic aspects of the object relations. *International Journal of Psycho-Analysis*, 49(1):44–45.

———. (1971). Theory and practice of intensive residential treatment of adolescents. In: *Adolescent Psychiatry*. Vol. 1. *Developmental and Clinical Studies*, ed. S. C. Feinstein, P. L. Giovacchini, and A. A. Miller. New York: Basic Books, pp. 479–509.

———. (1972a). Special education for adolescents in residential psychiatric treatment: A contribution to the theory and technique of residential school. *Unpublished manuscript*.

———. (1972b). Residential treatment of the adolescent. In: *American Handbook of Psychiatry*, ed. G. Caplan. In press.

——— (1972c). The adolescent inpatient: Patterns of depersonification. *Psychiatric Quarterly*, 45:1.

———, and Hall, D. D. (1962). Psychiatric hospital treatment of adolescents: Parental resistances as expressed in casework metaphor. *Archives of General Psychiatry*, 7:286–294.

Schmideberg, M. (1959). The borderline patient. In: *American Handbook of Psychiatry*, Vol. 1, ed. S. Arieti. New York: Basic Books, pp. 390–410.

Spitz, R. A. (1965). *The First Year of Life*. New York: International Universities Press.

Winnicott, D. W. (1958). The capacity to be alone. In: *The Maturational Processes and the Facilitating Environment*. New York: International Universities Press, 1965, pp. 29–36.

———. (1960). The theory of the parent-infant relationship. In: *The Maturational*

Processes and the Facilitating Environment. New York: International Universities Press, 1965, pp. 37–55.

———. (1962). Ego integration in child development. In: *The Maturational Processes and the Facilitating Environment.* New York: International Universities Press, 1965, pp. 56–63.

———. (1963a). The development of the capacity for concern. In: *The Maturational Processes and the Facilitating Environment.* New York: International Universities Press, 1965, pp. 73–82.

———. (1963b). From dependence towards independence in the development of the individual. In: *The Maturational Processes and the Facilitating Environment.* New York: International Universities Press, 1965, pp. 83–92.

———. (1963c). Psychotherapy of character disorders. In: *The Maturational Processes and the Facilitating Environment.* New York: International Universities Press, 1965, pp. 203–216.

———. (1963d). Hospital care supplementing intensive psychotherapy in adolescence. In: *The Maturational Processes and the Facilitating Environment.* New York: International Universities Press, 1965, pp. 242–248.

Zentner, E. B., and Aponte, H. J. (1970). The amorphous family nexis. *Psychiatric Quarterly,* 44:91–113.

Zetzel, E. R. (1971). A developmental approach to the borderline patient. *American Journal of Psychiatry,* 7:127.

Zilboorg, G. (1941). Ambulatory schizophrenias. *Psychiatry,* 4:149–155.

15] THE ADOLESCENT PROCESS AND CHARACTER FORMATION: CLINICAL ASPECTS—WITH REFERENCE TO DR. MASTERSON'S "THE BORDERLINE ADOLESCENT"

PETER L. GIOVACCHINI

The borderline syndrome, in spite of its diagnostic ambiguity, has recently received considerable attention from clinicians. Regardless of one's theoretical or therapeutic orientation, this syndrome has gained in importance because of the large number of patients seeking therapy who cannot be fit into previous diagnostic categories, such as the "classical" psychoneuroses. Here, I do not wish to make distinctions between various conditions that have many similarities (and some differences) and have been known by various names, such as characterological disorders (Boyer and Giovacchini, 1967), narcissistic personality disorders (Kernberg, 1968), borderlines (Knight, 1953), "as if" personalities (Deutsch, 1942), and other designations that refer to ego defects, primitive fixations and pregenital characteristics. Instead, I wish to refer to some structural characteristics of disturbed patients in general and the therapeutic implications gained from such understanding. Furthermore, the role of the adolescent process in character formation has considerable relevance and can be scrutinized further.

Dr. Masterson also believes that the borderline syndrome is important and discusses it from both a theoretical and therapeutic perspective. I propose to discuss the significant points Dr. Masterson makes and then expand the theme beyond the borderline adolescent to include developmental factors and their vicissitudes as they stem from the adolescent period, the implication being that adolescence may be a phase that has etiological significance for adult character structure.

To begin with, Dr. Masterson's theoretical exposition emphasizes that the borderline adolescent patient can be understood in terms of special fears regarding abandonment which originate somewhere between the symbiotic phase and what Mahler and Furer (1963) have called the separation-individuation phase of development. The patient's behavior is, to a large measure, determined by defenses designed to achieve repression of the fear of abandonment. These defenses include acting out, projection, denial, and various obsessional mechanisms. As with all protective and adaptive maneuvers, they tend to become accentuated during moments of stress, which in these patients often refer to separation from persons on whom they are dependent, a separation that may be subtle and far from obvious in its manifestations.

Such profound fear of abandonment has its antecedents in a disturbed, early relationship with the mother or the nurturing source, which impedes the achievement of separation and individuation. The previous symbiotic phase is not successfully traversed (the ego remains fixated at early developmental periods). I believe that Dr. Masterson is eminently correct in emphasizing these particular areas of impairment. The fear of abandonment is especially operative in determining future malfunctioning and in many instances acting out, whose purpose is to deny the value of object relationships.

Dr. Masterson's interest seems to be primarily clinical, that is, he appears to want to achieve theoretical understanding so he can apply it to the treatment of patients rather than for its own sake. This is a laudable pursuit and one in which I believe he succeeds.

Still, no theoretical exposition can ever be complete or final, and here, too, one can make meaningful extensions. For example, viewing psychopathology in terms of repression and defenses, though a traditional outlook, is a unilateral psychodynamic approach, especially when dealing with patients whose difficulties stem from what might be considered faulty structuralization.

My experience with patients suffering from ego defects has taught me that the majority of such cases are not able to successfully institute repression. Repression is a psychic mechanism that is usually associated with an ego that has achieved a relatively high degree of integration. My patients do not seem to have the ego organization required to sustain such a sophisticated defense.

Ordinarily, when considering repression, one is usually referring to the repression of an unacceptable instinctual urge, sexual or destructive.

270

Dr. Masterson refers to the repression of fear of abandonment, a repression that is maintained by specific defenses.

Is it conceptually consistent to make formulations about the repression of fear or anxiety rather than an unacceptable impulse? Fear refers to a reaction to external danger, in this instance real or symbolic abandonment by the nurturing source, and anxiety is a reaction to an internal danger (Freud, 1926). Though the distinction between these phenomonologically similar affective states is not so clear-cut as had been initially postulated, it seems clear that these feelings are the consequence of failure of repression or the return of the repressed. Therefore, it is not fear that is defended against by repression but the aberrant impulses that threaten to break through to consciousness. According to this thesis, fear of abandonment is, in itself, a reaction to inner disruptive forces.

Thus, in order to understand such psychic processes further, one has to go beyond the concept of repression. The psyche must be viewed in terms of specific ego systems and their faulty functioning. For example, preoccupation with identity is constantly found in severely disturbed patients, as well as the ordinary adolescent. In the borderline patient, the self-representation is precariously constructed, and he suffers from the perplexing and confusing feelings of not really knowing who and what he is, his place in the world and his purpose in life.

Such a vaguely defined identity, in situations of acute stress often reaching the intensity of an existential crisis, is accompanied by low esteem, extreme feelings of inadequacy, helplessness, and vulnerability. In moments of decompensation these feelings become accentuated to the point of panic. Consequently, these patients often have to guard against regression, which threatens to become unmanageable and results in loss of control of feelings and the terrifying ego state of nonexistence.

These patients have to defend themselves against what they fear to be the total dissolution of their identity. Because of a variety of characterological problems that also affect the ego's executive system, they find themselves unable to adjust to many facets of the external world. This lack of adjustment is experienced as failure and leads to further frustration as the patient feels thwarted in mastering what to him are the inordinate complexities of reality. His self-esteem receives another blow with each successive failure and each lowered state, in turn, makes him even more incapable of relating to problems that others would consider pedestrian.

In many instances, an external object is sought, and when this occurs in the transference during therapy, it becomes apparent that the patient is seeking an omnipotent sustaining relationship that will rescue him from the hateful, destructive aspects of his inner self.

The relationship to the external object can be considered a defense against inner chaos. However, the concept of defense, as used here, is much broader than the usual one of a mechanism erected to maintain repression of an unacceptable, instinctual impulse. As the transference so frequently reveals, patients suffering from characterological problems often assign omnipotent wisdom and goodness to the therapist and psychically fuse with him in order to gain surcease from their painfully amorphous, empty inner world. This can be considered a defense, but one where the person's total integration is involved. He gains sustenance and power from such a relationship, hopefully rising above his helpless misery. In daily life the just described fusion is also experienced, sometimes by becoming involved with a cause rather than a person. In any case, so much is expected of the relationship that it is doomed to failure. Magical expectations lead to inevitable frustrations. Again, a vicious circle is set up. The patient seeks omnipotence and fails. Thus, he finds himself at the mercy of a more unlovable and unworthy self. He then requires an even more omnipotent relationship than previously, and the cycle endlessly repeats itself.

The fear of abandonment and painful reactions to separation that Dr. Masterson describes are easily understood in view of such a precarious adjustment.

The supporting person also maintains meaningfulness from another perspective, that of need fulfillment, which again relates to the symbiotic phase and excessive disruptive reactions to separation. In the symbiotic unity, it is surmised that the child, in some poorly understood fashion, feels that all his basic requirements will be met. Though it is imprecise to assign complex mentational responses to the immature neonate, this stage of development has often been referred to as a state of omnipotent wish fulfillment. In the adult or adolescent who has a relative fixation on such early developmental phases, the need to be gratified is prominent. Wishes, even though they are incapable of being articulated, since they originate from preverbal states, have an urgent, pressing quality and have to be gratified instantaneously. The fact that the external world cannot comprehend the nature of the need because of its primitive quality, or respond with the magic assigned to archaic fusion states intensifies both frustration and disruptive reactions to separation. The discrepancy between what is felt to be needed and its inevitable frustration leads to further loss of self-esteem and feelings of vulnerability.

In certain psychotherapeutic relations and often during adolescence, some stability based on the belief that such primitive needs are being met is achieved. During treatment, there may be a reciprocal interaction between the patient and therapist regarding the assignment of omnipotence. The therapist, usually unconsciously, accepts the role projected onto him. He attempts to respond to the patient's needs in the same frame of reference that they are presented to him. He allows himself to intrude into the patient's life and participate in its management. This constitutes a reenactment of the symbiotic phase, and both patient and therapist are involved in the mutual delusion that primitive needs are magically and omnipotently gratified. This relationship may, on the surface, appear rational and reality oriented, but, underneath, there are many primary-process elements operating. Though some such relationships may endure indefinitely, most of them eventually lead to the inevitable frustration just described and, in extreme cases, suicide.

Needy adolescents attempt to create a situation similar to the above therapeutic relationship. Rather than seeking omnipotent reciprocity from a person, they search for causes and ideologies that transcend everything in the present reality. Thus, they achieve an orientation that combines the belief that they are receiving magical fulfillment (note the adolescent's preoccupation with astrology, oriental philosophy and religion, scientism, for example) and a hostile rejection of current values that express their massive anger, as described by Dr. Masterson, and represents their reaction to being reduced to a state of helpless vulnerability.

There are many aspects of such psychopathology that require clarification from a developmental perspective. Dr. Masterson believes that the borderline patient is fixated somewhere between the symbiotic and the separation-individuation phase. This viewpoint can be scrutinized further.

In a sense, one cannot be "between" developmental phases. Our theory contains concepts which view emotional development as a sequential, progressive structuralization, one phase gradually merging into the next. No previous phase is entirely obliterated; it becomes part of an hierarchically elaborated structure, and it is capable of exerting influence on the psyche. Still, when examining the psyche from a cross-sectional axis, so to speak, there is a predominant organization characteristic of the particular developmental phase.

The borderline patient often behaves in a fashion that suggests that he has very few qualities indicative of the separation-individuation phase. His amorphous self-representation emphasizes that individuating

273

characteristics have been poorly structured. On the other hand, there is considerable evidence, such as the transference reaction described, pointing to a fixation at the symbiotic phase.

I believe this view can be reconciled with Dr. Masterson's if instead of considering a fixation between phases, which is conceptually inconsistent, the emphasis is placed on turmoil and conflict within the symbiotic phase itself. These patients do not have sufficient psychic structure to relate to an environment where autonomy is required. Their orientation is based on the psychic mechanism of fusion, but within the symbiotic context they are vulnerable and fear annihilation and engulfment. Consequently, they have to construct defenses that utilize fusion mechanisms but, at the same time, protect them from ego dissolution.

Developmental Factors

The early developmental precursors of psychopathology frequently manifest themselves in adolescence, or perhaps reach their symptomatic peak at that time as has been emphasized; now, it becomes pertinent to focus on the adolescent period itself. Is there continuity between the experiences of childhood and adolescence, a continuity that is reflected in psychic processes responsible for either development or maldevelopment?

If one views ordinary emotional development as a progressive structuralization, the smooth upward flow of our conceptual curve seems to reach a plateau somewhere during midadolescence. Shortly following puberty, there seems to be accelerated development, characterized by adult preoccupations. Accompanying the often seen physical growth spurt (height, voice, secondary sexual characteristics, and so on), one often sees a similar emotional spurt, where childhood values seem to be relinquished, and in some instances repudiated.

If there have been emotional problems, the behavioral accompaniments of psychopathology become more acutely manifest, and decompensations are frequent during adolescence. The behavior of many adolescent patients seems to represent an attempt to achieve a defensive stabilization.

Freud conceptualized the infantile neurosis in the context of the etiological significance of early childhood experiences. Though he constantly believed constitutional factors were important, the influence of early object relationships was always kept in the foreground. He formulated emotional development in terms of progressively elaborated psychosexual stages and viewed neonatal relationships with parents or parental surrogates as crucial in determining the direction of psychic structuralization. (These ideas were formulated in a psychodynamic frame of reference, psychopathology being conceptualized as a clash between inner conflicting forces, between the id and the ego as he later stated.)

Borderline patients produce material that can be best understood in terms of the "anatomy" of the psyche—executive and integrative ego systems, the self-representation, levels of self-esteem, and disruptive rage—in other words, in terms of an ego-psychological focus. Similarly, the adolescent is also more easily conceptualized in ego-psychological terms, though id factors, such as seeking outlets for sexual drives, are never completely excluded. This is simply a question of emphasis.

When problems of early deprivation express themselves during later periods of life (adolescence and adulthood), they are more clearly viewed in characterological terms rather than simply frustration and helplessness. Specifically, the fear of abandonment during adolescence or adulthood has often become elaborated into the fear of getting close to someone, at first because of not wanting to experience once again the catastrophic pain of further disappointment and later because of the fear of being swallowed up, annihilated, and reduced to an amorphous mass. The patient's reactions are caused by a destructive maternal introject, which has hindered the integration of later beneficial experiences with the external world and has led to the construction of constricted characterological modalities that are incapable of mastering the problems of the surrounding reality. This failure of adaptation becomes manifest, especially during adolescence, because, in our culture, more autonomy is demanded of the adolescent and his problems become increasingly complex. Because of childhood deprivation (it must be emphasized that the word deprivation here is used in its broadest sense), the ego has not developed sufficient integration of character structure required for the acquisition of adaptive techniques to cope with the increased vicissitudes of biological maturation and the cultural world of the adolescent. To summarize, adolescence is a time of life when ego defects involving characterological adaptations of the ego-executive system become especially prominent.

Thus, there is an interplay between drive development and faulty psychic structure throughout the course of childhood development which reaches its most obvious symptomatic manifestations during adolescence. As Dr. Masterson's chapter emphasizes, patients suffering from severe psychopathology highlight this interplay in their acting-out behavior.

The previously mentioned adolescent developmental plateau is, in part, explainable by the ego's recognition that it is inadequate to master pedestrian problems. During prepuberty childhood, because of his accepted and acceptable dependence, the child's ego did not need complex, adjustive techniques, and their nonexistence or the lack of potential for their formation was not keenly felt. Being unprepared for the complex adult world, which, in a sense, is precipitously thrust on the adolescent, accentuates his characterological inadequacy, and he is at the mercy of his helplessness and unformed adult identity.

True, there are many experiences that attempt to make the introduction of the adult world gradual, and much of the child's developmental experience consists of preparing him so that he can deal successfully with future situations and problems. The borderline patient, however, cannot avail himself of such potentially helpful and integrative interactions, because he does not have the introjects of previously beneficial relationships available that would make him able to assimilate this benign class of transaction. The borderline patient is also unable to recognize the positive qualities of any situation because of suspiciousness and distrust stemming from the disruptive quality of the early symbiosis.

Consequently, the adolescent's ability to integrate himself into a world of increasing complexity will depend on how much freedom of interaction introjects acquired during childhood permit him. Patients suffering from severe psychopathology have to make special efforts to effect an adjustment.

Adolescent Adaptations

During the course of acquiring adjustive techniques, which eventually become consolidated and result in character synthesis, the adolescent may exhibit peculiar and bizarre behavior. This occurs during what has been referred to as a moratorium (Erikson, 1956), which signifies a psychic pause so the ego can further scrutinize both the inner and outer world. In his attempt to achieve autonomy, the adolescent has to search for standards and values he feels are truly his own. Depending on how much early objects related to him as narcissistic extensions of themselves, and not recognizing him as a separate person, the more the adolescent has to repudiate the values of the current establishment and seek his own values, which usually are antithetical to the major stream.

Some patients demonstrate that though the adolescent seems to orient himself in a totally different fashion from his parents, he is, in fact, really identifying with what may be considered the parents' core personality (Giovacchini, 1968). Frequently, parental values such as money, prestige, and even the compulsion to be happy represents defensive superstructures covering up painful feelings of hopelessness and futility. The adolescent is merely rejecting the superstructure but has incorporated the deeper levels of the parents' personality. The problem becomes even more compounded, for instead of achieving autonomy by his apparent rebellion, he cements himself closer and closer to the parents self-image and becomes further dissolved in the destructive symbiotic fusion.

In general, however, patients are seeking new introjects on which they can erect a foundation for an autonomous identity. Thus, adolescence can be a second chance to achieve ego integration to make up for the pathogenic influences of childhood, which have distorted the path of the developmental drive. During adolescence, a setting can be created for the initiation of experiences that set psychic processes in motion that lead to the synthesis of the adult character.

Success in achieving a stable character is directly related to the amount of autonomy already achieved. In terms of the theoretical orientation here, autonomy depends on how well the symbiotic phase has been resolved. Though the early self-representation and the corresponding identity sense concerns childhood patterns, the child still can feel that the boundaries between himself and others are distinct. During adolescence he has to add to his self-representation to give it adult qualities. The better consolidated the child's identity sense, the more smoothly it can integrate adult characteristics. There is a congruence between the preadolescent self-representation and the elements that have to be further incorporated into it. Since these adult accretions are concerned with autonomy, the amount of discreteness and autonomy the child has gained proportionately facilitates the expansion of the self-image.

As stated, the achievement of character synthesis takes place through the formation of new introjects. Elements of these object representations gradually blend into the self-representation and give it the expansion just described.

Though there seems to be a discontinuity in the developmental process occurring during adolescence, from the viewpoint of ego processes, structural changes occur in a relatively smooth, continuous fashion. The old introjects do not conflict with the new introjects required to deal with the tasks of the adult world. On the other hand, during the process of acquiring new introjects, there may be a behavioral discontinuity. Phenomenological changes, however, reflect inner processes that need

277

not be discontinuous. The new introjects are not discontinuous and are not essentially different from the old ones; they become structural extensions of the latter, which, during childhood, help the ego develop executive techniques appropriate to that period of life. Now, executive techniques become refined in order to deal with adult complexities.

I believe that the reason for the adolescent's striking behavior can be explained by the need for accelerated emotional development. Whereas ego structuralization and the corresponding acquisition of adaptive techniques occurred relatively slowly and gradually during childhood, the sudden appearance of puberty and the correspondingly increased societal demands requires a speeding up of the timetable. From the ego's perspective this is simply a speeding up of processes that are qualitatively similar, so there is no real discontinuity involved.

The situation is different with persons who suffer from developmental psychopathology, such as borderline patients. Their introjects are hostile and devouring and are not compatible with potentially helpful experiences. They cannot assimilate new introjects and effect structural extensions. For example, a nineteen-year-old patient described the situation graphically in a fantasy in which he had envisioned an inner powerful force that swallowed and destroyed everything that he tried to learn.

Traumatic Significance of Adolescence

I believe that patients with characterological problems experience a fresh trauma when they reach adolescence. A role is imposed on them that they are unable to fulfill. There is a marked discrepancy between their abilities and the problems that confront them. Thus, the expectations of the outer world constitute a trauma that operates as a negative feedback by lowering self-esteem and intensifying feelings of inadequacy. These reactions, in turn, make the patient even less capable of dealing with reality, and the cycle is endlessly repeated.

Adolescence is a crucial period, and when considered traumatic as just described, it gains in importance as a time of life that has *etiological significance* for the production of psychopathology. In this sense, it is similar to infancy as a stage of life when experiences are particularly important in determining the developmental sequence and whether one's adjustment will or will not be psychopathological.

The outer world makes demands and the adolescent suffering from an ego defect cannot meet them. The situation is reminiscent of the helpless vulnerability the abandoned child feels. The adolescent does not have and cannot develop adaptive techniques. In addition to his devouring and constrictive introjects, he cannot turn to external objects for help. He feels truly and hopelessly abandoned this time, not because, in contrast to infancy, there are no gratifying objects, but because, despite their presence, he cannot benefit from a relationship with them. His loneliness thus assumes extreme proportions during adolescence and, in severe cases, can lead to psychic collapse which may be related to the frequent occurrence of schizophrenia at this time.

The adolescent's defenses against what primarily is an alienation from his environment and against a poorly structured, inadequate self-representation contribute significantly to his adult character structure. Adolescence has often been considered a transition period where consolidation of the psyche and character synthesis occurs. In persons suffering from severe psychopathology, the relatively precipitous and sudden demands of reality represent the trauma, as has been discussed, and the consolidation of character is dominated by elements that are essentially *defensive* reactions against feeling abandoned and vulnerable. *Thus, the adult personality is psychopathologically constructed insofar as it is the outcome of reactions against what has been experienced as a traumatic adolescence.*

To consider adolescence, on the whole, a stage of life that has similar etiological significance as infancy is an unwarranted generalization. This is still a question that has to be explored. However, patients suffering from characterological defects such as the cases Dr. Masterson has called borderline fail in availing themselves of the second-chance aspect of adolescence and, instead, experience this period as traumatic and one that has profound significance for their future development. It may well be that only patients with severe ego defects assign adolescence such etiological significance, since their difficulties are mainly characterological, and adolescence generally is a period when the permanent character structure begins to form.

Adolescence may simply be a transition phase for persons who do not particularly suffer from the consequences of ego defects. Though the developmental process, at this time of life, may contain many complex factors, it is possible very little occurs during adolescence per se regarding interactions with the external world that introduce new elements to the formation of the adult character. One can conceptualize adolescence as a transition period when childhood memory traces incorporate experiences that are similar in kind, though more complex and mature. The traumatic aspects of adolescence are minimal or nonexistent.

Still, the transitional nontraumatic and the traumatic etiological aspects of adolescence are not antithetical absolutes. Rather, here again, one is dealing with a continuum which makes the question of causal factors in the development of the psyche a relative one.

With obvious psychopathology, etiological factors may be clearly discernible. On the other hand, when the psyche seems to be relatively well integrated, the qualities and significance of formative experiences are not so obvious. In the well-adjusted personality, the etiological factors responsible for such integration can be understood only in a broad sense; specific details become obscured since early beneficial experiences become amalgamated into the ego as modalities and do not manifest themselves as destructive and disruptive nonintegrated, discrete introjects.

Therapeutic Implications

Dr. Masterson finally deals with the treatment of the borderline adolescent patient, and he gives us a detailed description of the successful treatment of an acting-out female patient. Basically, he details opening maneuvers designed to establish contact and the later interpretative approach. The first part of the treatment was mainly managerial, but the therapist tried not to react as the patient expected in view of her past traumatic experiences. His attempts were directed toward being supportive in a realistic fashion.

Since the focus of this exposition is on the adolescent process and character formation, a detailed discussion of therapeutic technique would be tangential to the main thesis. However, parenthetically, I want to mention that I find the division of treatment into supportive and analytic phases an artificial distinction (Giovacchini, 1970a, 1970b) and that often attempts to adopt a supportive stance are both therapeutically self-defeating and make the later pursuit of analytic insight impossible for the same therapist. Apparently, this did not happen with the patient described by Dr. Masterson, but in order to ascertain how much ego integration she has achieved will require a long follow-up. In summary, I believe that the analytic approach from the beginning provides intrinsic support, especially for patients suffering from characterological pathology.

The reactions of adolescent patients during treatment teach us considerably about both the adolescent and the therapeutic process, and also emphasize some similarities to early childhood. I have noted during the treatment of both adolescents and adults that there often is an amnesia for certain experiences that occurred during adolescence, similar to infantile amnesia. Anna Freud (1958) mentioned this same amnesia, which is, of course, not so total as infantile amnesia, but which is sometimes lifted during the course of analysis. The traumatic adolescent events that come to the surface are relived in the transference and have the same etiological significance as the infantile neurosis. Thus, treatment operates on the same principle of recovery of unconscious memories and working through in the transference context Freud describes, and once again indicates something important about experiences occurring during the formative and, in some instances, vulnerable period of adolescence.

More specifically, because of the character fluidity of the adolescent, he is particularly amenable to treatment designed to achieve structural change. True, his resistances, which often take the form of rebellious withdrawal and aloofness, may make the initial contact difficult to establish, as was described by Dr. Masterson. Still, these are often superficial resistances, and if the therapist indicates respect for the patient's autonomy and does not try to impose his own values, the adolescent frequently relaxes and the therapeutic process spontaneously begins to unfold. This is an identical situation to the analytic treatment of adults, but, in a sense, more so, since the adolescent's need for autonomy is even greater than the adult's, the latter possibly having achieved a little more security regarding his identity.

Since the adolescent's character, defensive or otherwise, is not firmly fixed, he is able to regress with relative ease during treatment. He can also regress without treatment, as his erratic behavior sometimes flamboyantly illustrates, but the therapeutic setting can supply order and organization rather than let the regression proceed chaotically.

The patient, if he has developed trust, may let himself regress back to a period before the traumatic constricting introjects were firmly established. The borderline patient regresses to the symbiotic phase which is manifested by fusion with the therapist.

Insofar as traumatic introjects are still operating during regression, the reliving of the symbiotic phase is conflictive and painful. The patient expresses his disruption with anxiety, in some instances very severe, and in fantasies of being swallowed or engulfed and destroyed. The latter refers to obliteration of their meager and precarious identity.

Patients who will react in such a disruptive fashion usually defend themselves vigorously against the symbiotic fusion with the therapist, and this defense may take the form of hostile acting out in the external world. Still, when one has the opportunity of carefully examining cases that have had such an outcome, one finds that the therapist has either consciously or unconsciously attempted to direct the patient in a manner that the latter finds similar to the treatment that he received from early objects, persons who were instrumental in determining the course of his emotional development. This may occur even when the patient directly asks for guidance, and the therapist's reaction seems to be a helpful response to his request.

If the therapist directs his interest exclusively on understanding how the patient's mind operates, he is creating a unique situation. The patient cannot find any similar person or situation in his life. The experience of the therapeutic relationship and the perception of the therapist, in these circumstances, have no counterparts in the patient's memory system.

Not to impose one's principles on the adolescent patient creates an atmosphere where autonomy is possible. It also permits the patient the freedom to regress.

The therapist's exclusive preoccupation with the patient's psyche also indicates that he is interested in the patient's productions as phenomena worthy of study rather than frightening tragedies. This is a reassuring situation. Thus, therapy aimed primarily at understanding, rather than managerial manipulation, is *intrinsically supporting*.

Regression under these circumstances involves, as does any regression within the transference context, the projection of archaic imagoes on the therapist. However, from the very beginning of therapeutic contact, the adolescent has increasingly recognized that the therapist is different from any person he has ever met. This permits him to have two views of the therapist: (1) in terms of the content of his infantile imagoes as he is the recipient of the patient's projections, and (2) as a person who is dedicated to fostering his autonomy by increasing his range of control through integrative insight. These perspectives make the regression manageable and less disruptive.

The borderline adolescent, when reliving the initially traumatic symbiotic phase in treatment, finds himself fused with an object that has another meaning and significance, as well as the traumatic, engulfing qualities of the original infantile imagoes. He can also recognize a nonengulfing element to his fusion if the therapist's attention has been exclusively devoted to intrapsychic processes and he has not behaved in a manner congruent with the projection of infantile elements.

Thus, the resolution of the symbiotic transference has considerable potential for the acquisition of an ego that is not hampered in its autonomy by constrictive introjects. Insofar as the regressive fusion, though it recapitulates the symbiotic phase, is different and contains, in addition, a percept of the maternal imago that includes the therapist's structuralizing role, the resolution of the fused state need not be overwhelmingly disturbing and can lead to a relatively stable separation-individuation phase. The patient regains lost parts of the self through the transference resolution of the symbiotic phase.

My purpose here has been to discuss the therapeutic process generally and to view intrapsychic shifts as they are particularly relevant to the understanding of the treatment of the borderline adolescent who has a very unstable character. The latter, even though it may be manifested in disturbing symptoms and acting out, could be a factor that leads to sufficient transference regression to make the patient therapeutically amenable.

These are broad principles. When discussing the treatment of a particular patient, one can apply such principles within a specific technical context. Dr. Masterson discusses technical maneuvers from a traditional viewpoint. I believe the ego-psychological perspective presented here would make *deliberate* supportive maneuvers technically unnecessary and, contrary to our usual conceptions, even detrimental to patients suffering from severe psychopathology.

Still, as Dr. Masterson's clinical exposition so beautifully illustrates, the well-intentioned therapist who has considerable understanding about the patient's psyche can exercise a certain amount of *relaxed flexibility* in his relationship with the adolescent patient. One can only applaud the therapist's sensitivity and be grateful for the result.

Summary

The borderline adolescent is discussed from both a theoretical and therapeutic perspective. Using Dr. Masterson's concept about these patients' basic fear being separation from the nurturing object as a point of departure, the concepts of conflict, defense, and fixation are examined further. Theoretical elaboration leads to a consideration of etiological factors in determining the ultimate formation of character. It is finally postulated that the adolescent period has similar etiological significance for the development of psychopathology in persons suffering from ego defects as the infantile period, through the construction of the infantile neurosis, has for the development of the adult neurosis. An expansion of this theme leads to the often-reached conclusion that adolescence, because of its fluidity, represents a second chance where characterological synthesis can be achieved that is not hampered in its autonomy by archaic, constricting, and disruptive introjects.

In conclusion, the implications of these theoretical formulations are examined in the treatment process. The transference regression of borderline patients reaches back to the stage of symbiotic fusion. The more the therapist is perceived as a person whose purpose is to foster autonomy, rather than deliberately providing support by environmental manipulation or direction, the more likely the resolution of the symbiotic phase will achieve characterological stability and individuation.

REFERENCES

Boyer, L. B., and Giovacchini, P. L. (1967). *Psychoanalytic Treatment of Characterological and Schizophrenic Disorder.* New York: Science House.

Deutsch, H. (1942). Some forms of emotional disturbance and their relationship to schizophrenia. *Psychoanalytic Quarterly,* 11:301–321.

Erikson, E. H. (1956). The problem of ego identity. *Journal of the American Psychoanalytic Association,* 4:56–121.

Freud, A. (1958). Adolescence. *Psychoanalytic Study of the Child,* 13:255–278.

Freud, S. (1926). The problem of anxiety. Standard Edition, 20. London: Hogarth.

Giovacchini, P. L. (1968). Compulsory happiness: Adolescent despair. *Archives of General Psychiatry,* 18:650–658.

———. (1970a). Modern psychoanalysis and modern psychoanalysts: I. *Psychiatry and Social Science Review,* 4:3.

———. (1970b). Modern psychoanalysis and modern psychoanalysts: II. *Psychiatry and Social Science Review,* 4:4.

Kernberg, O. (1968). The treatment of patients with borderline personality organization. *International Journal of Psycho-Analysis,* 49:600–619.

Knight, R. (1953). Borderline patients. *Bulletin of the Menninger Clinic,* 19:1–12.

Mahler, M., and Furer, M. (1963). Certain aspects of the separation-individuation phase. *Psychoanalytic Quarterly,* 32:1–14.

16] RESPONSE OF UNMARRIED ADOLESCENT MOTHERS TO INFANT OR FETAL DEATH

PETER BARGLOW, ISIS ISTIPHAN,
JEAN E. BEDGER, AND
CLAUDIA WELBOURNE

> Sleep on my little one sleep.
> It grieves me so, to see you go,
> For you have fallen asleep;
> Never, never to waken to me.
> *By sixteen-year-old mourning girl*

Psychiatric studies of maternal response to infant loss have appeared only recently in the scientific literature (Kennell, Slyter, and Klaus, 1970; Wolff, Nielsen, and Schiller, 1970). Several articles have described parental response to the fatal illness of a child (Friedman, 1967; Futterman and Hoffman, 1970; Natterson and Knudson, 1960; Nolfi, 1967). On the other hand, there has been an extensive interest in childhood responses to parental object loss (Bowlby, 1960; Fleming and Altschul, 1963; Freud, 1917; Pollock, 1961). Several authors have written specifically about the pathology of adolescent mourning for the death of a parent (Furman, 1968; Laufer, 1966; Wolfenstein, 1966). As far as we can determine, this is the first essay devoted to the study of adolescent reactions to the death of a fetus or infant. We found multiple overt signs and symptoms of mourning in almost every instance.

Method

The setting for this study was the Crittenton Comprehensive Care Center, an outpatient community service program for pregnant unwed girls.[1] The focus of our investigation consisted of four questions: (1) Which criteria define successful mourning of an infant (or fetal) loss during adolescence? (2) What clinical postloss behavior, signs, or symptoms distinguish adequate adaptive mourning from pathological mourning? (3) Which factors facilitate or interfere with successful mourning? (4) What are appropriate therapeutic guidelines for this group?

We evaluated the social work, teacher, nursing, and medical records[2] of thirty-five patients who had lost a fetus or infant and who could be contacted by telephone. Efforts were made to interview psychiatrically all of those patients (twenty-nine) who had not previously been completely evaluated by a psychiatrist. Twenty of these patients were given a semistructured research interview using a data sheet. The data sheet was constructed utilizing the psychiatric literature on mourning and preliminary impressions obtained from six patients originally evaluated. (Psychiatric consultation had been requested because of major psychiatric symptoms.)

Insufficient data excluded two patients. One patient was eliminated because she had had a therapeutic abortion. Another girl was excluded because she had been married at the time of child loss.

Adequate data was accumulated on thirty-one patients,[3] of whom twenty-four had been seen by a psychiatrist. In all instances where there were early indications of psychopathology, a follow-up examination was conducted after the initiation of therapeutic interventions. Median age of patients was seventeen and one-half years with extremes of nineteen and thirteen years. All patients were unmarried at the time of loss, and the majority lived in single-parent homes. All patients were black, and most were poor (family of four with income less than $5,000 per year).

One-third of the patients (ten) had had spontaneous abortions during the second trimester of pregnancy; one-third (ten) had lost a fetus during the third trimester; and one-third (eleven) had lost an infant at term or within two months after birth. About one-half (sixteen) of the sample was observed during the first five months following loss, most (twelve) within a one- to three-month postloss period. The other half (sixteen) was studied at times that ranged from half a year to three years following child death.

Criteria for Successful Mourning

The following criteria were utilized to define adaptive, adequate mourning: (1) Some evidence of a progressive typical sequence of emotional reactions to the loss. The acute phases of mourning described by Pollock (1961), are (a) shock with initial denial of loss, (b) grief, (c) pain phenomena, and (d) separation reactions (often with anger). All stages should end within a few months. This description was more useful for our observations than Bowlby's (1960) "protest-despair-withdrawal" description, of childhood mourning responses. (2) A capacity to utilize available sources of emotional support from a parental figure, a helping professional, or a boyfriend. (3) Gradual realistic acceptance of the loss with a re-establishment of realistic goals, social relations, and educational progress. (4) Active efforts at mastery of disruptive loss sequelae that were usually characterized by effective interpersonal communications or by new sublimations.

We utilized clinical phenomena that were overt and common, that required little interpretation of unconscious affects or ideation. Most of our criteria for adaptive or pathological mourning correspond to the clinical manifestations described in the literature dealing with object loss in adults and adolescents (Bowlby, 1960; Cain and Cain, 1964; Deutsch, 1937; Furman, 1968; Lindemann, 1944; and Wolfenstein, 1966).

The criteria for successful mourning were met by a group of ten patients. Case No. 1 illustrates several of these:

A seventeen-year-old girl was seen seven months after she lost a term infant due to cord prolapse. She recalled "I didn't accept that the death happened. I had a dream that he was alive and what he looked like. . . . Then I was hurt, surprised, and bitter, and I almost lost hope." She blamed the doctor's ineptness and was furious at the hospital staff because she was not permitted to see the baby. For a month she cried often, had anorexia, insomnia, and frequent gastric distress.

When she first got home and heard her neighbor's baby cry, she became upset, thought for a moment it was hers. Then a week later "I had a dream the baby was lying on an operating table without breathing. I started crying in my sleep and that was it. He was dead!"

She gradually recovered and returned to school. "I wanted to go back quickly to my old friends and prepare for college." She felt the program nurse was extremely helpful to her, much more than her own mother. When seen the last time she had definite plans to begin on contraceptive pills, though she had not been dating. She had been accepted by a college. "I feel more grown up. I have experienced more than my friends and know a great deal about sex, boys, and pregnancy."

Active efforts to master the loss utilizing emotional and verbal communications or new sublimations were usually directly related to successful mourning. Some girls became leaders in helping nurses or health educators teach groups about infant care. The young woman who wrote the introductory poem was later considered to have made an optimal adjustment to her loss.

Short-term denial of the reality of child death seemed to be a universal phenomenon. However, the intensity of the denial, florid psychiatric symptoms, and the degree of initial reality distortion may not always predict the long-term success of mourning processes. The therapy notes in case no. 2 demonstrate this important fact:

1/11 A sixteen-year-old adolescent lost an infant girl during a difficult breech delivery. She could not remember details of her labor since she had a total amnesia for the day of labor and for the first postpartum days.

1/23 Patient was quite agitated and depressed. She believed she had caused the loss of the child by overeating during pregnancy, or by becoming pregnant out-of-wedlock.

2/5 Patient feels very guilty. "They should have saved her and let old nasty me die. God punishes me for not taking better care of myself and baby." (During the first four weeks following delivery she had consciously accepted the reality of the infant's death.)

2/11 The patient imagines the baby is alive. Often she mistakenly calls her three-year-old sister by the baby's name. When alone she pretends to feed, change, and dress the baby and imagines the infant sleeping next to her. She dreams repeatedly about a tiny baby coffin, but never looks inside. She awoke yesterday and saw an infant's head rising out of a set of drawers. She has severe insomnia and is unable to stay alone in her home.[4]

2/17 Dream: "I picked my baby up from the bassinet, fed and burped it." She awoke, experienced sharp chest pains and thought she was having a heart attack.

2/18 Dream: "I came home, and the baby wasn't in her bed. I asked mother where she was and she started to cry. Suddenly I knew my baby was dead."

3/4 She has become interested in her boyfriend again. She is able to sleep, leave the house without fear, and can return to school. She won't discuss the loss with anyone except her social worker.

3/11 Patient has recovered to approximately her prepregnancy emotional state.

The long-range criterion for successful child-loss mourning would be the capacity to satisfactorily complete adolescent developmental tasks (Freud, A., 1965). It implies the achievement of independence from parental figures, leading ultimately to a reality-oriented marriage, responsible motherhood, or work roles. We will elaborate on this issue at the time of our follow-up evaluation.

Criteria for Pathological Mourning

We found the following four factors consistently related to unsuccessful mourning: (1) evidence of persistent or abnormal affective states; (2)

the appearance of an acute psychosis or psychotic hypochondriasis; (3) new self-destructive acting out (some "replacement pregnancies" may have had such a motivation); (4) prolonged persistent denial of infant or fetal loss.

We considered fourteen patients to be in this category. All were felt to have difficulties in at least three of these areas of psychopathology. Each criterion will be briefly illustrated and discussed.

Pathological affective states most often recorded were inappropriate rage, guilt, and depression. Depression accompanied sometimes by marked withdrawal, apathy, or feelings of emptiness occurred with the highest frequency and had the most serious prognosis. Case no. 3 follows:

A fifteen-year-old adolescent was seen a month after the loss of an eight-month fetus. She answered the interviewer's questions with monosyllables. There was psychomotor retardation, masked facies, apathy, and withdrawal. History revealed that her beloved father had died after a prolonged illness two months before she lost her pregnancy. She had often had various bodily symptoms and depression since childhood.

Two months later the patient complained of peculiar abdominal sensations, which were responsible for frequent school absences. No organic basis for these symptoms was detected. "It is a rumbling, thumping, kicking feeling, like it was when I was pregnant." (See Brown and Barglow, 1971, regarding relationship between pseudocyesis and depression.)

The patient had neglected her personal cleanliness and appearance. She performed poorly at school and refused to help with household chores. She was preoccupied with her lost father and lost child. Since her depression seemed to be worsening the patient was given antidepressant medication. Subsequently she made a suicidal gesture with these pills and required psychiatric hospitalization.

Guilt reactions characterized by self-accusations (case no. 2) were common but often transitory. Guilt seemed to be relieved by atonement and suffering. The patient who consciously tried to make herself ill demonstrates this phenomenon (case no. 7). Guilt related to ambivalence toward the fetus was considered to lie behind self-destructive behavior in several instances (see case no. 5).

Rage states usually alternated with depressive reactions, guilt, or mild paranoid states (seven patients). However, patients who were chronically angry were sometimes difficult to evaluate diagnostically. Two such patients described postpartum, postloss medical care that seemed unkind or even brutal. One of these adolescent girls couched her criticisms in earthy black racist terms.

Case no. 4: A fifteen-year-old girl had denied the existence of a pregnancy for the first three to four months. She had an intensely negative response to the verification of pregnancy. She experienced intense shame and self-hatred.

During the second trimester of pregnancy, she hurled herself down a flight of stairs in an effort to abort.

She delivered prematurely (and spontaneously) but the infant died after two days. She angrily blamed the attending physician. One week later she reported a dream in which she saw an angel with a dead baby. However several months later she had a daytime vision of the same angel with a dead infant standing behind her infant brother. She picked up the brother in her arms and pretended he was the lost child.

Shortly thereafter she was seen by a psychiatrist because she feared her body had been irreparably injured in delivery by Cesarean section. She had a variety of pelvic symptoms, but refused a pelvic examination. Investigation revealed the patient had been delivered from below. The dynamic of ambivalence toward the fetus will be discussed below.

New or exaggerated self-destructive acting out was a third criterion of inadequate mourning. This may involve suicidal gestures, antisocial acts, promiscuity, premature leaving of school, or an early replacement pregnancy. Shoor and Speed (1963) described sexual acting out as a grief equivalent in adolescents who lost a parent.

Twelve patients became pregnant again within one year. The psychodynamic evaluation of quickly repeated pregnancy was difficult. One reason for this was the unreliability of retrospective reconstruction of emotional experiences following the child loss and preceding the next pregnancy. Traces of mourning reactions were often wiped out by the emotional and hormonal repercussions of the repeat pregnancy and its sequelae. Two adolescents who had had a second pregnancy were considered to have successfully mourned the lost infant.

There was a second obstacle to understanding the motivation for a new pregnancy. This involved the problem of differentiating an unrealistic self-destructive variant of mourning from the motivational forces contributing to the original out-of-wedlock pregnancy. We were unable to make a mourning rating in five instances. Because of these investigative handicaps we designated a "quick repeat" pregnancy as clearly maladaptive in only five out of ten instances. In these there was definite clinical evidence that satisfied our main criteria of pathological mourning. Case no. 5 was the best example of this.

An eighteen-year-old girl lost a fetus she had conceived with a man who was twice her age. He was a chronic alcoholic who abandoned her when she became pregnant. She was upset that the "baby" was immediately placed in a bag and taken away without her knowledge. She never learned the infant's sex or weight, nor was she even shown the death certificate. She consciously accepted the situation as "God's will" but secretly doubted that the "baby was really dead."

During the next year she was promiscuous. (The defensive use of promiscuity as an adolescent reaction to the death of a parent has been emphasized by Shoor and Speed, 1963.) Though she never used contraceptives she did not become pregnant. Both parents were Black Muslims opposing birth control, and her mother said the contraceptive pill would produce cancer. She became pregnant at the end of this year, but had a spontaneous first trimester abortion. She was terrified at that time that she would never be able to have a live child.

She did become pregnant again, this time by a man of forty-four. Three months after delivery she was pregnant again. She had no prospects for marriage, was economically destitute, and was without familial help.

The patient just described was observed to be extraordinarily involved with her new baby. This mother-infant interaction may, of course, be the product of many influences. We had an opportunity to study in some detail another girl who had lost one of a pair of twins. It was felt that she too was an overprotective, overanxious mother with the surviving child.

These two suggestive instances are reminders that child-loss sequelae can have a pathogenic effect also on the next child. One of the authors has analyzed an adult female patient, born six months after the death of her infant brother. This patient's fragile ego boundaries and problems with self-object discrimination could be traced backward in time to her mother's pathological mourning reactions to child loss. Similar observations have been made by Cain and Cain (1964).

All cases of nonadaptive mourning were characterized by an intense or prolonged denial that the fetal or infant object had been permanently lost. It is necessary to distinguish this long-term denial from the short-term denial previously illustrated (case no. 2). To emphasize this observation another brief example is valuable.

Case no. 6: An older adolescent girl was evaluated six months after she had a third trimester eclampsia leading to fetal death. The patient herself had been comatose and near death for many days at that time. She told the psychiatrist that she was not physically well enough to become pregnant again and the psychiatrist suggested it would be better to wait a few months with such an important decision. She replied "All right I'll wait six months. Then Joan (the name of the lost baby) will have (instead of would have had) her first birthday." She was confronted with this slip of the tongue and agreed that it suggested she had not accepted the reality of the infant's death. Subsequently, it became clear that the maintenance of this illusion originated in a defensive denial that she herself had been near death.

Several girls, when they had another pregnancy with a surviving infant, clearly conceived of it as "child number two." They retained distinct separate memories and images of the lost child. Freud (Binswanger, 1957) wrote the following words three decades after the death of his daughter: "Everything that comes to take the place of the lost object, even if it fills it completely, nevertheless remains something different."

The explanation for this truth is not mysterious. Some intrapsychic representation of the fetus-infant-child antedates even the famous "gleam in the mother's eye." It consists of expectations, fantasies, memories, and perceptions of the self and of parental figures. As pregnancy progresses the fetal representation encompasses bodily sensations and object representations of the loved, hated, feared, or admired future father. Impressions of labor, delivery, and even the obstetrician are not irrelevant. Such a rich associational creation can never be duplicated.

Factors That Influence Mourning Processes

These factors will be divided into extrapsychic and intrapsychic categories. Such an artificial separation is made for purposes of explication only, since internal and external variables are interacting constantly. In discussing these factors reference will be made to the above clinical material.

1. Extrapsychic factors refer to relatively discrete and highly visible experiences that contribute to the traumatic potential of the child or fetal loss. Rape, incest, or additional object loss clearly represent additional stress that may overtax mourning capacities. For example one patient gave birth after a thirty-hour labor to a badly deformed infant. A few weeks later she became catatonic, made a suicidal attempt, and had to be hospitalized. Intensive investigation revealed a history of incest.

Prolonged or very painful labor, fetal malformation, and concurrent medical or obstetrical illness were similar traumata. Extreme poverty, overworked, indifferent, or poorly trained obstetrical personnel, and rejection by family members are other negative environmental influences. On the other hand, a loving boyfriend, or a warm, empathic social worker tended to protect patients from the more extreme, acute disturbances. Parents, particularly mothers, were often underutilized as sources of aid and comfort. This phenomenon will be discussed further from the intrapsychic point of view.

The age of the fetus or infant seemed to have little effect on mourning reactions. We compared and contrasted the second trimester, the third trimester, and the postterm loss groups in terms of mourning processes. At the time our evaluation was made, there were no significant statistical differences among the three groups.[5]

2. Intrapsychic factors refer to mourning response patterns determined primarily by psychiatric history, stage of adolescent psychosexual development, and emotional conflicts specific to crises of pregnancy, delivery, or motherhood.

PSYCHIATRIC HISTORY

The patients who suffered the two most severe emotional disturbances, profound depression (case no. 3) and an acute psychosis had a history of severe prepregnancy psychiatric problems. Both required postloss psychiatric hospitalization. Most other girls with less disabling but nevertheless disruptive postloss reactions had a lifelong history of psychosomatic complaints, school problems, intolerance to life's everyday pressures, or minor psychic symptoms.

A great variety of psychiatric disabilities and symptoms have been illustrated above. By contrast, in a study of fifty older women's reactions to stillbirth no significant psychiatric difficulties were found (Wolff, Nielsen, and Schiller, 1970). Both the incidence and severity of psychopathological responses far exceed those of our program nonloss population. Eight (26 percent) of our thirty-one patient sample required extensive psychiatric intervention. Two (6 percent of the total group) of these needed psychiatric hospitalization. This finding contrasts with 2 percent of the control nonloss population that required psychiatric attention and 0.1 percent (1 / 800) that required psychiatric hospitalization.

We assume that the incidence of prepregnancy ego weakness and psychiatric problems are roughly the same in the child-loss and nonloss population. Therefore specific interactions of adolescence, pregnancy, and mourning must explain this high incidence of emotional disorders.

INFLUENCE OF ADOLESCENT DEVELOPMENT ON MOURNING

The psychological events that signal the beginning of early adolescence are initiated by pubescence. Pubescence is defined as a biological phase characterized by a hormonally induced growth spurt (Offer and Offer, 1971). This biological state temporarily strains the adaptive capacities of the ego (Josselyn, 1952).

The perceptual and emotional experiencing of these bodily changes contributes to vulnerability of maturation in the spheres of body image, ego boundaries and self-concepts. The physical and physiological aspects of pregnancy are capable of intensifying difficulties in these crucial developmental areas. This fact could account for the frequency of bizarre bodily preoccupations and distortions and psychosomatic symptoms among our youngest adolescent girls.

Psychologically, early adolescence is characterized by an increased

293

urgency of sexual and aggressive drives and by the intensity of affects. Nevertheless, in the normal adolescent, there is a time gap of several years between the time when the adolescent is "biologically able to produce children and the time the adolescent is engaged in intensive heterosexual activities" (Offer and Offer, 1971). This gap usually enforced by psychosocial prohibitions was generally absent in our study group.

We expected that younger adolescents would have greater difficulties with mourning than older girls. Such an impression is consistent with articles detailing developmental attainments as prerequisites for mourning (Furman, 1968; Wolfenstein, 1966). We compared ages of the seventeen-patient pathological mourning group with the ages of the ten-patient group who seemed to be mourning successfully. However, we found a median age of seventeen years for both groups. The absence of any age difference can be explained in two ways. Often there is a lack of correlation between chronological and maturational age. And, in our study sample, there were other highly variable crucial influences on loss sequelae.

In spite of the absence of statistical corroboration, we felt that very young (thirteen- to sixteen-year-old) patients constituted a distinct category. Typical signs and symptoms of mourning reactions were sometimes hidden or absent. Overt grief or intense preoccupation with the lost child were rare. Reactions tended to be evanescent and characterized by bizarre concerns, a stunned withdrawal, or apathy. Other very young patients adapted regressively, giving us the typical appearance and defenses of tomboyish latency girls. These observations are consistent with the tenuousness of object constancy, the fragile mastery over strong affects, and the regression readiness of early adolescence.

It has been stated that the childhood absence in the home of a strong father figure could contribute to problems of sexual identity and self-object differentiation in this unwed mother group (Barglow *et al.,* 1968). These two factors in turn would predispose to emotional decompensation (particularly depression and psychosis) when combined with other psychic pressures.

Middle adolescence (adolescence proper) involves a loosening of emotional ties to powerful parental images. It has been compared to mourning (Blos, 1961; Laufer, 1966). Analysts speak of a decathexis of internalized object (parent) representations and hypercathexis (concentration) of psychic energy on the self-representation. Clinically this process is experienced as feelings of emptiness, estrangement, and loneliness. Such narcissistic shifts in object relations complicate mourning processes, and favor the development of depressive conditions.

In a previous article we described a specific motivation for premature sexual relations in unwed adolescent mothers (Barglow *et al.,* 1968). This consisted of unconscious efforts to sever the frightening dependent maternal tie by a leap into adult womanhood (Blos, 1957). The result was often a pregnancy conceived against the massive opposition of the (conscious) wishes of the mother. After delivery and child loss, the struggle with the mother seemed to become revitalized. This dynamic might explain why mothers were found not to be of much help to our girls with mourning work.

The late adolescent phase should be characterized by a shift from defensive to adaptive reality structure. The question "Who am I?" has been answered, and there is a shift to the question "What kind of person am I?" There is considerable autonomy and independence permitting a realistic choice of love object, successful marriage and motherhood, or vocational role. Four out of five members of our loss group who attained this degree of maturation were among those (ten patients) considered to have mourned successfully (note case no. 1). These patients apparently learned and grew emotionally from the stimulation of the entire experience. (See Patt, Rappaport, and Barglow, 1969, for a similar observation of therapeutic abortion.)

INFLUENCE OF PREGNANCY ON MOURNING

Benedek (1970) has described pregnancy as a narcissistic state of introversion, self-preoccupation, and increased passive dependent strivings. This psychic condition is viewed as an intensified replica of the progestational phase of the menstrual cycle. These features make depression and psychosomatic oral problems the most characteristic psychopathology of pregnancy.

These elements clearly add their weight to the narcissistic imbalances typical of adolescence and also of object-loss sequelae. They may account for the frequency that we observed hypochondriacal and psychosomatic symptoms (cases 2, 3, and 4). Furthermore, postdelivery hormonal level drops probably contribute to the etiology of postpartum depression and psychosis (Wilson, Barglow, and Shipman, 1971). The bodily changes of pregnancy can exacerbate the disruptive personality effect of the body-image distortions of early adolescence.

As pregnancy progresses a woman gradually conceives of the fetus as a separate potential being, intrapsychically distinguishable from the self. Our adolescent patients were frequently found to have symbiotic identifications with their fetus or infant. This situation may further interfere with self-object (self-representation: infant representation) distinctions. Again there would be a predisposition toward depression in response to loss instead of time-limited adequate mourning.

The unwed mother usually experiences and expresses marked ambivalence toward her fetus. The wish for spontaneous abortion was common, and there were several abortion attempts.[6] Powerful negative feelings are usually no longer conscious by the third trimester, but it is likely they do persist. These destructive or hate wishes would be seen as magically fulfilled by the death of the child. This was considered to be an important dynamic factor in the hypochondriasis of the patient (case no. 4) who attempted to abort herself actively. Death wishes toward the fetus, with rage turned back against the self, also contributed to depressive states and to chronic guilt responses shown by case no. 7.

A sixteen-year-old girl was psychiatrically interviewed a little over a year following the death of her two-week-old child. During her pregnancy she consciously rejected and hated the future child. She related to the interviewer, "In the month afterwards I had sort of a nervous breakdown. I thought the death was my fault. I tried to make myself sick by going out into the winter cold without wraps." (The patient had a history of severe chronic bronchitis and asthma.) She visited the cemetery several times where the baby was buried. The family was too poor to afford a marker, and she never located the grave. At the time of evaluation she was depressed and still blamed herself for the loss. She felt her life had been unalterably and hopelessly changed for the worse.

"Mourning becomes more complicated or even pathological if the relationship of the mourner to the lost object was an extremely ambivalent one" (Fenichel, 1945). A transient identification with the dead ambivalently loved infant was seen frequently. Such a reaction in itself was not considered pathological.

Implications for Therapeutic Intervention

The comment has been made that "the loss of a child can never be fully integrated and totally accepted by the mother or the father" (Pollock, 1961). The severity and frequency of intense, incapacitating emotional sequelae of child loss detailed above constitutes indications for active therapeutic efforts.

We concluded that all adolescents who suffered a child loss should be carefully screened by means of an individual diagnostic interview prior to their return to school. Patients with acute emotional decompensations can be referred for further evaluation and emergency care. As shown by case no. 2, a few patients manifest acute grief reactions that only appear to be ominous or dangerous. Such patients need to be followed up frequently and cautiously in an effort to discern remissions or new dangerous trends.

Assessment should also be made of the optimal timing for the return to school. A girl's preference to return to a special program school, rather than public school, should be considered sympathetically. This request may represent an effort to "speak up—not hush up" (Lindemann, 1944) and to make it possible for the girl to share her grief with other adolescents who have experienced pregnancy and childbirth. On the other hand, the choice of a return to public school may signal a readiness to accept the loss and resume customary modes of life.

There is general agreement among psychiatrists that "fully independent mourning which can occur regardless of external support or milieu" (Wolfenstein, 1966) cannot be accomplished prior to the completion of adolescence. Only two of our thirty-one patients were felt to have completed adolescence. Many girls were found to have just entered adolescent maturation. For this reason the sensitive, supportive actions and reactions of adult figures to the grieving adolescent have a pivotal, crucial significance.

There are two essential therapeutic steps to help a child with an object loss (Furman, 1968): (1) the fulfillment of the child's reality needs; (2) the appropriate assistance with painful or conflictive feeling responses. Abreaction is of central importance.

Better housing, improved medical and educational facilities, and an adequate diet constitute reality needs for many of our adolescents. The provision of these necessities is the major domestic problem of contemporary America.

Who can best assist the adolescent girl with the task of mourning? For reasons noted above, related to adolescent development, the mother's capacity to help seems to be limited. It is likely also that the adolescent's mother may feel a secret sense of relief in the grandchild's demise. Evidence of the stigma of unwed motherhood is canceled. There will be one less mouth to feed. The daughter can continue her education and/or money-producing work. The adolescent girl who detects such attitudes will turn against her mother with fury.

If there is no father or boyfriend or other family member available to be mobilized for help, the social worker, nurse, or teacher may have to assume a surrogate parental function. This helping professional must cope with both the patient's and his own responses to the loss.

He must be trained and willing to discuss openly the medical and emotional details of the pregnancy and the infant's death. There should be some effort to compensate the patient for the paucity of hospital death rites and the absence of communicated information between overworked doctor and adolescent girl. "At present when a newborn infant dies in the hospital, all evidence of his existence is often removed with amazing rapidity" (Kennell, Slyter, and Klaus, 1970).

Follow-up interviews and evaluations are essential to ensure that premature denial of loss or unexpected outbreak of life-threatening psychopathology do not go unnoticed. Often, at least transitory encouragement for the adolescent to utilize family planning may be a protective time-gaining practice.

The seriousness of these problems must not be underestimated. Poverty is the pervasive and oppressive environment of these adolescent girls. Against this background there is adolescence, pregnancy, and infant loss. Each of the three phenomena taken in isolation is a normative crisis. But taken together they constitute a crushing stress of traumatic proportions.

Summary

We psychiatrically evaluated thirty-one adolescent unwed mothers who had lost a fetus or child. Criteria were established to distinguish successful adolescent mourning. Using these criteria we described a group of fourteen patients with pathology of mourning and ten patients who mourned adequately. We were unable to make a valid mourning judgment about five patients with a second pregnancy and two patients with intense rage reactions.

We found a very high incidence of severe psychiatric difficulties. Two out of thirty-one loss adolescents required psychiatric hospitalization in contrast to one hospitalization per 800 in nonloss adolescents. The explanation of this finding lies in a combination of factors unfavorable to adaptive mourning: (1) psychopathology leading to illegitimate pregnancy; (2) a failure to have attained sufficient adolescent maturation; (3) specific emotional and hormonal aspects of pregnancy, one of the most important of these being marked ambivalence toward the fetus; (4) multiple real environmental stresses. These four factors have many implications for a therapeutic approach.

NOTES

1. Description of program aspects have appeared previously in the psychiatric and social work literature (Barglow, Bornstein, Exum, Wright, and Visotsky, 1968; Bedger,

1969, 1971; and Wright, 1966). The program is administered by Florence Crittenton Association of America, Inc., under contract with the Chicago Board of Health. It is also funded by USPH Maternity and Infant Care Project #502.

2. This Crittenton program emphasizes comprehensive outpatient services and includes three components: (1) social work and mental health services, including individual and group therapy; (2) medical services, including prenatal and postnatal care for mother and child; (3) educational services, including an accredited academic and home arts curriculum at elementary and high school levels (provided by the Chicago Board of Education).

3. Our patient sample is small and our present clinical findings are of a preliminary nature. For this reason no statistical analysis of data was done.

4. Greene's (1959) description of the "vicarious object" is useful for an understanding of the sister's meaning. Feelings and attitudes toward the dying or dead object are displaced onto a significant living person. This vicarious object may be exposed to chronic misidentifications and traumatic pressures related to the lost object.

5. The memories, perceptions, and fantasies produced by an older infant should be greater in number and intensity than those stimulated by the immature fetus. We would have expected, therefore, that the older the lost child, the more difficult would be the task of mourning. The fact that our findings did not verify this hypothesis is probably related to the variability of our sample and the imprecision of our diagnostic evaluations.

6. There is a paucity of information about the emotional sequelae of abortion during adolescence. This is true of spontaneous, therapeutic, and illegal abortion. The authors felt our focus would be diffused if we included first trimester abortions within our research group.

REFERENCES

Barglow, P., Bornstein, M., Exum, D. B., Wright, M. K., and Visotsky, H. M. (1968). Some psychiatric aspects of illegitimate pregnancy in early adolescence. Unpublished manuscript.

Bedger, J. E. (1969). *The Crittenton Study: An Assessment of Client Functioning Before and After Services*. Chicago: Florence Crittenton Association.

———. (1971). *Teen-Age Unwed Mothers' Behavior Changes*. Washington, D.C.: American Psychological Association, Experimental Publication System, Issue 11–Ms. 419–5.

Benedek, T. (1970). The psychobiology of pregnancy. In: *Parenthood*, ed. E. J. Anthony and T. Benedek. Boston: Little Brown, pp. 137–151.

Binswanger, L. (1957). *Sigmund Freud: Reminiscences of a Friendship*. New York: Grune & Stratton.

Blos, P. (1957). Preoedipal factors in the etiology of female delinquency. *Psychoanalytic Study of the Child*, 12:229–249.

———. (1961). *On Adolescence: A Psychoanalytic Interpretation*. New York: The Free Press.

Bowlby, J. (1960). Grief and mourning in infancy and early childhood. *Psychoanalytic Study of the Child*, 15:9–52.

Brown, E., and Barglow, P. (1971). Pseudocyesis: A paradigm for psychophysiological interactions. *Archives of General Psychiatry*, 24:221–229.

Cain, A. C., and Cain, B. S. (1964). On replacing a child. *Journal of the American Academy of Child Psychiatry*, 3 (3):443–456.

Deutsch, H. (1937). Absence of grief. *Psychoanalytic Quarterly*, 6:12–22.

Fenichel, O. (1945). *The Psychoanalytic Theory of Neurosis*. New York: Norton.

Fleming, J., and Altschul, S. (1963). Activation of mourning and growth by psychoanalysis. *International Journal of Psycho-Analysis*, 44:419–431.

Freud, A. (1943). *War and Children*. New York: International Universities Press.

———. (1965). *Assessment of Pathology: Normality and Pathology in Childhood*. New York: International Universities Press.

Freud, S. (1917). Mourning and melancholia. Standard Edition, 14:239–258. London: Hogarth, 1957.

Friedman, S. B. (1967). Care of the family of the child with cancer. *Pediatrics,* 40:498–507.

Furman, R. A. (1968). Additional remarks on mourning and the young child. *Bulletin of the Philadelphia Association for Psychoanalysis,* 18(2):51–64.

Futterman, E. H., and Hoffman, I. (1970). Transient school phobia in a leukemic child. *Journal of the American Academy of Child Psychiatry,* 9:477–494.

Greene, W. A., Jr. (1959). Role of a vicarious object in the adaptation to object loss: II. *Psychosomatic Medicine,* 21:438–447.

Josselyn, I. M. (1952). *The Adolescent and His World.* New York: Family Service Association.

Kennell, J. H., Slyter, H., and Klaus, M. H. (1970). The mourning response of parents to the death of a newborn infant. *New England Journal of Medicine,* 283(7):344–349.

Laufer, M. (1966). Object loss and mourning during adolescence. *Psychoanalytic Study of the Child,* 21:269–293.

Lindemann, E. (1944). Symptomatology and management of acute grief. *American Journal of Psychiatry,* 101:141–148.

Natterson, J. M., and Knudson, A. G. (1960). Observations concerning fear of death in fatally ill children and their mothers. *Psychosomatic Medicine,* 22:456–465.

Nolfi, M. W. (1967). Families in grief; The question of casework intervention. *Social Work,* 12(4):40–46.

Offer, D., and Offer, J. (1971). Four issues in the developmental psychology of adolescents. In: *Modern Perspectives in Psychiatry,* ed. J. C. Howells. Edinburgh: Oliver & Boyd, pp. 28–43.

Patt, S. L., Rappaport, R. G., and Barglow, P. (1969). Follow-up of therapeutic abortion. *Archives of General Psychiatry,* 20:408–414.

Pollock, G. H. (1961). Mourning and adaptation. *International Journal of Psycho-Analysis,* 42(4–5):341–361.

Richmond, J. B., and Waisman, H. A. (1955). Psychologic aspects of management of children with malignant disease. *Journal of Diseases of Children,* 89:42–47.

Shoor, M., and Speed, M. (1963). Delinquency as a manifestation of the mourning process. *Psychiatric Quarterly,* 37:540–557.

Solnit, A. J., and Green, M. (1959). Psychologic considerations in the management of deaths on pediatric hospital services: I. The doctor and the child's family. *Pediatrics,* 24:106–112.

Wilson, J., Barglow, P., and Shipman, W. (1971). The progress of post partum psychosis. Paper presented to the American Psychiatric Association, Washington, D. C.

Wolfenstein, M. (1966). How is mourning possible? *Psychoanalytic Study of the Child,* 21:93–123.

Wolff, J. R., Nielsen, P. E., and Schiller, P. A. (1970). The emotional reaction to stillbirth. *American Journal of Obstetrics and Gynecology,* 108(1):73–77.

Wright, M. K. (1966). Comprehensive Services for adolescent unwed mothers. *Children,* 13(5):170–176.

PART IV

PSYCHOTHERAPY OF ADOLESCENCE

INTRODUCTION

The following chapters deal with specific psychopathology and treatment issues. Treatment can be considered from various viewpoints and can roughly be divided into those therapies that are primarily directed toward behavioral change through management and those whose primary goal is the production of insight and the fostering of autonomy. Both these approaches as well as combinations of them are discussed in this part. In general, residential treatment usually involves considerable management whereas insight-producing treatment is more often conducted in a one-to-one outpatient relationship such as that found in the psychoanalytic consultation room. Still, this issue is not resolved, and Bertram J. Cohler discusses psychotherapy in a residential setting from a psychoanalytic viewpoint, while Julian I. Barish and William A. Schonfeld review the recent development of comprehensive residential treatment programs in psychiatric hospitals.

Should the adolescent patient be considered different from other patients to the degree that he requires special techniques? Opinions about this point are divided, but most experienced clinicians seem to agree that in some instances the adolescent patient is especially difficult to treat. Frank S. Williams approaches these issues by discussing the value of family therapy in the total treatment regimen for adolescents, its use for diagnostic purposes, and its value in exposing symbiotic family resistances. Jerry M. Lewis, John T. Gossett, Joe W. King, and Doyle I. Carson present a treatment approach based on group process in which the adolescents must assume responsibility for the entire group's behavior. This they believe fosters a protreatment attitude.

It is not necessary here to enumerate the various characteristics that have been described as impediments to treatment; instead, the therapist's discomfort with these patients is discussed by Robert W. Shields and D. W. Winnicott, who emphasize how the adolescent has to behave in a fashion that is both objectionable and painful to the adult so that he can progress developmentally. Indeed, it is stressed that the adolescent has to make the adult suffer in order to achieve ego integration.

Therapists are adults and often suffer when treating adolescents. They often suffer when treating other adults; still, the provocative techniques patients in general use frequently have an adolescent quality. If the patient achieves emotional integration by using certain types of provocations, such as those described by Winnicott as the antisocial tendency, they should be understood in detail so that evoked countertransference attitudes do not upset the therapeutic equilibrium.

Those of us who treat adolescent patients psychoanalytically find that disruptive countertransference attitudes are provoked when the patient rationally attacks an area that the analyst values. It is the patient's rational approach that creates difficulty, because it contains the psychopathological core. The latter cannot be reached because it is protected by the armor of the secondary process, and the analyst feels particularly helpless because he is threatened by the encroachment on an aspect of his ego ideal and identity. Paranoid patients often have a well-developed ability to clothe their projections in rationality; the adolescent's particular ability resides in his skill in detecting areas upon which the therapist's personal identity is based.

Furthermore, the adolescent patient projects his self-image, which he considers amorphous and empty, onto the therapist. The patient then treats the therapist as if he were nonexistent. If the therapist is unaware of what is happening, this can become a disruptively painful situation, with the patient's behavior seeming to be withdrawn and concrete, not making any access to feelings possible. This type of behavior has often been considered characteristically adolescent and infuriating. Because of the projection of an amorphous self-image, the therapist feels shut out.

One can see that the study of the adolescent in a psychotherapeutic frame of reference has relevance in many areas. The therapeutic process, in general, for all classes of patients is elucidated as we learn more about transference-countertransference aspects and the impact of the environment, which seems to be especially important to the adolescent.

17] NEW WAYS IN THE
TREATMENT OF EMOTIONALLY
DISTURBED ADOLESCENTS

BERTRAM J. COHLER

Psychoanalysis has taught us that adolescence must be a time of inner turmoil and struggle if maturity is to be attained (Freud, 1946, 1958; Eissler, 1958; Deutsch, 1967; Masterson, 1967; Erikson, 1968). Of course, the most important event associated with this phase of the life span is that, for the first time, the young person has the capacity to realize his sexual fantasies through genital sexuality (Spiegel, 1951). Attainment of sexual maturity makes possible greater pleasure, but it also imposes greater burdens and responsibilities. The outcome of this battle between impulse and control is an important determinant of the adolescent's subsequent ability to resolve developmental tasks associated with adulthood (Blos, 1962).[1]

Adolescence and Social Change

Some adolescents deal with their newly discovered sexual drives by acting impulsively, whereas others are so terrified that in order to keep these impulses under control, they establish complex and rigid rules. In some instances the young person may adopt an ascetic attitude and become involved in a complex religious or philosophical pursuit, such as Zen, which denies the importance of impulses and teaches inner control. Much of the fascination that adolescents have with the peace movement stems from their desire to suppress aggressive and sexual impulses. Another response to this increase in sexual impulses is to become rigid and

305

inflexible, refusing to give, take, or compromise with others; this rigid stance only reflects the inner struggle to maintain a tight reign on impulses.

Adolescence is also that point in the life span when it is necessary to resolve the wish to be cared for by one's parents in order to go out into the world and find a partner with whom to make a new family of one's own (Freud, 1958). Frequently, there are strong ties to a parent which have not been resolved. In the process of finding emotional satisfaction outside the family, there may be a phase in which the adolescent develops an important relationship with a teacher, athletic coach, or minister. Sometimes the adolescent may deny the importance of his family by rebelling against his parents. Young people who feel unable to cope with these new burdens may retreat from greater involvement with contemporaries, and may lose interest in school or work. Rather than rebelling against the family, such young people may show a heightened dependence and even a fear of leaving the house.

Given the amount of internal turmoil, adolescents require a well-structured environment that can offer support in their struggle. Significant social changes during the past five years have created additional problems for young people, leading to an increase in the incidence of such signs of impairment as serious suicide attempts (Caplan and Lebovici, 1969). Changing norms sanction the expression of sexual impulses in sexual intercourse at a far earlier age than has previously been true. The focus in sex education classes in many high schools is no longer on problems that arise from early sexual experimentation but rather on the problem of preventing conception. As families become increasingly comfortable financially, young people are less and less often required to work; liberal allowances mean that there is no need to anticipate the future or to delay present desires for the future. Without sufficient encouragement to postpone gratification, society makes less necessary the inner control that so many adolescents require.

It is not only in the area of control of impulses that changing values are having an impact on the adolescent's ability to deal with inner conflicts. It is important for a young person to attain independence from childhood attachments to his parents. We are seeing today a blurring of the generational distinction that makes it impossible for the young person to distinguish between adolescence and adulthood and to perceive adults against whom to define himself. At least in the middle class, adults often emulate teenage dress and manners and join in such adolescent activities as smoking marijuana in an attempt to remain eternally young. If struggle between the generations is so important in order to break ties with the past, the inability to distinguish between youth and maturity makes such a struggle seem pointless, and the young person is not able to successfully resolve childhood attachments or to assume the responsibilities of adulthood.

Unique problems are posed for young people today by the lack of effective social control over troubling sexual impulses and by the failure to maintain generational boundaries, which is necessary in order for the adolescent to be able to deal with the past. Though it is true that the majority of adolescents are able to attain adulthood with few more psychic scars than their parents (Offer, 1969; Offer, Marcus, and Offer, 1970), a sizable minority of young people are experiencing more distress than ever before in recent history. For these adolescents, life has become an extreme situation, not unlike that described by Bettelheim (1956, p. 511) who, in his discussion of the concentration camp, noted that

What characterized this situation was its deep impact on the individual, for which he was totally unprepared; its inescapability; the expectation that it would last for an indefinite period, potentially a life time; that, throughout its entirety, one's very life would be in jeopardy at every moment; and that one could do nothing to protect oneself.

Under such extreme conditions, profound and lasting personality changes are likely to occur.

An adolescent who has been able to successfully resolve the psychosocial conflicts associated with early childhood will be most able to resolve subsequent conflicts between internal needs and the demands and expectations of the social environment (Erikson, 1968). On the other hand, when there is already a residue of conflict from childhood, leading to feelings of mistrust of others, extreme concern with self-control, and feelings of lack of efficiency, the pressures created by the environment become especially intolerable. Adolescents who perceive their life as an extreme situation are likely to escape from an unpleasant reality into less painful but also less adaptive fantasies. Such an escape makes it difficult to function at home, in school, or at work. Under such extreme conditions, profound personality changes are bound to occur, including the growing unwillingness to accommodate to the demands of reality.

Psychiatric Treatment for Disturbed Adolescents

At the present time, there is an acute shortage of facilities for those adolescents who require psychiatric help during adolescence (Buckle,

1969). Outpatient psychotherapy with even fairly well-integrated adolescents is extremely difficult (Holmes, 1964). There has long been controversy within psychoanalysis as to whether adolescent patients can profit from classical psychoanalytic treatment (Gitelson, 1948; Eissler, 1958). The initial defiance of many adolescents makes it difficult to establish contact in any form of psychotherapy (Noshpitz, 1957; Hendrickson, Holmes, and Waggoner, 1959; Holmes, 1964; Rinsley and Inge, 1961). A part of the problem in psychotherapy with adolescents arises from the fact that young people are trying to emancipate themselves from relationships in which they must rely so greatly on another at the same time that they are being asked to form such a relationship with a psychotherapist (Rinsley, 1965). The tendency among many disturbed adolescents to flee rather than to examine feelings and motives makes it additionally difficult to maintain a relationship during treatment.

The problem of providing adequate treatment facilities is even more difficult for the adolescent who experiences a serious emotional disturbance. Typically, these young people make desperate pleas for help such as suicide gestures, refusal to eat, or the development of such psychotic symptoms as hallucinations.

The psychiatric hospital, modeled after the general medical hospital, is often the only alternative for the disturbed adolescent. Both because of its organization and its treatment philosophy, such a facility often fails to provide the help the disturbed adolescent so badly needs.[2]

Adolescents are often placed on wards together with adult patients (Greaves and Regan, 1957; Hartmann *et al.*, 1968; Garber and Polsky, 1970). Though the explicit rationale for this practice is that the ward should be like a family, the implicit rationale is that mixed adolescent-adult wards provide better discipline. There is concern that by placing adolescents together on one ward, they will find strength in numbers and become uncontrollable. However, by having adolescents together with adults, the young person soon learns the role of an outcast or social deviant from adult patients, many of whom have had multiple hospitalizations and have lapsed into a chronic disturbance.

The staff structure in such a hospital is immensely complex with both psychiatrists and a number of other professionals, each with assigned duties. Typically those who have the most contact with the patient, the aides or attendants, are also those personnel with the least training. Such marginal personnel are often recent expatients or other persons with profound psychological difficulties not unlike those of the patients they are supposed to be helping (Stanton and Schwartz, 1954). In addition, seriously disturbed adolescents are unable to relate to the variety of persons with whom they are supposed to form such relationships.

The treatment philosophy of the psychiatric hospital is based on the belief that the hospital is a bad place to have to stay and that all efforts must be expended on as rapid a discharge as possible (Beckett, 1965). Patients are started on a variety of medications aimed at controlling symptoms, and frequently intensive work is begun with the patient's family in order to prepare parents or relatives to deal with any additional symptoms. Particularly with adolescents, the hospital staff believes that this period of the life cycle is so important and enjoyable that every effort must be expended to facilitate a rapid return to the community. So-called regressive behavior is discouraged in an attempt to help the young person appear as adequate and normal as possible. An adolescent who makes demands on the staff, refuses to take responsibility for personal grooming, or loses interest in typical teenage pursuits is a source of concern to the hospital's administration.

In an attempt to discourage regression and in order to facilitate the earliest possible return to the community, many psychiatric hospitals have been employing behavior modification during the past few years. Token economies have been promoted as especially effective means for developing more socially appropriate behavior. (Atthowe and Krasner, 1968; Aylon and Azrin, 1968; Phillips, 1968; Forehand, Mulhern, and Rickard, 1969). In exchange for such socially appropriate behavior as good table manners, good personal hygiene, cooperation in psychotherapy, or participation in required social activities, patients are given some sort of coupons or tokens which may be exchanged for such tangible goods as ice cream or for such privileges as a weekend at home or greater freedom of movement within the hospital. Behavior modification tends only to further dehumanize the patient, enhances his own belief that his symptoms have no meaning as expressions of important feelings and motives, and encourages rapid return to the environment that was previously experienced as overwhelming without any better capacity to resolve the inner conflicts that such extreme situations had previously evoked. If the young person has developed no new structures to deal with this extreme situation, the original conflict is likely to continue, leading to multiple admissions and continuing personality disorganization following discharge (Masterson, 1967; Hartmann *et al.*, 1968; Garber and Polsky, 1970).

If the feeling of impending inner disorganization that characterizes psychiatric disturbance in adolescents may be viewed as an extreme reaction to an environment that appears to the young person to place his very existence in jeopardy, the ideal treatment environment for adolescents would be one in which there is only minimal pressure and in which the daily routine is sufficiently simplified that the young person may feel comfortable (Bettelheim, 1948, 1949, 1950, 1955, 1956, 1960; Bettelheim and Sylvester, 1947, 1948, 1949; Easson, 1969; Noshpitz, 1962; Redl, 1949, 1951, 1959). With minimized demands to socialize and a less complex life, symptoms would begin to disappear as soon as the adolescent would no longer feel his life to be in danger. He could then begin to feel that he has control over his environment and would then begin to feel protected and safe (Cumming and Cumming, 1963). Since adequate supervision would be available, he would begin to feel that he could achieve control over his disturbing impulses and that he could be protected from his own impulses (Aichhorn, 1935). As Bettelheim (1956, pp. 516–517) commented,

to begin life anew, the total extreme situation which destroyed autonomy must be replaced with a total living situation over which he can exercise control. As he was overwhelmed by his environment, he must now be able to control it. . . . This means that it must be simple; it must not offer complex challenges nor make complicated demands. . . . When living under such conditions, even a very weak ego can begin to function more adequately.

The Application of Milieu Therapy in the Treatment of Disturbed Adolescents

The University of Chicago's Sonia Shankman Orthogenic School provides a treatment environment consistent with this concept of a positive therapeutic milieu. Though much has been written on the school's treatment of psychotic children (Bettelheim, 1948, 1949, 1950, 1955, 1960), including the treatment of autism (Bettelheim, 1967), it is less widely known that the school has pioneered in the treatment of disturbed adolescents.

In contrast to the psychiatric hospital, the school has a very simple organizational structure, one that can be understood by even the most confused adolescent (Henry, 1954, 1957a, 1957b). All the staff work directly with the children and have only one task, that of providing for a particular youngster the care most congruent with his needs. Typically, the adolescent lives in a group of six to eight young people, with two regular therapist-counselors who have been trained in a variety of skills that, together, contribute to the reconstruction of the young person's personality.

The school's staff, most of whom are either candidates for advanced degrees or mental health professionals, devote their entire effort to the young people with whom they work, in order to provide these young people a renewed feeling of trust and hope. As Rosen (1963), Bettelheim (1966), Bettelheim and Wright (1955), and Wright (1957) all have noted, the counselor's own personality enters directly into the treatment, and it is only with the achievement of greater self-understanding that a staff member is able to offer the young person the care most appropriate to that adolescent's unique needs. To this end, daily staff meetings are focused primarily around the staff member's inner attitudes and the meaning of his emotional reactions to the children with whom he works, rather than exclusively with the young person's present problems and their etiology (Bettelheim, 1966). Since it is only through greater self-understanding that a counselor can be of greater help to the young persons with whom he works, staff members are also helped toward a greater understanding of themselves and, when appropriate, are encouraged to arrange for their own personal treatment.

THE CONCEPT OF REPARENTING

Perhaps the most important treatment modality employed at the Orthogenic School is reparenting. If an adolescent had been able, during early childhood, to feel a sense of sufficiency, trust, autonomy, and efficacy, he would have been better prepared to withstand the inner turmoil of adolescence. An important part of his treatment consists of being well cared for in order that he can develop the sense that all is right with himself.

Frequently, young people whose basic needs for care have not been met react to overwhelming pressure in adolescence by refusing to eat or by losing all interest in food. Though they may manipulate their families by refusing to eat, such young people are really unable to hold down their food and may even gag or vomit when they eat. Anorexia nervosa is one of the most troubling adolescent maladies and one that may even threaten life itself. Ultimately, such young people must be fed intravenously and, even when being fed by tube, are so able to control their metabolism that they reject the nourishment and die of the consequences of their self-starvation. In the beginning, eating is an act that symbolizes caretaking; it is the most basic expression of parental love. If an anorexic youngster is again to become able to eat, it will be only in the context of a relationship with an adult who cares about the adolescent and for whom it is important whether he or she lives or dies:

Jane, a fifteen-year-old young woman from an educationally ambitious family, was enrolled at Orthogenic School following a very serious weight loss.

311

A compulsively successful student, who overstudied for her examinations and who was anxious to please, Jane had a crowded schedule, which included dancing classes, horseback riding, and skating classes, with numerous medical and dental appointments sandwiched into her free hours. Summers were spent at an exclusive girl's camp where the cabins were organized into competitive teams.

Competition and achievement were dominant family themes. For example, Jane pressured her mother into purchasing women's underclothing for her when she was barely ten years old. With all this achievement pressure, her only satisfaction had been raiding the refrigerator, but both she and her mother were concerned about her weight. Her ideal body image at this time was that of the model Twiggy, who was known for her skinny build.

Six months prior to enrollment, Jane stopped eating regular meals but would snack when her parents were not looking. When they complained about this, she stopped eating altogether and said she had lost all interest in food. She drank dietetic beverages and began to lose weight drastically. This continued during the summer when she again went to camp and by the middle of the season, she was so bony that her physical appearance frightened her cabinmates, and she lacked sufficient energy to participate in camp activities.

When she was enrolled at the school, it was obvious that if, within forty-eight hours, she did not resume at least some intake of fluids, she would have to be hospitalized. Her counselors made it very clear to Jane that she would have to eat and that they wanted her to eat. Even before her suitcase had been unpacked, her counselor brought her a frosty glass of milk and, when she refused to drink, her counselor offered to hold the glass for her. Jane was then taken to the candy closet (a built-in cupboard, about six feet wide, stocked with generous quantities of a wide variety of candy, cookies, and crackers). Jane asked for some saltine crackers and then said that they tasted good with a particular brand of peanut butter. Another of her counselors went out at once and purchased the specified brand of peanut butter.

Periodically, for the next few days, for minutes on end, Jane would just go down and stand in front of the candy closet and stare at the selection. Gradually, she made a wider selection of candy, which she stocked in her chest of drawers until she had a large quantity of candy. She enjoyed having her favorite counselor hold her milk glass while she drank out of it, and also enjoyed being fed. Out of their concern for her well-being, her counselors encouraged her to eat, and sat with her several hours at a time until she had eaten a nourishing portion. She asked for but was refused dietetic drinks. Providing these dietetic beverages, like offering water instead of milk, conveys the opposite of the intended message, that of lack of pleasure in eating instead of enjoyment in eating. By the end of her first week in the school, Jane had gained fifteen pounds and showed a marked increase in her energy level.

The school's success in helping Jane was largely derived from her counselors' awareness of their own feelings concerning food and eating. Staff meetings in the days preceding Jane's enrollment were concerned with the staff's feelings about food and eating. Particular attention was paid to childhood feelings of deprivation and the ways in which these feelings were re-enacted with the young people at the school.

One of Jane's prospective counselors commented on how angry she became when the young people in her group grabbed the serving bowl at dinner to help themselves to more food or when they demanded larger portions. This anger was, in turn, related to her jealousy about how much the girls in her group enjoyed eating and to her memories of her own childhood when her mother had been so busy with community activities that she had complained about the inconvenience of having to prepare meals for her children. Another counselor, talking about her feelings about eating, expressed her concern that she might become too heavy. Such concern with her own body, when communicated to a disturbed adolescent, would lead the young person to feel that her counselor did not want her to eat, gain weight, and regain her health.

As a result of these staff meetings, Jane's counselors were able to resolve many of their own feelings about eating and were able to help Jane to want to eat and to enjoy her food. However, eating was placed in a human context not unlike that of a mother offering nourishment to her infant, rather than being regarded as medicine to be swallowed. Equally important, concern that Jane begin eating had to be but one part of a total relationship and not just one designed to get her to eat.

It is not only in these dramatic life and death gestures that such re-parenting can be observed. Recently, a counselor purchased a new bottle of bubble bath that had been requested by a seventeen-year-old girl in her group. However, she did not simply hand it to her or put it on her bed. Rather, she attached a note wishing Joan "many happy baths." Such a simple act conveys to the young person the feeling that her counselor has not simply done an errand but that the counselor has given her youngster something that she hopes will allow her to have a more comfortable life.

Typically, adolescents at the school live in groups with some younger children. Such a mixed group is intentional and permits the adolescent to come to recognize his own basic needs; frequently, an adolescent's first understanding of his own wishes comes from hearing a younger member of the group express these same wishes. It is also reassuring to see these younger children being well cared for; if the counselor can provide for a younger child then there is hope that the adolescent may be well cared for as well.

SYMPTOMS AS A RESPONSE TO AN EXTREME SITUATION

For the disturbed adolescent, the school offers the possibility of a much simpler and easier life than that before coming to the school. The daily routine is kept as simple and structured and free of regulations as possible, and there are few surprises or unanticipated events. There is no achievement or academic pressures: Young people are assured that when they are ready to learn in school, there will be little problem with academic matters. At the outset, we do not even expect the young person to begin talking about feelings. An adolescent who comes to the school is told that the most appropriate step is to rest and take it easy. This, in itself, is extremely difficult for an adolescent who has been pushed for so many years to excel and who has both internalized this pressure and revolted against it. The effect of such a simplified life is striking, for we find that symptoms begin to disappear and that, for the first time in many years, a youngster feels more comfortable.

An eighteen-year-old girl came to the school immediately following her high school graduation. At the time of her enrollment, she showed a severe hand-washing compulsion. Margaret was unable to complete her toilet because everything she touched became contaminated. When she touched the washbasin, it became contaminated, and she had to wash again. This phobia of contamination then spread to all her belongings, and if she touched her bedspread she would, once again, have to go through her extensive washing ritual. Finally, this ritual consumed all her time and energy during the day and involved her in frequent conflict with her parents.

The ritual was begun following a summer spent at a youth camp, where there was a good deal of contact between boys and girls with little supervision, and were associated with Margaret's feelings of guilt regarding her sexual fantasies. At the school, our first concern was to make her ritual as easy for her as possible while at the same time respecting her need to carry out such rituals.

One part of the ritual required her to dispose of tissues and towels used to wipe her hands in the toilet rather than in a wastebasket. Since the wastebasket seemed the more usual place to dispose of these towels, it seemed to us that Margaret must attach special meaning to the disposal of tissues in the toilet. For this reason, we refrained from unstopping the toilet for her, but only made it easier for her to do so if she wished, by providing her with a plunger. At the same time, we arranged for the plumber to come in each day and clear the main drain in order that other toilets would not become clogged. Since touching the metal cover of the tissue dispenser involved an additional ritual, we arranged for her to be able to tape it back if she so wished.

Though the staff did everything they could to help Margaret be more comfortable while carrying out her ritual, we did little to interfere with the ritual itself. Our hope was that we could help her attain greater self-understanding through a growing awareness of the meaning of this ritual. In addition, respect for her ritual provided, as Bettelheim (1950) has shown, a feeling of greater autonomy and freedom.

As Margaret saw that we respected her ritual and its importance for her, and that we were greatly interested and concerned with understanding its meaning for her, she began to allow her favorite counselor to stay with her while she was in the bathroom and to talk with her. This contrasted sharply with her refusal, before coming to the school, to allow another member of the family in the bathroom while she was carrying out her ritual.

Margaret was able to tell us some months later that the reason she attempted to stop up the toilet was that she feared she would be flushed away; she tried to stuff the toilet in order to prevent this from happening. Had we unstopped the toilet for her, as she had at first demanded that we do, we would have unknowingly acceded to her worst fears as well as her wish for self-destruction, while believing we were helping her. By the end of her fourth month at the school, Margaret had cut the time spent each day on her rituals by more than half and, whereas she formerly had had to stay up half the night in order to complete the ritual, she was now able to be in bed by 10:30 P.M.

Through experiences such as this, we have come to appreciate the extent to which symptoms are means of protection or defense acquired in response to extreme situations. However, making the symptom become less central to the young person's life creates its own difficulties. While much time was formerly spent worrying about the symptom, whether a compulsion, failure in school, or antisocial behavior, the young person inevitably becomes depressed when he begins to see that the symptom served to avoid the real issues and begins to see the work that such self-exploration entails:

Marci, a sensitive nineteen-year-old college sophomore, was enrolled at the school following a suicide attempt and a delinquent episode in which she forged a prescription in order to obtain diet pills (amphetamines). Marci's parents were determined that she would not have to experience the privation that had haunted them since their own childhood, and provided her with everything possible in the way of material possessions. Then, when Marci was fourteen, her mother was discovered to have advanced cancer. After her death, a year later, Marci became seriously disturbed and, despite outpatient psychiatric treatment, tried to escape from dealing with her feelings by traveling with a fast crowd, by her preoccupation with clothes and other possessions, and by frantic overeating, which led to obesity. Her father described her as "spoiled rotten" and as "unable to tolerate even the smallest frustration."

The first weeks at the school were very difficult for Marci. The change from her fast life at college was especially difficult. As her counselor gained her confidence, Marci was able to reveal the extent of her delinquency for the first time, and to describe her extensive fears about her own body. She ran away one afternoon during her first week at the school but returned the same evening and was amazed when her counselor, rather than being angry

315

with her, told her about how worried she had been and how pleased she was to see Marci. She then provided Marci with hot chocolate and freshly baked rolls.

Marci now began to talk in earnest about her feelings. As she was able to give up her delinquency and overeating, she became extremely depressed and was often unable to get out of bed in the morning or to concentrate on such simple activities as sewing or reading a popular novel. She talked frequently about how difficult it was to recapture the sadness from which she had tried to escape during the previous four years. During these first months, she did begin to form an important relationship with a staff member who began seeing her in individual sessions.

As she began to relive her memories of her mother's death and her feelings about her father, with whom she had a seductive relationship, she continued to face her sadness and was able to gain considerable inner strength and lost much of her excess weight.

MANAGEMENT OF REGRESSIVE BEHAVIOR

After an initial period of fighting the school, the young person settles into the comfortable daily routine and begins to make it his home. He may now begin individual psychotherapeutic sessions with a favorite teacher or counselor; these sessions are of some value in the reconstruction of personality, but it is only because of the special milieu that the school provides that intensive psychotherapy can have such impact.

It has been suggested that in a milieu such as that provided by the Orthogenic School, adolescents are encouraged to regress and are unable to take part in traditional adolescent activities such as dating and competitive sports. We are not convinced that adolescents typically enjoy adolescence. Rather, it is a very difficult time of life, to be endured and mastered as soon as possible. The concept of regression is a complex one, but is typically used to refer to the reliance on forms of behavior that were socially appropriate at some earlier point in childhood but that are now inappropriate.

Many adolescents rely on social skills in order to mask internal distress. If, when the threat is removed, the young person readily gives up these skills and accomplishments, such attainments were never really an integral part of personality and had little meaning for the young person. Much inpatient treatment of adolescents is geared to concealing such emotional disturbance in order that the young person can return to the threatening environment that previously evoked his symptoms. Regression then becomes a threat to the goals of the institution, which discourage long-term intensive treatment aimed at personality reconstruction.

Since the treatment philosophy of the school is one of personality reconstruction, we believe that it is necessary for a young person to give up such superficial forms of adjustment as a part of treatment:

John came from a broken home. Early in his life, John experienced both emotional and physical traumata and when, at an early age he contracted a serious neurological illness, it was misdiagnosed and he received poor medical care. Afterwards, it was believed that he suffered from a permanent organic impairment that affected his psychological functioning.

Though John attended a private school of high academic standing he graduated from high school without having mastered elementary academic skills. During his first semester in college he had increasing trouble with his work; he took drugs, withdrew from his professors and classmates, and eventually became suicidal.

Upon enrollment at the school, John became increasingly disinterested in the sophisticated life he had led before. His clothing looked disheveled and his personal appearance was unkempt. He would frequently go unshaven and without even a change of underwear for weeks at a time. It was also very important for him to be able to wear his shirts with the tails sticking out.

John enjoyed receiving the stuffed animal which the school provides each new young person who is enrolled, and insisted that his favorite counselor take special care of this stuffed animal, including tucking the animal into bed with him at night. He also asked her to feed him milk and cheese and enjoyed being able to put his head on her lap and being reassured that she would take good care of him. Somewhat later, he asked her to give him a baby bottle and talked of wishing that he was her child.

In many psychiatric hospitals, such behavior would be a cause for alarm. At the school we view such behavior as an indication that, for the first time, a young person is able to feel in control of his own life. If an adolescent needs to wear dirty clothes, and John was insistent that no one provide him with clean clothes, then such behavior is accepted.

It is particularly important that the staff understand the meaning of an adolescent's style of dress. In John's situation, the fact that he chose to wear his shirttails out had particular significance: as a child, toilet training had been an especially difficult situation. His stepfather, the only important male figure in his life, had numerous bizarre fantasies about elimination, which he discussed with John and which had added to John's concern about his body. In addition, John's illness at the age of three, together with prior illnesses, increased his concern about his body. The shirttails, worn out, served as armor to protect John's behind from danger.

When he first came to the school, John felt that it was dangerous to even use the school's toilets and selected special toilets in another university building. Only as he was able to feel safer at the school could he begin to use the school's toilets. Talking with John about his shirttails provided an opportunity to begin exploring his fantasies about elimination and his body. As he was able to begin to talk about his feelings, his physical appearance began to change. When he once began to shave and to change his underwear each day, it was because these aspects of personal hygiene were part of his desire to take good care of himself and to feel self-respect.

CONTACT WITH FAMILY AND COMMUNITY

Adolescents who live at Orthogenic School have less contact with their families than is true in most other residential treatment centers. When a young person is enrolled at the school, he is told that he will not see his family for many months. Prior to his enrollment, members of our staff talk with the adolescent himself in an attempt to determine whether we can be of help, and talk with each parent in order to obtain a complete history of the young person, his family, and his development. A decision to accept a child or adolescent is a total staff decision and depends, in large part, on our feeling that he can profit from the intensive treatment we offer. Following his enrollment, it may be a year or more before his first visit. Such a visit is arranged for a part of one day; we discourage home visits until there have been a few trial day visits. Since we have a small staff and spend so much of our time directly with the children, our commitment is to the young person himself and to helping him achieve the independence that will enable him to decide whether he wishes to live his own life with or outside of his family.

This procedure has numerous benefits. In the first place, it permits the family to reorganize its emotional resources. Typically, during the years before a young person comes to us, the relationship between the young person and his family has become progressively difficult. Increasingly, the family's emotional resources are spent trying to understand and contain the disturbed adolescent. For example, Margaret's compulsive hand-washing and bathroom activities in the only bathroom in the house became the focus of both realistic struggles, as well as intense emotional struggles, with other family members. In another family, the daughter's sexual acting out and her involvement in drugs became the focus of frequent family quarrels.

Typically, after a young person has been with us for several months, we learn from his parents how much better things are for the family. Fathers report that they are able to concentrate on their work for the first time in several years. Mothers report that they are now able to devote more energy to caring for brothers and sisters. Often the young person's disturbance has been part of a complex marital conflict. With the adolescent out of the home, the parents are better able to deal with problems in their marriage.

From the perspective of the school's work with the adolescent, there are numerous benefits to be gained from infrequent visits. The young person is told when he comes to the school that he is beginning a new life. Indeed, we do not even announce his name when we tell the others that a newcomer will join us. When an adolescent wishes to change his name, we encourage him to do so since this emphasizes the fact that his entrance in the school marks the beginning of a new life. Shielded from the extreme situation that intensified his disturbance, the defensive protection offered by his symptoms becomes less necessary. Work can proceed with continuity from day to day and from week to week, not subject to the interruptions that occur when patients are allowed to have visitors or to leave the institution for the weekend. Finally, there is the important advantage to be gained, especially among drug-using adolescents, by protecting both the young person and his dormmates from continued accessibility to drugs. Since there is little exposure to the outside world, there is little opportunity to experiment with drugs during a time when the young person is rebuilding a very shaky internal structure.

There is little difficulty at the Orthogenic School with problems frequently found in psychiatric hospitals, such as drug use, delinquency, or other forms of antisocial behavior. This is largely because young people like the school and feel safe and well cared for:

Susie traveled with the fast crowd which hung around Berkeley's Telegraph Avenue and the West Coast hippie communes. She had experimented with a variety of drugs, including "Speed," LSD, and "STP," and had carried on affairs with numerous writers and musicians. She finally developed a series of bizarre rituals which had to be carried out at exact times during the day; she had several bad trips and had finally begun to refuse food and to lose weight.

During her first weeks at the school, Susie attempted to organize her dormmates in a rebellion against the staff. They looked at her with amazement. When she asked them how they could stand to live in such a prison, they explained to her that they liked the school and that, for most of them, their counselors were the first adults in their lives ever to attempt to understand or care for them. Why, they asked her, should she want to run away, and where could she go that would be better than the school?

At the party to celebrate her coming to the school, Susie was given a box of elegant, scented, imported soaps. That first evening, she watched in amazement as her counselor ran baths for the girls, talked and played with them while they were in the bathtub, helped them to wash their hair, and so on.

Though Susie was not yet ready to allow her counselor to care for her in this way, the fact that she saw this kind of care being given to her dormmates was, as she was later able to tell us, very reassuring for her. The soap she had been given was a sign that her counselors wanted to provide such care for her when she would be able to accept it. It was very gratifying to watch, several months later, when another girl came to the school, as Susie explained to her what a good place the school was.

During the four to seven years that young people are at the school, all available resources are brought to bear on personality reconstruction. In the dormitory, individual psychotherapeutic sessions and, in the classroom, the entire day is viewed as a part of the treatment process. Academic work is individually tailored to a young person's needs and adolescents spend a part of the school day talking with their teachers who, like the counselors, are educational therapists. Adolescents who have had difficulty in school are helped with their work, but only as they become able to profit from such instruction. The decision to begin a more active program of studies is, like all other decisions at the school, one that depends on our understanding of the individual adolescent and his unique psychological needs.

Preparation to leave the school and to return to the community is a gradual process. A young person may begin by taking some courses in the local public high school or college while living at the school. In other cases, vocational training programs are arranged so that he can develop necessary job skills. This permits us to help him explore feelings about such a move before he is actually ready to leave. Many of our adolescents attend public high school for one or two years before leaving the school and beginning life on their own.

If the young person chooses to stay in Chicago, we then encourage him to come back to the school two or three times a week for individual sessions during the first year or two on his own. After they leave the school, some of our adolescents go on to college, while others join the military service or go directly to work. Whereas about eight of every ten adolescents who leave the school are able to make a good life for themselves, there are some adolescents who still lack the inner strength to deal with life outside the school. We try to help these people find professional help in the community and are, ourselves, ready to be of continuing help. However, in no instance does a young person who has left the school have an opportunity to return. The decision that he is ready to begin a new life is an important decision, and it is for this reason that it must be considered for months or even years prior to leaving.

Conclusions

The treatment philosophy of the Orthogenic School is based on a view of adolescence as a time of inner turmoil which, in a young person who has previously experienced conflicts in his own development, and who finds a lack of environmental support for his attempt to develop internal control, may lead to an emotional disturbance that is actually only a response to a life-threatening situation. Clearly, neither the manipulation of outward behavior nor the provision of a better façade of adjustment will succeed in helping the adolescent to resolve this disturbance and to achieve a better adaptation. However, reparenting, combined with intensive individual psychotherapy, in an environment structured around the adolescent's unique psychological needs, has led to a more effective adaptation in the vast majority of young persons with whom we have worked.

NOTES

1. The author wishes to thank Bruno Bettelheim and David Hall for their helpful comments regarding previous drafts of this chapter.

2. Reviews of the literature concerning administrative and therapeutic issues involved in the treatment of the adolescent in a psychiatric hospital are available in Beskind (1962) and Easson (1969).

REFERENCES

Aichhorn, A. (1935). *Wayward Youth.* New York: Viking Press.

Atthowe, J., and Krasner, L. (1968). Preliminary report on the application of contingent reinforcement procedures (token economy) on a chronic psychiatric ward. *Journal of Abnormal Psychology,* 13:37–43.

Aylon, T., and Azrin, N. (1968). *The Token Economy: A Motivational System for Therapy and Rehabilitation.* New York: Appleton-Century-Crofts.

Beckett, P. (1965). *Adolescents Out of Step: Their Treatment in a Psychiatric Hospital.* Detroit: Wayne State University Press.

Beskind, H. (1962). Psychiatric in-patient treatment of adolescents: A review of clinical experience. *Comprehensive Psychiatry,* 3:354–369.

Bettelheim, B. (1948). Closed institutions for children? *Bulletin of the Menninger Clinic,* 12:135–142.

———. (1949). A psychiatric school. *Quarterly Journal of Child Behavior,* 1:86–95.

———. (1950). *Love Is Not Enough.* New York: The Free Press.

———. (1955). *Truants from Life.* New York: The Free Press.

———. (1956). Schizophrenia as a reaction to extreme situations. *American Journal of Orthopsychiatry,* 26:507–518.

———. (1960). *The Informed Heart.* New York: The Free Press.

———. (1966). Training the childcare worker in a residential setting. *American Journal of Orthopsychiatry,* 36:694–705.

———. (1967). *The Empty Fortress.* New York: The Free Press.

———, and Sylvester, E. (1947). Therapeutic influence of the group on the individual. *American Journal of Orthopsychiatry,* 17:684–692.

———. (1948). A therapeutic milieu. *American Journal of Orthopsychiatry,* 18:191–206.

———. (1949). Milieu therapy: Indications and illustrations. *Psychoanalytic Review,* 36:54–68.

Bettelheim, B., and Wright, B. (1955). Staff development in a treatment institution. *American Journal of Orthopsychiatry,* 25:705–719.

Blos, P. (1962). *On Adolescence: A Psychoanalytic Interpretation.* New York: The Free Press.

Buckle, D. (1969). Mental health services for adolescents: An introduction. In: *Adolescence: Psychosocial Perspectives,* ed. G. Caplan and S. Lebovici. New York: Basic Books, pp. 363–371.

Caplan, G., and Lebovici, S. (1969). Editors' introduction: Depression and suicide. In: *Adolescence: Psychosocial Perspectives,* ed. G. Caplan and S. Lebovici. New York: Basic Books.

Cumming, J., and Cumming, E. (1963). *Ego and Milieu.* New York: Atherton.

Deutsch, H. (1967). Selected problems of adolescence: With special emphasis on group formation. *Psychoanalytic Study of the Child,* Monograph 3.

Easson, W. (1969). *The Severely Disturbed Adolescent.* New York: International Universities Press.

Eissler, K. R. (1958). Notes on problems of technique in the psychoanalytic treatment of adolescents. *Psychoanalytic Study of the Child,* 13:223–254.

Erikson, E. (1968). *Identity: Youth and Crisis.* New York: Norton.

Forehand, R., Mulhern, T., and Rickard, H. (1969). Effects of token reinforcement in a therapeutic camp. *Psychological Reports,* 25:349–350.

Freud, A. (1946). *The Ego and the Mechanisms of Defence* (1936). New York: International Universities Press.

———. (1958). Adolescence. *Psychoanalytic Study of the Child,* 13:255–278.

Garber, B., and Polsky, R. (1970). Follow-up study of hospitalized adolescents. *Archives of General Psychiatry,* 22:179–187.

Gitelson, M. (1948). Character synthesis: The psychotherapeutic problem of adolescence. *American Journal of Orthopsychiatry,* 18:422–431.

Greaves, D., and Regan, P. (1957). Psychotherapy of adolescents at intensive hospital treatment level. In: *Psychotherapy of the Adolescent,* ed. B. Balser. New York: International Universities Press, pp. 130–143.

Hartmann, E., *et al.* (1968). *Adolescents in a Mental Hospital.* New York: Grune & Stratton.

Hendrickson, W., Holmes, D., and Waggoner, R. (1959). Psychotherapy of the hospitalized adolescent. *American Journal of Psychiatry,* 116:527–532.

Henry, J. (1954). The formal structure of a psychiatric hospital. *Psychiatry,* 17:139–151.

———. (1957a). The culture of interpersonal relations in a therapeutic institution for emotionally disturbed children. *American Journal of Orthopsychiatry,* 27:725–734.

———. (1957b). Types of institutional structure. *Psychiatry,* 20:47–60.

Holmes, D. (1964). *The Adolescent in Psychotherapy.* Boston: Little, Brown.

Masterson, J. (1967). *The Psychiatric Dilemma of Adolescence.* Boston: Little, Brown.

Noshpitz, J. (1957). Opening phase in the psychotherapy of adolescents with character disorders. *Bulletin of the Menninger Clinic,* 21:153–164.

———. (1962). Notes on the theory of residential treatment. *Journal of the American Academy of Child Psychiatry,* 1:284–296.

Offer, D. (1969). *The Psychological World of the Teen-ager.* New York: Basic Books.

———, Marcus, D., and Offer, J. (1970). A longitudinal study of normal adolescent boys. *American Journal of Psychiatry,* 126:917–924.

Phillips, E. L. (1968). Achievement place: Token reinforcement procedures in a home-style rehabilitation setting for pre-delinquent boys. *Journal of Applied Behavior Analysis,* 1:213–223.

Redl, F. (1949). New ways of ego support in residential treatment of disturbed children. *Bulletin of the Menninger Clinic,* 13:60–66.

———. (1951). The concept of ego disturbance and ego support. *American Journal of Orthopsychiatry,* 21:273–284.

———. (1959). The concept of a "therapeutic milieu." *American Journal of Orthopsychiatry,* 29:721–736.

Rinsley, D. (1965). Intensive psychiatric treatment of adolescents. *Psychiatric Quarterly,* 39:405–429.

——, and Inge, G. (1961). Psychiatric hospital treatment of adolescents: Verbal and nonverbal resistance to treatment. *Bulletin of the Menninger Clinic,* 25:249–263.

Rosen, J. (1963). Personality factors in the reactions of child-care workers to emotionally disturbed children. *Psychiatry,* 26:257–265.

Spiegel, L. (1951). A review of the contributions to a psychoanalytic theory of adolescence. *Psychoanalytic Study of the Child,* 6:375–393.

——. (1958). Comments on the psychoanalytic psychology of adolescence. *Psychoanalytic Study of the Child,* 13:296–308.

Stanton, A., and Schwartz, M. (1954). *The Mental Hospital.* New York: Basic Books.

Wright, B. (1957). Attitude toward emotional involvement and professional development in residential child care. Unpublished doctoral dissertation, University of Chicago.

18] FAMILY THERAPY: ITS ROLE IN ADOLESCENT PSYCHIATRY

FRANK S. WILLIAMS

Much of the pioneer work in family therapy during the past twenty-five years has centered around the young schizophrenic adult, or the older schizophrenic adolescent and his family. During more recent years, the literature has included a growing number of reports of family therapy with the neurotically disturbed adolescent (Minuchin, 1971; Brown, 1970; Wynne, 1965; and Williams, 1968). Though most psychiatrists recognize the interplay between an adolescent's intrapsychic conflicts and his family's interpersonal dynamics, there is disagreement among clinicians regarding the use of family therapy with adolescents.

Quite often, when child psychiatrists refer to family therapy with an adolescent, they mean that they actively involve the mother and father in the total treatment program (but separate from the adolescent's individual therapy). The family therapy that I shall be considering in this chapter, however, refers to a family interviewing technique that includes the adolescent and his parents seen together in the same room with the psychotherapist.[1] Such family interviews may be employed for one or two diagnostic evaluation sessions; may occur in series over a period of several weeks or months as part of an ongoing treatment program, which in turn may include marital therapy for the parents and additional modalities, such as group or individual therapy for the adolescent; or may remain the primary or sole form of therapeutic intervention with an adolescent and his family by regular weekly family interviews over a period of many months.

There is no doubt that a disturbed adolescent needs much assistance in breaking his ambivalent family ties as he strives for identity and independence. Some therapists feel this can only be done by his developing a highly confidential one-to-one relationship with an adult outside the family, his psychotherapist. Some psychotherapists are unique in their capacity to rise above ensuing familial resistances to the establishment of such out-of-the-family relationships. They are able to develop with the teenager a most powerful new corrective relationship. However, I believe that in most situations the familial resistances will prevail, block, and overcome progress. As a child enters adolescence, these parental resistances to his forward development can be quite severe. For instance, at no time in a woman's life is her own identity more threatened than at that point when her maternal role must give way in light of her last child's adolescent maturity. This is particularly so if her marriage is not a rewarding one. Mothers at such points of personal crisis may unwittingly hold on to their teenage sons and daughters, stifling their psychosocial growth. Seeing the adolescent together with his parents allows for a mutual working through of these resistances. Some of the questions raised by those who are reluctant to see the adolescent with his family include: Will family therapy help individuation or promote an even greater continued symbiosis? Will not such family meetings result in a break of confidentiality with the adolescent? The complex familial field that surrounds an adolescent often perplexes the clinician. This perplexity overwhelms many therapists to the point of avoiding working with adolescents and of adopting a stance of therapeutic nihilism. Some teachers avoid the perplexities by presenting students with an oversimplified exposure to adolescent psychiatry, primarily a one-to-one dyadic approach. Varying flexible and multitreatment techniques are not sufficiently introduced early enough in the student's or resident's training. Unfortunately, the reassurance that a beginning student attains from working in the one-to-one, easy to control, uncovering psychotherapeutic approach with adults often collapses when he faces an adolescent and the multiforces within the family that he, the therapist, cannot control. I should like to suggest that therapists who feel in control while working exclusively in the dyadic one-to-one relationship with an adolescent actually have very little control, merely the illusion of it. Whittling away goes on behind the scenes in the form of overt and subtle sabotage within the family field.

I should like to discuss the indications for family therapy in adolescent psychiatry, both for assessment and for treatment. Attention will be paid to the most serious dilemma for the adolescent and his family, the age-old conflict between autonomy and individuation as it comes into conflict with dependency-control attachments, particularly in the next to impossible to treat symbiotic type family. The author encourages flexibility of approach within the total treatment program for the adolescent, a flexibility that includes therapeutically timed mixtures of one-to-one therapy and family treatment.

Major Conflicts of Adolescence

Before attending to indications and contraindications for family inter-viewing techniques, I should like to briefly review some of those major conflicts of adolescence for which families can either offer resolution or stifling perpetuation.

INDEPENDENCE VERSUS DEPENDENCY ATTACHMENTS

The adolescent, in his struggle to achieve freedom from his family, often threatens, within himself and his parents, very primitive fears of object loss and separation from symbiotic involvements. Brown (1969) indicated how the transactional field of the family is often used to reaf-firm and preserve the internal infantile object constellation in an effort to ward off fantasied separation grief and anxiety. Minuchin (1971) de-scribed how in working with very close-knit families the therapist must be aware of the powerful familial forces that impede maturity for the adolescent. He further stressed the need for clinicians to find effective ways of overcoming these forces.

Today, many adolescents attempt to solve their own intrapsychic and their family's problems over independence and dependency attachments by leaving home at an early age. Unfortunately, what often results from such attempts to jar loose from the family is a state of pseudomatura-tion. The underlying sense of weakness and object loss frequently per-sists and represents itself in a growing need for drugs and new attach-ments within hippie-type crash pads or communes (Williams, 1970). Such dependency attachments to peers—without the development of significant mutuality and intimacy—can result in a group of adolescents holding together like orphans in a storm, merely playing at the game of maturity. Some succeed in developing, in spite of the game; others fail and remain symbolically attached to their families, through the fanta-sied family objects in their new surrogate peer parents. Williams (1970) described how adolescents in a hippie commune display an exquisite at-tempt to work through the attachment-autonomy conflict with the use of drugs. He offers examples in which the adolescent parent nurses his peer child back to health from a bad trip. At a later point, that same former child-patient becomes the mother and nurses his former peer parent back to health from a similar bad trip. Unfortunately, very little in the way of sustained day-to-day experiences in maintaining a role of growing leadership seems to occur.

326

RECRUDESCENCE OF OEDIPAL CONFLICTS

The sexual conflicts stirred up within the adolescent, by nature of his physical and psychosexual growth, often lead to the development of dramatic distancing mechanisms between parents and their sons and daughters. Mutual fears of fantasied hetero- and homosexual erotization of the parent-child relationships are often represented in extreme defensive hostile pushing-away maneuvers in some families. In others, the parents become overly involved in the sexuality of their sons and daughters. This may be reflected in either direct seductive contact, or in subtle cueing mechanisms, wherein a mother, for example, using the rationalization of instilling "a healthy wholesome attitude," overeducates her daughter about sex and elicits detailed descriptions from her young adolescent daughter of sexual fantasies and encounters.

The role of the parents and siblings in the reappearance of threatening incestuous fantasies in adolescence has received little emphasis in the literature. Family interviewing techniques offer opportunities to observe directly those subtle seductive stimuli from sisters and brothers, as well as from parents, usually not gleaned from sessions with the parents alone. The adolescent faced with symbolic or real incestuous provocation often finds it difficult to sublimate his feelings in the direction of nonsexual familial intimacy experiences. This is, in most families today, owing to a lack of experiences with intimate sharing of feelings between parent and child, after the initial maternal-infant symbiosis and parental-preschooler closeness. The adolescent is therefore trapped. He either leaves and looks for intimacy outside his home, or he remains within the family and suffers the fantasied and/or part reality threat of massive regression to those types of early oral and anal intimacy experiences he knew as a young child and as an infant. Should he choose to leave home, in an effort to seek love and intimacy, he has very little intimacy capacity with which to sustain himself. He often winds up substituting pseudosexual intimacies and the pseudointimacy of the hippie or drug scene.

INTEGRATION OF ANGRY AFFECT

In adolescence, significant real physical strength is available for the first time. Too, the capacity for calculation related to carrying out of crimes and physical harm is readily available. Adolescents are often frightened by their rage and destructive potential, particularly in relation to their parents. The rage often relates to inner struggles over autonomy and is projected onto the parents. Should the parents have intense problems regarding letting go, the projection, of course, becomes much easier to accomplish and more readily fixated. At other times, the teenager's rage represents a defense against emerging positive erotic feelings toward parents or siblings. Completely separating the adolescent's therapy from his family's therapy may parallel the negative effect of a teenager's premature leaving of home, as far as rage is concerned. When the adolescent leaves home (made easy today by the availability of hippie communes or crashpads, which will provide food and shelter), he does not have an opportunity to fight out certain rage-inducing conflicts with his parents and siblings. Fighting it out can help the adolescent test the extent and limitations of his own murderous rage in terms of potential action, as well as the extent and limitations of his parents' and siblings' murderous rage in terms of potential danger. Some adolescent peer groups maintain an ideology of love. The proclamation, "We love everyone, including the parents who hassle us!" may serve as a defense against the eruption of repressed or suppressed feelings of rage toward family members. Family therapy offers a safe and constructive setting in which to fight it out.

Much can be inferred regarding that portion of an adolescent's problem with angry affect, which stems from familial relationships, by seeing parents in separate diagnostic or therapeutic sessions. Family interviews, however, which include the parents and adolescent together, offer an *in vivo* opportunity to determine whether the rage relates to defensive paranoid projection on the part of the adolescent, or to reality-oriented parental precipitants. Such a differential assessment helps in determining intrapsychic fixation and potential for the later handling of rage feelings once separation from the family does occur. Brown (1964) described an example of parental stimulation of inappropriate anger in a young teenage boy with self-destructive tendencies. In several interviews, which included the boy, his mother, father, and sister, a fascinating interplay between the boy's problem with inner controls and familial interpersonal relations was elicited. In part the therapist was able to observe how the father's avoidance of decisive discipline helped to perpetuate the youngster's problem with controls. He was also able to observe, within the nuances of the familial interactions, how the father and son made a regressive alliance, a focal symbiosis, in which they both retreated from their phallically feared mother and in which the father used his son both as a retreat and as a symbolic expression of his own rage toward his wife.

IDENTITY AND CAPACITY FOR INTIMACY

The adolescent's capacity for intimacy and his ego identity—his separateness—are affected by his family's attitude toward his individuation. Some families with very powerful familial identities display a wholesome working togetherness, but unwittingly squelch the individual identities of the various family members. Adolescents sometimes flee from such families in a desperate attempt to achieve a sense of individuality. Once with a new family peer group, they are supersensitive and on guard in relation to fears of their becoming possessed and of losing separateness. A question pertinent to the field of family therapy is, "Can an adolescent work through his struggle between his desire for intimacy and his fear of loss of individuation, within the context of family therapy sessions, or separate from his family in an individual new intimate one-to-one relationship with a therapist?" My own bias is in the direction of a flexible combination of both modalities for adolescent therapy. The family can often be helped to encourage the teenager toward independent individuation; the teenager's role in undermining that potential encouragement from his parents is most observable and available for confrontation in family meetings.

Indications for Family Therapy with Adolescents

ASSESSMENT

Regardless of the treatment modality eventually decided on for an adolescent, family interviews during the diagnostic phase help the therapist to understand the multitude of outer forces perpetuating and contributing to the adolescent's internal conflicts. Family interviews can be helpful during the initial work-up, as well as at major points of resistance, during an ongoing individual treatment. One or two initial diagnostic family interviews help the therapist with prognostic considerations. He is able to determine more accurately those factors in the family that will serve as major resistances to the uncovering work of one-to-one individual therapy with the adolescent. There are at times certain affects hidden within the adolescent, related to past tragic family traumas. These affects may be continually held down via subtle parental cues, in an effort to protect the parent from the pain of affective recall, memory, or expression. For example, a severely depressed thirteen-year-old boy was desperately in need of psychotherapy to help relieve him of self-destructive tendencies and his gloomy preoccupation with the hopelessness of failing peer relationships. Seeing the boy and mother in separate diagnostic sessions elicited historical material about the father's death several years earlier. Neither mother nor son showed the slightest affect while presenting the material about the father's sudden death. Mother's monotone presentation was noteworthy. When seeing the boy and mother together in a family interview, it was striking to note that whenever the boy attempted to discuss his feelings about his father's death, he immediately evoked from his mother a gentle but definitive prohibition against further ventilation. The boy's eyes would well up with tears as he would start to say with sadness that he "remembered when his father . . ."; the mother would immediately say something to the effect of, "Your father was a good man and it isn't proper to talk about him." Even when it was apparent that the boy was about to say something positive about his father, the mother would again prohibit such expression by changing the subject or by indicating the potential hurt she would feel if one "dredged up the past." In this particular case, a series of family interviews was helpful in freeing the mother to give her son permission to uncover and ventilate his feelings of depression and rage about the loss of his father. One might have attempted to get this boy to reach the same point in individual therapy. I feel, however, that in so doing one could readily create new conflicts for the youngster, as he would have to blindly struggle with his conflict over loyalty to his own wish for relief and his mother's wish for continued burial of affects. Paul and Grosser (1965) described the values of uncovering such buried affects from the traumatic past during family interviews.

Diagnostic family interviews help to assess whether the intrapsychic distortions of the adolescent are firmly fixated and resistant to changes within the environment, or whether such distortions are still in a state of fluidity and primarily reinforced, daily, by parental cueing. I recently treated a sixteen-year-old girl with severe anorexia nervosa. The original diagnostic work-up reflected some of the classical conflicts over fear of separation from mother and fear of her adult female sexual impulses. In individual diagnostic sessions, Marie tearfully told of how her wish to have a boyfriend, and how her dreams of sex with boys made her feel "trampy." She was openly anxious as she discussed her desire to eventually live away from home. In the parents' separate diagnostic history-taking interview, the mother convincingly indicated her own healthy approach toward sex, as far as her daughter was concerned, and stressed how she encouraged Marie to date and to learn about sex from both books and from questions put to the parents. In marked contrast to the tone of the individual sessions was one family interview, in which the question of Marie's dating and leaving home came up. As Marie's tears and anxiety level lessened, she began to talk of a boy she met at school who wanted to take her out. Marie's father blanched; her mother sat forward and said, "What do you know about him?" She then turned to me and said, "Doctor, we know that there are some nice boys, but my father was a policeman, you know, and I've learned about all the rapes and murders that go on, particularly with young girls; you never know what a boy is really like; he may just be putting on a friendly front!" The next day in an individual session with me, Marie appeared extremely frightened. She described how she had not eaten all day and how uncertain she felt about her feelings in relationship to boys and dating. This is a striking example of an observable direct influence by the parents on the unresolved autonomy and sexual conflicts of an adolescent.

When doing family interviewing, one has an opportunity to note such overt as well as certain subtle cueing mechanisms. At times mothers and fathers will discuss with seeming frankness their concerns about hetero- and homosexuality and will, at times, show zealous interest in their adolescent son's or daughter's sexual activities. The family therapist is in a position to see those cues that admonish or prematurely encourage sexual involvement. These cues are often missed in the more traditional diagnostic interview.

One has an excellent opportunity in family meetings to observe directly double-bind communications. For example, a fifteen-year-old boy lived alone with his divorced mother. In her initial individual intake session, the mother complained of her son's lack of friends; she wanted the clinic to "help him get out of his shell and make more meaningful friendships." In a diagnostic family meeting, the boy discussed his wish for friends, but added his concerns about his mother's loneliness. Mother broke into tears, saying, "I want you to go out, you need to be away from me, somehow I will survive; it is important for you to have your own life!" The boy was torn in that his mother had given him permission, but at the same time had indirectly indicated that she might die without him.

Family interviews during the diagnostic phase often elicit marital disharmony or potential disharmony, which is covered up by the scapegoating of the problem teenager. Frequently, one of the siblings is the first to uncover the disharmony. Brown (1970), in his description of family therapy, indicated how family meetings can promote a readiness to deal with change in the marital relationship. He particularly noted how siblings who are not directly caught up in the pathologic family dyads may move this process along. The scapegoated problem adolescent serves to ward off a threatened potential break in the family equilibrium should the parents' underlying hatred or intimacy deficit be brought to the surface. The designated teenage patient often loyally accepts his role as the sick one, though ashamed of it, in an effort to hold his parents and family together. In family meetings, one can observe the exquisite and precise timing of some of the shifting of attention to the teenager's problems, as the therapist or one of the family gets close to touching on the underlying marital conflict. A sibling may point out the lack of time mother and father spend together, or the lack of romantic feelings between the parents. Suddenly, and apparently out of context, the designated patient or one of the parents will draw attention to the adolescent's symptoms. In several family treatment situations, we have noted how symptom complexes such as aggressive behavior disorders, predelinquency, and poor school performance abate once the parents are able to ventilate their anxieties about the instability of their marriage. In these cases, the treatment of choice is often conjoint marital therapy without any therapy necessary for the adolescent.

In diagnostic family interviews one obtains a sense of whether a family will be of help in attempts to reverse an adolescent's intrapsychic distortions. In an interview with a sixteen-year-old boy with sleep problems, school failures, and a lack of friends, the youngster indicated severe conflicts regarding his wish to go to a nonparochial school. He feared his father, a long-time religious devotee, would condemn his wish to attend a coed school. He further feared that he would bear the brunt of peer ridicule if he wore his religious skullcap in a coed setting. The father, in a meeting with the boy and the therapist, shared his own mixed feelings about the matter, but convincingly encouraged the boy to go to a coed school and to remove his skullcap. It became clear that much of the work to be done in individual therapy would need to focus on the boy's underlying fears of sexuality, and that his father would probably be an ally, or at least not a sabotaging agent.

OVERCOMING RESISTANCES

In individual or group therapy, the clinician often faces what appears to be a major resistance to continue treatment. Those of us who work a great deal with adolescents are all too familiar with the frequency of missed sessions, latenesses, and the boredom that often sets in, particularly at times when painful affects are expressed. As one gets close to a teenager's underlying struggles with sex or aggression, it is important to note whether an ensuing resistance is primarily motivated by the adolescent's anxieties or by the parents' discomfort with newly emerging affects and desires, which are communicated at home.

Earlier, I mentioned Marie, a sixteen-year-old girl with anorexia nervosa. As Marie began to write letters to an eighteen-year-old, apparently healthy young man who liked her, she simultaneously reported dreams of having sexual intercourse with this young man and with older men. She suddenly began to miss sessions and indicated her wish to stop treatment. Interpreting the transference elements in her feelings did not dissuade her. She continued to express the feeling that we were wasting time and that she was not getting better fast enough. This was in spite of a twenty-pound weight gain over a period of four and one-half months. Seeing Marie together with her mother and father at this critical point in her treatment was quite revealing and helpful. The father kept looking at Marie with tearful, "basset hound" eyes, saying "I don't mind that you don't want to go camping with me any more; if you are too busy writing to Marty, that's all right! I can always bury myself in work; I have to support you all and send you to college, so that you can see your boyfriend more anyway!" Mother, on the other hand, stated that she was very glad that Marie was now interested in dating, but quickly shifted the subject to an article that she had read in the paper about a coed girl being murdered in a parking lot. She added her convictions that the murderer must have been a sex deviant. It became apparent that the parents needed to be involved in either a parallel conjoint marital therapy or a total family therapy with Marie, to help them all separate out the parental fears and guilt-provoking affects from Marie's own psychosexual internal conflicts.

At times, passive young adolescent boys will be in individual therapy for many months, and will eventually become more assertive and aggressive, both verbally and physically. To the therapist's astonishment, they may suddenly be taken out of treatment by their parents, who are unable to tolerate their new expressions of anger. Seeing such adolescent boys and their parents together, at these moments of resistance, can elicit both the parental anxieties in response to the patient's aggression, as well as those ways in which the teenage boy may be unwittingly provoking his parents by an exaggerated display of his newfound power. An additional problem with such families, particularly in the case of the predelinquent adolescent, lies in confused communication patterns. There may be prohitition of direct expression of aggression at the same time that there is much subtle cuing from the parents provoking antisocial behavior.

Williams (1967a) described how a predelinquent boy was attacked by his parents for investigating areas of the therapist's office that were obviously out of bounds, after they had cued his exploration with their own questions about the restricted area.

The value of seeing the family at these points of resistance is in seeing how the adolescent himself helps start or rekindle the familial anxiety patterns that then act to put down the threatening affects. For example, the adolescent beginning to struggle in individual therapy with his wish to separate from home may in family meetings continue to drop hints about his self-destructive potential once away from his parents. He might state: "Maybe I'd smoke a joint once in a while! Don't worry, I'll find a pad to sleep somewhere." The parents' anxieties are then reawakened in terms of their own reality separation and loss feelings, and in terms of fantasied distortions within them. These intrapsychic distortions may have to do with violence, loss of controls, self-destruction, annihilation, and death, which seem imminent when one separates from parents.

CRISES IN FAMILIES

Series of family meetings aimed at opening up lines of communication can help an adolescent through major points of transitional crisis in a family's life. Crises can be particularly disruptive at points of significant separation, as in divorce, a move to a new neighborhood, a youngster's going away to school, hospitalization, or death. Very often the affects and anxieties that parents feel at times of major crises are repressed only to appear in exaggerated forms within their youngsters. Sudden school phobias or sudden aggressive predelinquent activity frequently occur on the threshold of a divorce or other imminent separation. Also, violent exacerbations of psychosomatic illnesses, such as ulcerative colitis or severe asthma, may occur in an adolescent following the death of a close grandparent or ambivalently loved sibling. Family meetings at such times of crisis allow for an equal sharing of the burden of affect experiences for every member of the family.

With encouragement and selective sharing of his own genuine affects, the therapist can serve as a model to the family, for expression of a range of emotional feelings. He can help the family to express sadness and rage rather than let them dwell on positive sides of major transitional crises. Parents often emphasize the positive at such times to both reassure their youngsters and to keep repressed their own underlying potential for affect eruption regarding tragic separations.

In preparation for placement of an adolescent outside the home, either in a hospital or in a foster home setting, family meetings can be of great value in bolstering the potential success of the placement. Parents may mask unresolved guilts regarding certain wishes to get rid of a troublesome teenager by resisting a necessary placement. Too, the adolescent may struggle with guilt feelings about leaving his family behind, particularly if there is an unconscious or preconscious awareness of the marital discord that might erupt when the problem teenager is no longer the focus of concern. Such mutual guilts and anxieties, when openly discussed in a series of family meetings, are often worked through and seen in their proper perspective.

334

THE HOSPITALIZED ADOLESCENT

Schween and Gralnick (1965) and others, in their work with hospitalized patients, have during the past few years underlined the necessity for concomitant family therapy while treating the hospitalized patient. The hospitalized adolescent's family particularly needs a family interviewing approach for two reasons. (1) The teenage patient usually returns to the family. (2) Should the therapist see only the designated patient, he is not in a position to consistently deal with the familial resistances to change in the patient. These resistances usually manifest themselves after hospitalization, and alter the gains the adolescent has made by corrective relationships in the hospital milieu. Family meetings while the adolescent is hospitalized permit the therapist and patient to deal with familial, including sibling, resistances to change at every step of the adolescent's gain. The family sessions also help the therapist gauge the optimal therapeutic pace for his adolescent patient with which the family can keep step. This is most important when the plan is for the patient to definitely return to his original family environment.

Recently, a hospitalized, self-destructive, seventeen-year-old boy made frequent attempts to elope from the hospital, usually after visits from family members. Rather than discontinuing the visiting, family meetings were held on the ward, with the patient, his divorced parents, his mother's fiancé, and his older sister. After several meetings, it became clear to all involved that the patient was acting out the entire family's ambivalence regarding the initial divorce, as well as the mother's imminent remarriage. The patient eventually communicated his loyalty conflicts and his wish for a closer relationship with his estranged father. In addition to the total family meetings, weekly father-son meetings were introduced. The elopement attempts soon subsided.

THE SYMBIOTIC FAMILY AND ADOLESCENT IDENTITY

For myself, and many of my colleagues, the problem of the locked-in adolescent symbiosis has continued to present a major challenge and therapeutic dilemma. In viewing certain family symbioses, we note a precarious balance between the identity of the adolescent and the diffusion of that identity within the family, within the family identity so to speak. In some families, a family identity is completely lacking; everyone truly "does his own thing." In others, however, the family identity may be so strong as to blot out individual uniqueness. In working with one such family, a professional vaudeville-type stage group, I readily sensed a wholesome family spirit as they discussed with warm feelings their group excitement and pleasures related to traveling around the country together performing as a musical team. However, it took much time and effort to pinpoint any individual, distinct personality differences for the various family members. The parents themselves, as well as the children, frequently confused each other's names, as did the therapist. In that particular family, as well as in one described by Minuchin (1971), the teenager's autonomous identity was lost and submerged by the family's needs. In Minuchin's case, the boy's individuation broke through in the form of an idiosyncratic and life-defying self-starvation, in the symptoms of anorexia nervosa. In the stage family I treated, one of the teenage boy's identity erupted in the form of drug usage and anti-social aggressive acts. Minuchin utilized ongoing family therapy as the primary modality in his treatment. His successful approach to this problem of severe adolescent symbioses led me to reconsider some of my own earlier views (Williams, 1968). I had made a case for the contra-indication of family therapy techniques in dealing with some symbiotic adolescents and cited some related negative therapeutic results. I suggested that such families often cooperated with a family treatment approach for long periods of time, just to stay together, paying ear service to but defeating therapeutic insight attempts. Minuchin, however, described a very active involvement by the family therapists in an effort to set up family tasks that highlight the family's internal power plays and eventually force a disruption of the family's pathologic equilibrium. The problem with a passive approach to the locked-in symbiotic family may lie in the probability that the family's homeostatic power is truly stronger than most doctors' therapeutic powers. In the past, my own therapeutic bias regarding the symbiotic adolescent was in the direction of feeling that he desperately needed a separate one-to-one relationship, outside of his family, to encourage his individuation. I believed that in one-to-one therapy, the therapist could demonstrate respect for the adolescent's autonomy, while offering the support necessary to incur trust of relationships outside the cloistered and somewhat paranoid symbiotic family. However, the results of long-term individual therapy with such adolescents, either in hospital or outpatient situations, are often minimal, as are some of the similarly long-term attempts with family therapy. Again, Minuchin emphasized the need for extensive activity by the therapist when working with such families. An example of a therapist-induced family task aimed at highlighting and breaking up control mechanisms within the family is seen in Minuchin's insistence that no one in the family was to eat as long as the anorexic boy would not eat. Since the youngster was already secretly in control of his entire family, with the symptom of anorexia, and since the parents were already helpless, the family task merely brought to the surface and underscored that the boy was truly the despot. The despot interpretation, and family-fasting task, led to all kinds of severe familial disruptions. The therapist had to be available day and night during the ensuing crisis to move in and encourage the forward movement and individuation at the point of crisis.

In certain families, teenage boys or girls "will not permit" their parents to go away without them to parties or on vacations. In exploring the value of family therapy and family tasks with such families, I have introduced the task of insisting that the parents go out, after many sessions of dealing with both the adolescent's and parents' resistances to such individuation and freedom. My experiences in this regard are similar to those of Minuchin in relation to the essentiality of therapist availability for crisis intervention. For example, when in response to the parents' first weekend away a teenage boy crashes his car, or a teenage girl makes a manipulative but dangerous suicide attempt, the therapist has to be ready to continue to push for the separation, while making himself and appropriate others available to the adolescent for physical and emotional help.

For the present I feel that a combined approach that utilizes individual treatment, series of family meetings, and major attention to encouraging peer relationships is necessary in dealing with the symbiotic adolescent and his family.

Conclusions

As therapists, but primarily as human beings, we like to know our own roles and identity, with a minimum of confusion. Psychotherapy with adolescents can be overwhelming for the therapist because of complicating family forces, peer crises, legal entanglements, the pressure for guidance, and direct advice. We may wish the adolescent to go elsewhere. On the other hand, we may handle our frustration by magnifying the value of confidentiality and, with our adolescent patient, "hide from the world." This unfortunate overemphasis on confidentiality can at times constrict the therapist's diagnostic vision, as well as foreclose an opportunity to utilize family interviewing techniques, a most helpful treatment modality when working with adolescents.

Family therapy offers a means to overcome resistance to an adolescent's psychosocial and psychosexual development. For some adolescent problems the family approach should be the primary therapeutic modality. In family sessions, the therapist can offer a point of view and an attitude that embodies respect for the individuation of the adolescent, as well as respect for the family group and its identity. He can encourage communication of affects and the expression of feelings of intimacy in ways which do not threaten regression to infantile or erotic ties. My overall recommendation is geared toward a flexible approach, which includes family and individual therapy and which permits direct observation of those dynamic familial interpersonal forces impinging on the adolescent's psyche.

Flexibility of approach encompasses many considerations: When do we involve the entire family in a regular ongoing treatment? When do we utilize one or a series of meetings for diagnostic purposes? Will family therapy help individuation or promote continued symbioses in certain symbiotic families?

Teachers and students of adolescent psychiatry need much greater exposure to family techniques if we are to acquire significant clinical wisdom regarding these questions.

One can feel overwhelmed by the chaos of an adolescent's intrapsychic life. One can feel still further overwhelmed when seeing an adolescent together with his family, in the same room, over long periods of time. Nonetheless, I feel that we need to expose students of adolescent psychiatry to the reality of these interdigitating, overwhelming forces. More so than with any other age group, the psyche of the adolescent cannot be understood without appreciating the impinging and shifting pressures of the familial field.

NOTE

1. The major portion of the theoretical formulations and related clinical studies described in this chapter represents experiences acquired by the author during some ten years of empirical clinical work in the field of family therapy, along with others on the senior staff of the Cedars-Sinai Department of Child Psychiatry, Los Angeles, California.

REFERENCES

Brown, S. L. (1964). Clinical impression of the impact of family group interviewing on child and adolescent psychiatric practice. *Journal of the American Academy of Child Psychiatry,* 3(5).
————. (1969). Diagnosis, clinical management and family interviewing. In: *Science and Psychoanalysis,* ed. J. Masserman, Vol. 14. New York: Grune & Stratton.
————. (1970). Family for adolescents. *Psychiatric Opinion,* 7(1).
Minuchin, S. (1971). Re-conceptualization of adolescent dynamics from the family point of view. In: *Teaching and Learning Adolescent Psychiatry,* ed. D. Offer and J. F. Masterson. Springfield, Ill.: Charles C. Thomas.

Paul, N. L., and Grosser, G. H. (1965). Operational mourning and its role in conjoint family therapy. *Community Mental Health Journal,* 1(4):339–345.

Schween, P. H., and Gralnick, A. (1965). Factors affecting family therapy in the hospital setting. *Comprehensive Psychiatry,* 7(5).

Williams, F. S. (1967a). Family interviews for diagnostic evaluations in child psychiatry. Paper presented to the American Orthopsychiatric Association, New York City.

———. (1967b). Family therapy: A critical assessment. *American Journal of Orthopsychiatry,* 37(5).

———. (1968). Family therapy. In: *Modern psychoanalysis,* ed. J. Marmor. New York: Basic Books, pp. 387–406.

———. (1970). Alienation of youth as reflected in the hippie movement. *Journal of the American Academy of Child Psychiatry,* 9(2).

Wynne, L. C. (1965). Some indications and contraindications for exploration of family therapy. In: *Intensive Family Therapy,* ed. I. Boszormenyi-Nagy and J. L. Framo. New York: Harper & Row, pp. 289–322.

19] COMPREHENSIVE RESIDENTIAL
TREATMENT OF ADOLESCENTS

JULIAN I. BARISH AND WILLIAM A. SCHONFELD

The admission of youthful patients to psychiatric hospitals, which began experimentally during the 1950s, has reached major proportions, with patients from twelve to twenty-five years of age comprising 50 to 80 percent of psychiatric hospital populations. During these twenty years there has been a corresponding proliferation of hospital facilities for adolescents (Hartmann *et al.,* 1968). The time-honored term "residential treatment," formerly reserved for a few special programs, is now applied ambiguously to a variety of treatment facilities. A current definition of the nature and use of extended residential treatment for adolescents in hospitals seems indicated.

There are residential adolescent treatment centers other than those in hospitals; these have, basically, a social work or educational orientation. Social work settings, the oldest historically, emphasize group living but also provide schooling and often psychotherapy, perhaps with psychological or psychiatric consultation. On the educational level, some special treatment schools and camps have a major focus on re-education, both in academics and in social relationships. These facilities, too, may consult with other disciplines and may utilize concurrent psychotherapy. In contrast, the philosophy in hospitals blends the dynamic orientation of psychiatry with the biological orientation of clinical medicine. Hospitals may or may not provide schooling or programs dictated by the special needs of adolescents. If generalizations may be made, the first two forms of residential care emphasize the mobilization of healthy aspects of personality, whereas psychiatric hospitals have tended to stress the relief of psychopathology.

Reprinted with permission from *Current Psychiatric Therapies,* ed. J. Masserman, Vol. 12 (1972). New York: Grune & Stratton, Inc.

Unfortunately, there has been no formal evaluation of the relative effectiveness of the social, educational, and psychiatric approaches to residential treatment. However, a wholesome balance and a complete program would appear optimal. During recent years, a few psychiatric units have been developing more and more in that direction. A new type of hospital service is emerging for which the term "comprehensive residential treatment of adolescents" is suggested.

Comprehensive residential treatment implies, first, that an institution provides a complete milieu, one that meets the social, educational, and other growth and health needs of its adolescent patients; second, it implies a particular kind of long-term treatment in residence, an organized therapeutic use of the milieu and an integration of milieu therapy with other treatment modalities into a unified approach toward definitive therapeutic goals. Finally, if it is to be designated comprehensive, a residential treatment service must pay full attention to aftercare, arranging follow-up treatment, supportive services, and a smooth transition of the patient back to the community.

In short, comprehensive residential treatment is more than the management and treatment of adolescents away from home. The designation is not appropriate for facilities that limit themselves to crisis intervention, short-term hospitalization, or partial hospitalization; nor does it apply to day schools, halfway houses, group residences, or foster family placements, though there is admittedly some overlap in facilities and functions and many of these services are, by definition, included.

Elements of Care

Allowing for local variations in emphasis and style, there are basic elements that comprehensive residential treatment centers ideally hold in common.

Most psychiatric residential treatment centers for adolescents have a psychodynamic frame of reference, with extensions to include family and group dynamics. Psychodynamics, defined as the study of goal-directed behavior and its motivational forces, is derived from psychoanalysis, psychiatry, and psychology. It offers concepts of personality development, of motivating forces, and of mechanisms by which environmental forces are internalized. Psychodynamics has limitations in accommodating data on biological and on sociological levels, and other theoretical approaches such as general systems theory are being added. Psychodynamics, however, remains the most useful frame of reference available for the purpose.

In a psychodynamic frame of reference, problems are seen in terms of motivation as well as behavior and are viewed longitudinally as a function of personality development. Consequently, therapeutic goals involve more than relief of symptoms or change of maladaptive behavior; when possible, they aim at modification of basic motivation and at personality reconstruction; always, they are concerned with fostering healthy growth and development. Since achieving definitive goals requires considerable time, a typical treatment program will involve six months to several years in the hospital and a like period of subsequent outpatient treatment.

The Patients

Most adolescents in residential treatment are diagnosed as schizophrenia, personality disorders, or borderline states. These diagnoses do not fully convey the diversity of clinical problems, but they do imply long-standing ego defects, severe motivational conflicts, and pervasive disturbances of functioning. The usual problems of adolescence, often tumultuous in themselves, are intensified and distorted. The customary themes and conflicts about impulse control, body image, dependency versus independence, peer relationships, sexual adequacy, identity, competition, authority, and so on, are presented. Also appearing in magnified form is the adolescent propensity for acting out: repetitive, symbolic, behavioral communication of anxieties and conflicts, at times in self-destructive and socially disturbing forms, which present both real dangers and unique opportunities for meaningful therapeutic intervention.

The number of adolescents makes a substantial difference in the character of a hospital milieu. A few adolescents may dominate a mixed adolescent-adult service, but without providing the minimum number necessary to make practical the required special staff and program. Moreover, the interactions in a sizable peer group are essential for residential treatment. Too large a number, however, makes management difficult. Units of ten to twenty adolescents offer a suitable balance.

Hospitals must be selective in the number and types of patients they treat. A single facility may not be able to deal with the full range of adolescent problems. The use of drugs, so prevalent in our adolescent subculture, is not managed easily, and some hospitals avoid drug problems. Other hospitals set an arbitrary age limit for acceptance; this should not supplant biological and social development as determining criteria. A serious deficiency in some states has been the exclusion of youths older than sixteen years from adolescent programs, not as a result of psychiatric judgment, but because education is not compulsory after sixteen.

Staff Requirements

Because of their energy, rebelliousness, and varied needs, adolescents require greater numbers of supervising personnel and a wider range of professional disciplines than do other age groups. More important than numbers, however, are the qualifications of professional staff, since therapeutic use of self is a sine qua non for all personnel in comprehensive residential treatment. The first qualification is the possession of certain difficult to define personality traits. One such trait is tolerance for adolescents, who do have a knack of threatening defenses and of evoking anxiety. Adolescents themselves say that attributes such as flexibility, firmness, sincerity, fairness, self-confidence, a desire to be of help, and the like are desirable.

Beyond personality traits, the paramedical professional staff requires expertise derived from training and, especially, experience. Key hospital personnel should be assigned to work with adolescents as their sole responsibility so that they may regard adolescents as a major professional interest. Some professionals see adolescents merely as troublemakers, which they often are; but an experienced and sensitive person will ask "Why?" and will react to the trouble appropriately. The psychiatrists who work with adolescents should also have special training and experience with this age group. (It is, in fact, important that all general psychiatric residents, as well as residents in child psychiatry, have supervised treatment of adolescents as part of their training. In addition, more opportunities for advanced training in adolescent psychiatry are needed to qualify psychiatrists as directors of adolescent services.)

Therapeutic Modalities

A comprehensive residential treatment milieu has immediately available a wide range of treatment modalities that can be integrated into individually planned programs. These include milieu therapy, individual psychotherapy, group therapy, family therapy, psychopharmacotherapy, and the organic therapies, plus the so-called ancillary therapies: educational, occupational, recreational, art, and perhaps music and dance

343

therapy, as well as counseling in family relationships, legal matters, social skills, and educational and vocational placement. Obviously, the choice and manner of application of these modalities varies considerably.

Milieu therapy, a vague entity, is not a specific treatment modality but is nonetheless a potent therapeutic force. It comprises all the basic elements of milieu described herein and serves as a vehicle for the other modalities of treatment, but it is more than the sum total of these. It requires a coherent social organization that provides an extensive treatment context that coordinates and integrates the various treatment modalities. According to Abroms (1969), the aim of milieu therapy is to direct social contacts and treatment experience synergistically toward specific, realistic therapeutic goals.

Whereas milieu therapy serves as a context and an integrating force for the therapeutic process, the core modality of treatment is individual psychotherapy, adapted by the therapist in his own style to each patient's needs. If milieu therapy is the vehicle of the treatment process, ongoing psychotherapy is its steering mechanism. Comprehensive residential treatment begins with a diagnostic evaluation in which a psychiatric case study is supplemented by the daily observations of professional staff. The therapist becomes the leader of a treatment team composed of representatives of various professional disciplines who interact with and try to understand the patients and one another. Individual psychotherapy provides an irreplaceable means of understanding a patient's unfolding dynamic pattern; further, the emotional context of the one-to-one relationship offers therapeutic leverage that is different from that of other modalities; finally, it serves as a check and balance for the otherwise group-oriented residential treatment.

Group therapy is also important in that it provides a controlled dynamic interaction and confrontation with peers. Psychopharmacotherapy is useful in relieving certain target symptoms such as excessive anxiety, depression, or decompensation so as to facilitate psychotherapy, education, and socialization.

The Structure

"Structure," in psychiatric jargon, refers to a regulated style of daily living. Patients are required to arise and retire on schedule, to eat meals at regular times, to attend activities and keep treatment appointments, to dress within prescribed modes, to observe telephone and visiting restrictions, to avoid behavior designated as objectionable, and to follow other local ground rules.

Each of these facets of living has its own set of psychodynamic meanings. Morning awakening, for example, can become a repetitive problem in which fear of failure, defensive anger, depression, and hopelessness are expressed. Similarly, going to bed at night elicits fears of helplessness and loss of control. The management of each requires skill and patience. However, these focal points of arising and retiring can also be the occasions of the most significant communication between patients and staff.

Structure helps recompensate a disorganized adolescent, sets limits for one who acts out, and gives all youth the symbols of authority to interact with. It provides the behavior control advocated by Hendrickson and Holmes (1959) as essential for residential treatment of adolescents. Structure and behavior control are necessary components of dynamic residential therapy; they should not, however, be so rigid as to prevent spontaneity or, indeed, all acting out. To reiterate, adolescent acting out often provides valuable opportunities for therapeutic intervention, through psychotherapeutic sanctions, peer disapproval, and, hopefully, insight as to motivation.

Activities

Whereas the scheduling of activities is an integral part of the structure of a hospital, and the need for a schedule is similar for adults, the type and variety of activities are different in an adolescent program.

Schooling is the customary occupation of adolescents and is appropriately the key activity in their residential programs. In some settings, the school is an integral part of the institution. It may be modeled after a community school, or it may operate along the lines of educational therapy. Individual tutoring and a flexible curriculum are needed in order to meet the requirements and adjust to the limitations of certain patients. It is important to offer high school credit for courses completed. In other institutions, adolescent patients attend the local junior or senior high school or are enrolled in neighboring tutoring schools. In still others, correspondence courses are utilized. Several universities with hospital programs for college students use their own academic facilities. Douady, Jeanguyot, Neel, Danon-Boileau, Lab, Brousselle, and Levy (1967) reported that a network of special hospitals for college students in France have the prerequisite of continuation of studies by each patient during treatment.

A variety of additional activities (physical, mechanical, artistic) are required to match the wide range of adolescent interests and are integrated into the therapeutic program. Nontherapeutic activities, too, are necessary to allow a respite from concentrated treatment. Youths also need a time and a place to which they may go off by themselves to read, think, or cry. Activities within the surrounding community also help to minimize the cloistered effect of residential treatment and ease transition back after discharge. Further, activities oriented to helping others serve as a counterforce to self-preoccupation and to the fascination with drug-induced perceptual experiences so currently common among adolescents.

Housing

There has been much debate, without reaching a definite conclusion, about adolescents in hospitals having separate quarters or sharing them with adults. There are advantages to each arrangement. With separate housing, a peer culture is established, more adolescents are amenable to treatment, and there is greater therapeutic leverage. With shared housing, particularly when adults greatly outnumber the adolescents, acting out is less and behavior control is easier. Ideally, both arrangements should be available, since some youths respond better to one than to the other. Realistically, the choice usually depends on local conditions, such as the availability of space and staff. Separate housing is of less consequence than separate programs and a well-trained multidisciplinary staff under the supervision of a psychiatrist specializing in adolescents' problems.

Families

The patient's family may not be living on the hospital grounds, but it is nonetheless a vital element of the hospital milieu. An effective system of communicating with parents is essential, since they can reinforce or undermine therapeutic efforts, depending on their own needs and on how well they are coordinated with the treatment. As a minimum standard for parents' involvement, they should be kept informed about the patient's status and progress and should have counseling to improve their understanding of the patient and their dealings with him. In many cases, of course, more elaborate treatment for families is indicated.

Group Dynamics

Conscious use of informal and planned interactions is an essential ingredient of a residential treatment program. Group dynamics may be defined simply as the interaction of individuals with one another and with social institutions, but under this rubric are found the most complex and least understood therapeutic phenomena. As Redl (1967) indicated, we do not have adequate concepts, or even the language, to describe fully the multiple, subtle transactions among people in a hospital. Yet, these transactions exert a powerful influence, both positive and negative, on the treatment process.

Aftercare

Abrupt discharge or faulty aftercare without adequate supportive and rehabilitative services can undermine an otherwise positive result of residential treatment. For gradual transition back into the community, a comprehensive service may be required to arrange continued treatment, educational or vocational counseling, school or job placement, housing or surrogate family, and social contacts. The range of services may be supplied by the institution itself or through cooperation with other agencies in the community. Perhaps, for most efficient operation, comprehensive residential centers should be part of a broad continuum of facilities so organized as to permit close cooperation and ease of transfer. This may be made possible by the community mental health program.

Indications for Comprehensive
Residential Treatment

Few authors mention specific indications for long-term residential treatment. Beckett (1965) noted that adolescents are usually referred for inpatient treatment because of behavior that "adult society considers boisterous, aggressive or violent," but use of that criterion alone would qualify most teenagers for residential treatment at some time during their development. Easson (1969) cited two basic criteria for residential

347

treatment of an adolescent: a deficit in ego strength manifested by an inability to control drives and impulses and a lack of emotional capability to form meaningful relationships.

There are other factors to consider. The prescription of comprehensive residential treatment should be made only after a thorough evaluation of the patient, his family, and his social environment gives positive indication that it is the treatment of choice. Furthermore, the recommendation should be carried out only if there is a hospital available that can treat him effectively. Each factor and the whole configuration must be considered. Is the adolescent's problem pervasive and severe enough to warrant such intensive and extensive treatment, and will it be amenable to a comprehensive residential approach? Is he maladjusted in multiple areas—family, school, social, and sexual? Is the family interaction pathogenic, and does it perpetuate the problem? Are there significant positive forces in school or in peer relationships that should be preserved? Can the adolescent and his family be helped to use the hospital experience constructively? Which of the hospitals under consideration is likely to manage the patient and his family most effectively? How long a period of treatment is needed? Is it financially feasible for the family? These are representative questions that a referring person or an admitting psychiatrist must ask himself. Aftercare planning should also begin at this stage. Can the patient return to his family after discharge from the hospital? What other arrangements will be necessary for aftercare?

Adolescents are at a particularly malleable stage of development. Comprehensive residential treatment, therefore, is a powerful therapeutic force, since it supplies a maximum of external support, direction, and influence. When carefully designed and properly used, such programs can effectively treat some problem adolescents who cannot be helped in any other way, and may be life-saving.

Conversely, comprehensive residential treatment can also be a destructive force. Easson (1969) cautioned that injudicious or ill-timed use of inpatient therapy may not only fail to benefit the patient but may also produce emotional regression and personality stunting. Unnecessary or badly planned hospital placement may handicap an adolescent emotionally and intellectually. Consequently, the prescription of comprehensive residential treatment must be made with great care. Less radical methods of treatment are to be considered first, keeping in mind, however, that procrastination in prescribing residential treatment when it is the method of choice may lose valuable time and may conceivably permit preventable tragedies. In short, fine clinical judgment is required. When in doubt, a trial period in a comprehensive facility may clarify whether extended treatment is indicated.

Comprehensive residential treatment may follow crisis-oriented therapy, but the indications for the two are quite different. Dangerous behavior or exposure to excessive stress may be sufficient indication for short-term psychiatric hospitalization but not for continued residential treatment. A youth who is a drug abuser or even a potential suicide is not necessarily a candidate for comprehensive residential treatment. Nor should hospitals be used as tools of popular prejudice to remove from society those youths who do not accept conventional concepts. Only those adolescents who show positive indications for, and who can benefit from, the experience should be considered.

The choice of a hospital is crucial. To judge whether an institution can be expected to treat a specific patient effectively, the prescriber should know the strengths and limitations of the institution's particular milieu, its treatment philosophy and practice, and its attitude toward aftercare. A poorly matched patient and residential service may result in a treatment failure or in equally undesirable custodial care.

Conclusions

By definition, comprehensive residential treatment should be part of a total treatment program for the adolescent and his family. For that reason its prescription is best made by a professional who not only can make a suitable evaluation but also, if possible, maintain contact with the hospital, the family, and the patient. He may be of immeasurable help in minimizing the anxieties and guilt inevitably evoked by the recommendation of psychiatric hospitalization, in overcoming family resistances as they arise during the course of treatment, and in ensuring continuity of care after discharge.

The prescriber of comprehensive treatment can give no positive prognostication or definite promise about its outcome. With such a new, potent, and complex tool, uncertain results are not surprising. Hopefully, as methods employed are developed further, their positive indications and inherent limitations will be more precisely defined.

REFERENCES

Abroms, G. M. (1969). Defining milieu therapy. *Archives of General Psychiatry,* 21:553–560.

Beckett, P. G. S. (1965). *Adolescents Out of Step: Their Treatment in a Psychiatric Hospital.* Detroit: Wayne State University Press.

Douady, D., Jeanguyot, M., Neel, D., Danon-Boileau, H., Lab, P., Brousselle, A., and Levy, E. (1967). L'organisation des cliniques médico-psychologiques de la fondation santé des étudiants de France. *Revue Neuropsychiatrie et d'Hygiene Mentale de l'Enfant,* 15:505–535.

Easson, W. M. (1969). *The Severely Disturbed Adolescent.* New York: International Universities Press.

Hartmann, E., Glasser, B. A., Greenblatt, M., Solomon, M. H., and Levinson, D. J. (1968). *Adolescents in a Mental Hospital.* New York: Grune & Stratton.

Hendrickson, W. J., and Holmes, D. J. (1959). Control of behavior as a crucial factor in intensive psychiatric treatment in an all adolescent ward. *American Journal of Psychiatry,* 115:969.

Redl, F. (1967). *Aggression in Adolescence.* Paper presented to the Society for Adolescent Psychiatry, New York City, October.

20] DEVELOPMENT OF A PROTREATMENT GROUP PROCESS AMONG HOSPITALIZED ADOLESCENTS

JERRY M. LEWIS, JOHN T. GOSSETT,
JOE W. KING, AND DOYLE I. CARSON

In a setting with treatment vectors that include intensive individual psychotherapy, group psychotherapy, family therapy, a full school program, and an active, confronting, interpreting milieu program, one still faces the disheartening observation that a significant number of severely disturbed adolescents do not achieve satisfactory social recovery after months, or even years, of hospitalization. The fact that such programs achieve only limited success provokes thoughtful inquiry, stimulates research hypotheses, and leads to program innovations. The focus of this chapter concerns one such set of innovations: our attempts to promote a protreatment group process among our hospitalized adolescent patients.

Protreatment Group Process

We use the term "protreatment group process" to describe the genuine internalization of positive treatment goals by a majority of the members of the inpatient adolescent group. Examples of treatment goals are: (1) acceptance of the fact that self-destructive and self-defeating behaviors are seriously maladaptive solutions to the universal problems of living; (2) acceptance of personal responsibility for maladaptive behavior (and the consequent giving up of tenaciously held rationalizations, minimizations, denials, and projections concerning these behaviors); (3) commit-

351

ment to personal change through sustained, often extremely uncomfortable, behavioral effort and cognitive insight; (4) commitment to the positive value of openness about one's thoughts, feelings, and behaviors (and the negative value of secrecy, passivity, and apathy); (5) commitment to direct verbal expression of one's thoughts and feelings (rather than acting out and manipulation); (6) commitment to honest relationships with peers, family, and hospital staff (with a sense of personal obligation to detect one's own distortions and repressions, and to refrain from suppression and lies); (7) willingness to observe therapeutically derived limits set on one's behavior, whether one agrees with those limits at the time or not; (8) acceptance of the prime value of human relationships (that is, viewing of one's ability to love, to give, to share, to receive, and to establish and maintain close, warm, trusting human relationships as a most important goal in the process of living); (9) concurrent acceptance of the value of meaningful, productive work (which includes continuing education, forming educational and vocational goals, and striving toward economic and personal autonomy through self-supporting, ego-enhancing activity).

No one individual patient achieves complete internalization of all these goals, but the list does describe a general pattern or style possessed in greater degree by patients characterized as protreatment. When most of the members of the inpatient group are working together toward such goals, their influence spreads throughout the group and we speak of a protreatment group process.

The Setting

The Timberlawn Adolescent Service is one part of a private psychiatric center and constitutes 26 of the 152 beds of the inpatient service. The development of this adolescent service, the administrative structure of the treatment team, the basic philosophy of the milieu program, and our clinical observations regarding the special resistances of a subgroup of highly drug-dependent adolescents have been the subjects of other reports (Lewis, 1969, 1970; King, 1969; Gossett and Lewis, 1969; Carson and Lewis, 1970; Lewis and Gossett, 1971). We emphasize that our treatment experience is with severely disturbed thirteen- to nineteen-year-olds for whom other treatment attempts have failed. Typically, hospitalization for such patients ranges from months to several years. The treatment program has evolved through several stages (Lewis, 1970); prior to February 1968, all adolescent patients were housed in primarily adult living units. During this phase of development as a service, in some rare instances we observed the crucial role played by spontaneously evolving protreatment cliques on newly admitted, highly resistant patients. Such peer-group contact appeared to reduce the intensity of early resistance, shorten its duration, and directly influence the course of treatment. Much more common was the formation of intensely antitreatment cliques whose members' resistance to treatment was greatly increased and prolonged as the teenagers supported one another's negative, self-defeating, and self-destructive attitudes. As our sensitivity to the tremendous impact of peer-group pressure grew, the writings of Redl (1951, 1966); Hendrickson, Holmes, and Waggoner (1959); Rinsley (1962, 1963, 1965, 1967); Rinsley and Inge (1961); and Holmes (1964) led us to attempt to influence the nature of the group process in a planned way. To implement this attempt, our adolescent service staff decided to effect two major changes in the treatment program.

Separate Divisions and Group Restrictions

First, all adolescent patients were moved to two separate divisions apart from adult patients; that is, the fourteen female adolescents were housed together, and the twelve male adolescents were housed together. As a second major change, we borrowed a technique from other settings, that of holding the groups responsible, in part, for the behavior of each member and, conversely, each member responsible to the group for his own behavior. At the time of transfer to separate living divisions, the boys' and girls' groups met with their division psychiatrist who described how they could influence the quality of life on their units by their participation in the four group meetings per week on each unit. These division meetings would be focused on their day-to-day feelings. Iron-clad rules would be few, but vigorously enforced. Behaviors considered by any staff member to be actually or potentially dangerous would result in loss of all privileges (parties, visits, unaccompanied absence from the living unit) for the entire division. Such behaviors include, for example, suicide attempts or gestures, physical assault, running away from the hospital, illicit drug use, or fire setting. This group restriction automatically cancels all privileges for all patients on the division regardless of who was actively involved.

The rationale for the group restriction is the staff conviction that very little disturbed behavior is truly spontaneous, impulsive, or without antecedents. We believe that such behaviors are almost always preceded by verbal or behavioral messages directed to other patients or to the staff. The responsibility for recognizing such messages and attempting to intervene is shared by staff and patients. If the group plays a marked role in the dangerous behavior of an individual member, the restriction is likely to be of a long duration. For example, if a patient elopes from the hospital and it becomes apparent that many of the other patients on that unit knew the plans in advance, a long group restriction is likely to follow. On the other hand, if the group's role was minor, the restriction may be much shorter. If a new female patient slashes her wrists on the first day of hospitalization, before other patients could know her, the group restriction is likely to be a short one.

Group participation in destructive behavior may be passive rather than active. For example, if a depressed, schizoid girl suddenly explodes into violence and attacks someone, and it becomes obvious in subsequent division meetings that this seriously disturbed individual had made a number of ignored attempts to communicate the degree of her internal rage, a lengthy group restriction is probable.

Though most group restrictions result from overt, aggressive behavior, it is clear that pervasive group apathy sometimes can be destructive enough to warrant a group restriction. For example, if some of the group are upset and on the verge of destructive acting out, staff members encourage the other group members to offer concern, support, and an opportunity to talk out rather than act out the conflicted feelings. However, if apathy, passivity, and indifference pervade the group, the support needed by the aggressive, acutely disturbed members does not appear. If repeated staff confrontations do not elicit a supportive, working together, helpful response, and group apathy continues, a group restriction results because such group indifference to acute problems invites destructive acting out. Group restriction continues until group members once again show concern, involvement, and active interest in one another's welfare.

Generally, group restrictions continue until three conditions are fulfilled: (1) each member in the group has explored his own role in precipitating (either actively or passively) the behavior that caused the group restriction; (2) there has been open expression of honest feelings about the patient whose behavior led to the restriction; and (3) the group has attempted to help the patient or patients who caused the restrictions to find alternate ways of handling the feelings involved in the harmful behavior. Group restriction may be terminated only by the division psychiatrist; he bases his judgment primarily on the degree to

354

which the group can meet the three requirements in their division meetings.

Rendering an active, dynamic process to written form leaves the impression that the process is somehow stylized or rigid. Actually this is far from so; the guidelines for group restrictions only define the context in which the staff formulates clinical judgment regarding individual and group behavior.

Development of a Protreatment Group Process

During the two years of this milieu there have been several clear-cut phases in patients' reactions. Initially, both the boys' and girls' groups reacted with intense resistance. The move to separate units was extremely stressful for our patients, most of whom had little trust in one another's benevolence and were rarely able to tolerate interpersonal closeness. Homosexual fears and fears of attack were stimulated in many patients. These fears, initiated by the forced physical closeness of the separate units, were augmented by the loss of fantasied staff omnipotence. Our demand that patients now become involved in the responsibility for preventing severely disturbed behaviors directly contradicted their expectation that since we were in charge we should be able to prevent anyone from harming himself or others. Many responded by increasing the frequency and intensity of demands on staff, thus communicating their need to be cared for by an omnipotent staff.

Anger, superficial demands, and a high level of anxiety characterized the four-times-a-week division meetings during this resistant phase. The initial group restriction on each unit provoked intense anger focused entirely on the staff rather than on the patient whose behavior had restricted the unit. They felt we were grossly unfair to restrict all of them for the behavior of one person. During these initial restrictions, the more manipulative and verbal youngsters (usually severe character disorders) led the discussions of factors and feelings involved in the group restrictions. A quality of phoniness pervaded these meetings. A girl who had precipitated a group restriction by cutting her wrist was told how much the group cared about her, how sorry they were that she had resorted to such behavior, and how much they regretted whatever their own role might have been. Their underlying anger was thinly veiled by such pseudoconcern. The unit psychiatrist confronted the group members repeatedly with their phoniness.

355

After a few group restrictions were invoked and resolved (which took several months) we moved into a second phase of patient reaction to the new milieu. The intense resistance softened as the patients became accustomed to the system, and a clear-cut difference between the male and female divisions appeared. Though the differences may have been a reflection of the differing styles of the two division psychiatrists, it was the impression of staff members who attended meetings on both divisions that this was not the primary factor.

The girls' group restrictions generally were caused by suicide gestures or runaway attempts, and were dealt with by slowly increasing openness on the part of the girls in their division meetings. Initially, they expressed angry feelings, but then moved into their genuine positive feelings for one another. This led to group discussions focused on anxiety related to homosexual feelings and fears of object loss. These meetings in the girls' division tended to center around discussions of closeness and fears of closeness.

A very different style developed in the boys' unit. Suicide gestures were extremely rare, and most group restrictions were provoked by runaway attempts, threats of physical aggression, or illicit drug use. The boys continued much longer than the girls to project their anger onto the division psychiatrist. Rarely did any male adolescent approach topics of closeness or fears of closeness directly, but they were much more open and direct about the true intensity of their angry, hostile feelings toward the staff, and eventually toward one another.

During this second phase, the teenagers whose family relationships involved persistent testing maneuvers repeated the same maneuvers with their groups. Frequent group restrictions resulted, and meetings were filled with anger, despair, and feelings of impotence. It appeared crucial for the staff to acknowledge these feelings and to confront the testing youngsters repeatedly with their impact on others. Group cohesion gradually appeared on both units, and the need for staff confrontation and interpretation diminished as the groups themselves became more active in these areas.

When openness about feelings became customary, a third phase coalesced as the majority of members in each group supported the goals of treatment. Patients began calling impromptu division meetings on their own because "Mary is withdrawn tonight, and sometimes that's followed by a suicide attempt," or "George is acting very silly and immature today, and he has a visit coming up this weekend which he can't handle if he acts the way he's acting this week." At such meetings, frequently the charge nurse was the only staff member present. Discussions of closeness (and resulting fears of homosexuality or abandonment) be-

came possible on both units. In the boys' unit (where drug usage occurred several times) an antidrug orientation gradually evolved as one
part of their protreatment attitude. It is our impression that this antidrug group attitude is crucial to the success of treatment efforts with such
youngsters (Lewis and Gossett, 1971). Patients can now discuss their
feelings about staff members openly. A division meeting may be devoted to a schizophrenic boy's intense fear of the school principal; and
though his and the principal's verbalizations do not magically undo the
fear, he may experience some relief as other youngsters talk about their
own frequently distorted images of various staff members. Currently,
when the group's attention is drawn to the degree of their participation
in allowing a withdrawn patient to remain withdrawn, efforts can be
made, on the spot, to involve the withdrawing person in more meaningful relationships and perhaps avert an elopement or suicide attempt.

Clinical Vignettes

Though it was possible to elicit discussions of suicide gestures and
threats, homosexual fears, illicit drug use, withdrawal, and physical aggression prior to the separate divisions and group restrictions innovations, it generally was not possible to persuade severely disturbed adolescents to show sustained helpful involvement in one another's specific
behavioral problems. Such problems not only reflect the teenager's inner
disturbances, but, in turn, disturb others. When forced into a very close
day-to-day living situation (without adult patients as buffers), the adolescents began to experience one another's problems in a very personal,
concrete, and significant manner:

When confronted in a division meeting with her recent withdrawal, Lois
said she cared deeply for all of them, but (tearfully) she simply couldn't express her genuine affection. At this, Mary responded angrily, "If we are so
damned important to you, why are you making plans to run away?"

Bill, a fourteen-year-old, handled his angry feelings by being provocative
and sarcastic to the other patients. He excelled at playing pool and would
do anything to win. He delighted in beating all the others, and then making
derogatory comments about them personally, somehow connecting this to
their "shabby pool playing." He provoked them in other areas as well until
finally the group confronted him with how many of them felt like "smash-
ing" him. Instead, the group elected to restrict him from the pool table for a
week. This had a tremendous impact, and his behavior improved considerably.

George, a very intelligent seventeen-year-old, had been hospitalized for
two years because of withdrawing, psychotic episodes. He had improved

357

enough to leave the hospital to go to public school; but, despite great strides toward recovery, he continued to function in a very maladaptive way in several areas. Individual staff members found it virtually impossible to get through his shield of denial and sarcasm. His quick wit (and quicker tongue) usually left them feeling as though it was a terrible mistake even to say good morning to him. However, confrontation by the entire group of eleven boys could penetrate his denial with examples of his behavior known only to them, and force his acknowledgment of the problems he was having in dealing with others.

In the current milieu, active involvement in one another's problems is not confined to group confrontations about irritating behaviors. What may begin as an angry confrontation often develops into substantial group empathy and support:

Marie, an eighteen-year-old girl, within a few days of discharge encountered Ann, younger and very severely disturbed. Ann ran up and hugged and kissed her, making her very uncomfortable. The other kids were all saying, "There goes Ann again with the homosexual crap." But Marie said, "I don't feel it that way. I felt that you were being a little baby with me, and you were asking for something from me that I can't give you. I can't do everything for you that your mother didn't do; but even worse than that, when you treat me that way, I can't even be Marie to you." The group focus shifted from angry confrontation to understanding support.

For a week, Hal, a fourteen-year-old, was increasingly irritating until finally several aggressive group members angrily demanded an explanation for his provocative behavior. Initially defensive, Hal suddenly broke into tears, "I can't see my therapist; he's sick and people aren't letting me know how sick he really is. I don't have anyone to talk to." This genuine anguish shifted the group mood from attack to support, and Hal could explore his fantasies of the therapist's death, the added loss of his best friend (who had recently been discharged), and the final blow, cancellation of a parent's visit due to a group restriction. As his genuine feelings of abandonment poured out, many group members shared similar feelings of loss, sadness, loneliness, and subsequent rage.

Finally, we think we get a different quality of patient-to-staff confrontation now that the adolescents feel some protreatment group solidarity. We have always received projections of blame, angry blasts, and attempts at guilt manipulation; these continue, but currently, in addition, the group's anger may be directed at real staff irresponsibility:

Tom and Susan, making their first explorations into boy-girl relating, held hands under the table while eating lunch. An aide observed this clear violation of the rule against physical contact but did not confront the patients or report the incident to other staff. Several days later the incident was reported in a group meeting by Susan herself who described very mixed feelings. It was fun to get away with hand-holding, but she knew she had been observed and was uncomfortable. As others joined in, several different feelings surfaced. Joan thought the rule was silly and didn't count if you didn't get caught. Marsha felt that it was okay since Tom and Susan were "in love." Mary hinted at more than hand-holding but said she was talking to her individual therapist about it, clearly implying that her rule-breaking was thereby sanctioned. At this point, Susan faced the aide who had observed her physical contact, saying that if there were good reasons for the rule then, by God, she expected staff to enforce it. The clear expectation of more strength and maturity from staff members came out as they revealed the anger they experienced when their irresponsibility was met by staff avoidance of confrontation.

Special Problems: Patient, Parent, Staff

Though moving to the all-adolescent divisions and instituting the group restriction policy have been extremely potent milieu maneuvers, no treatment techniques are without special problems. Our initial concern was whether it would be possible to treat psychotic teenagers in such a physically and emotionally close, all-adolescent setting where intense feelings are generated and handled directly and openly. With two years' experience, we feel that even very withdrawn and confused teenagers can be treated in such a setting even though such intense closeness and intimacy may at times precipitate or prolong psychotic regressions. These overtly psychotic teenagers are more likely to begin initial, groping attempts toward potentially healthy peer relationships in this setting, while previously they often settled into very childlike, dependent relationships with seriously disturbed adult patients. The clear, confrontation-of-reality expectation has a therapeutic impact on even hallucinating, delusional, and disoriented boys and girls. Occasionally a psychotic patient's insights penetrate into deeper levels of the group process; and, though he may move in close and then retreat to a more withdrawn stance over and over again, he may come to be valued by the group for his occasional, shattering insightfulness.

Impulsive, primitive, characterologically disordered teenagers also posed special problems in this milieu. During early weeks of hospitalization, the direct, angry group confrontations of such a patient's rationalization, minimization, denial, and projection of blame often result in heightened anxiety on the part of the new patient. When his family relationships have centered around pervasive, hostile jealousy and competitiveness, he often attempts to control or punish the group through consciously planned suicide gestures, physical attacks, or elopement. This usually happens when an envied group member is about to get a highly

359

valued visit, or shortly before another hated group member is to receive a high level of day-to-day privileges. Such attempted manipulation of the group is met by immediate termination of the group restriction by the division psychiatrist.

Finally, we note that the divisions tend to regress if several youngsters are discharged simultaneously. When many well-functioning patients are replaced by new, highly resistant individuals, the group stance may shift from a protreatment to an antitreatment attitude. For this reason, we space discharges as far apart as possible, and spend a great deal of time in division meetings preparing for the feelings aroused by the loss of old, highly valued members and the threats posed by new, generally disliked members.

We are aware of the possibility that the severity of the group restriction process invites patients to become skilled at pretending the openness, honesty, and interpersonal involvement they now frequently display. It is our strong impression that for many (if not most) of our adolescents, initial efforts in a protreatment direction are quite artificial and are engaged in more to satisfy the severe requirements of the system than as expressions of genuine caring. For many, however, experiencing themselves behaving in these new ways appears to augment the genuine incorporation of the previously pretended behavior patterns. Perhaps the most reliable index of the change from pretense to genuineness is not the verbal acknowledgment of protreatment goals but rather the demonstrated ability to tolerate the anxiety, related psychological depression, and pain associated with intensive self-exploration.

Parental resistance to the group restriction requires consideration in our family treatment program. When a group restriction caused by someone else's child cancels a long-awaited visit, parents have very strong negative feelings. Repeated explanations of the philosophy and process of group restriction are necessary. It has been helpful to have families participate in a division meeting as part of an all-day family program. For some parents, this emotionally charged experience creates a clearer understanding than staff explanations. However, many parents continue to be angry at paying a personal price to help other people's children.

In addition to these special problems with certain types of patients and parents, the new milieu created new staff stresses. Staff members also must participate in the division meetings, which place a premium on open, honest, direct, verbal communication of one's feelings in an interpersonal context. Such closeness and directness may be very unsettling to staff members who previously functioned in more bureaucratic,

360

distant, nonsharing treatment roles. It has become clear to us that not all treatment personnel can, or care to, function in this milieu.

Outcome

Though we have not yet developed a way to measure degrees of a group's protreatment attitude, it is our distinct impression that many of our patients have a much deeper commitment to treatment goals than they did during earlier phases of the service's development. We do not know how much of what we perceive is related to the all-adolescent division system and how much to the group restriction technique. The annual follow-up evaluation of all discharged patients has not generated sufficient numbers to enable us to make statistical correlations of outcome with the various phases through which the service has evolved. However, we think that we are tapping a treatment resource frequently overlooked, that of the impact of a protreatment group process as a function of intense peer-group influence on the individual members.

REFERENCES

Carson, D. I., and Lewis, J. M. (1970). Factors influencing drug abuse in young people. *Texas Medicine*, 66:50–57.

Gossett, J. T., and Lewis, J. M. (1969). Follow-up study of former inpatients of the Adolescent Service, Timberlawn Psychiatric Center. *Timberlawn Foundation Report*, no. 37.

Hendrickson, W. J., Holmes, D. J., and Waggoner, R. W. (1959). Psychotherapy of the hospitalized adolescent. *American Journal of Psychiatry*, 116:527–532.

Holmes, D. (1964). *The Adolescent in Psychotherapy*. Boston: Little, Brown.

King, J. W. (1969). The scope and impact of the group process in adolescents. In: *Troubled Youth in Today's World. Timberlawn Foundation Report*, no. 28, pp. 45–58.

Lewis, J. M. (1969). The organizational structure of the therapeutic team. *Hospital and Community Psychiatry*, 20:36–38.

———. (1970). Development of an inpatient adolescent service. *Adolescence*, 5:301–312.

———, and Gossett, J. T. (1971). The treatment of drug dependent adolescents: Impressions from a psychiatric hospital. *Timberlawn Foundation Report*, no. 56.

Redl, F. (1951). *Children Who Hate*. New York: The Free Press.

———. (1966). *When We Deal With Children*. New York: The Free Press.

Rinsley, D. B. (1962). Psychiatric hospital treatment of adolescents. *Archives of General Psychiatry*, 7:286–294.

———. (1963). Psychiatric hospital treatment with special reference to children. *Archives of General Psychiatry*, 9:489–496.

———. (1965). Intensive psychiatric hospital treatment of adolescents. *Psychiatric Quarterly*, 39:405–429.

———. (1967). Intensive residential treatment of the adolescent. *Psychiatric Quarterly,* 41:134–143.

———, and Inge, G. P. (1961). Psychiatric hospital treatment of adolescents: Verbal and non-verbal resistance to treatment. *Bulletin of the Menninger Clinic,* 25:249–263.

IN MEMORIAM

DONALD W. WINNICOTT

D. W. Winnicott died in January 1971 shortly after we received his essay for publication. His loss to psychiatry and psychoanalysis both in a therapeutic and developmental frame is immeasurable, and to those who felt close to him, he is irreplaceable.

The chapter published in this volume is illustrative of his customary charm, but the simplicity of his style should not mislead us; he expounds profound truths in a light but dexterous fashion. His description of the antisocial tendency and his distinction between privation and deprivation are important issues for those interested in clinical and developmental factors. His capacity to elucidate transitional elements and instill hope in those working with children are among his important contributions.

Sherman C. Feinstein
Peter L. Giovacchini

21] DELINQUENCY AS A
SIGN OF HOPE

D. W. WINNICOTT

Although the title of my talk has been put in the program in the following form: "Delinquency As a Sign of Hope," I would prefer to talk about The Antisocial Tendency. The reason is that this term can be applied to tendencies that appear at the normal end of the scale from time to time in your own children or in children living in good homes of their own, and it is here that one can best see the connection that I believe exists between the tendency and hope. By the time the boy or girl has become hardened because of the failure of the communication, the antisocial act not being recognized as something that contains an S.O.S., and when secondary gains have become important and great skill has been achieved in some antisocial activity, then it is much more difficult to see (what is still there, nevertheless) the S.O.S. that is a signal of hope in the boy or girl who is antisocial.

The second thing that I want to make clear is that I know I could not do your job. By temperament I am not fitted for the work that you do; and in any case I am not tall enough or big enough. I have certain skills and a certain kind of experience, and it remains to be seen whether there can be some pathway found between the things that I know something about and the work that you are doing. It might happen that nothing that I say will have any effect at all on what you do when you go back to your work. Nevertheless there might be some effect of an indirect kind because it must sometimes seem to you to be an insult to human nature that most of the boys and girls you have to deal with have this tendency to be a nuisance. You try to relate the delinquency you see in front of you to general matters like poverty, poor housing,

Presented to the Borstal Assistant Governors' Conference, Winchester, 1967. Reprinted with permission from *Prison Service Journal*, Her Majesty's Prison, Blundeston, Lowestoft, Suffolk, England, 1967.

broken homes, parental delinquency, and a breakdown of the social provision. I would like to feel that as a result of what I have to say, you may be able to see a little more clearly that in every case that comes your way, there was a beginning and at the beginning there was an illness, and the boy or girl became a deprived child. In other words there is sense in what once happened, although by the time that each individual comes into your care the sense has usually become lost.

A third thing that I want to make clear has to do with the fact that I am a psychoanalyst. I am not putting forward a strong claim that psychoanalysis has a direct contribution to make to your subject. If it has, this belongs to recent work, and I have taken some part personally in trying to formulate a theory, which is valuable because true and which derives to some extent from the general body of understanding that has come through psychoanalysis.

I now come to the main statement that I want to make which is really not at all complex. According to my view, which is based on experience (but as I freely admit on experience of younger children who are near the beginning of their trouble and who are not from the worst social conditions), the antisocial tendency is linked inherently with deprivation. In other words, it is not the general social failure that is responsible so much as a specific failure. For the child that we are studying it can be said that things went well enough and then they did not go well enough. A change occurred which altered the whole life of the child and this change in the environment happened when the child was old enough to know about things. It is not that the child could come here and give a lecture on himself or herself, but, given suitable conditions, the child is able to reproduce what happened because of having been far enough developed at the time to have been aware. In other words, in special conditions of psychotherapy the child is able to remember in terms of the material produced, in playing or in dreaming or in talking, the essential features of the original deprivation. I want to contrast this with environmental disturbances at an earlier stage of emotional development. A baby deprived of oxygen does not go around hoping to convince someone that if there had been enough oxygen things would have been all right. Environmental disturbances distorting the emotional development of a baby do not produce the antisocial tendency; they produce distortions of the personality which result in illness of a psychotic type so that the boy or girl is liable to mental hospital disorder or else he or she goes through life with certain distortions of reality testing and so on, perhaps of the kind that are accepted. The antisocial tendency relates not to privation, but to a deprivation.

The characteristic of the antisocial tendency is the drive that it gives the boy or girl to get back behind the deprivation moment or condition. A child who has been deprived in this way has first suffered unthinkable anxiety and then has gradually reorganized into someone who is in a fairly neutral state, complying because there is nothing else that the child is strong enough to do. This state may be fairly satisfactory from the point of view of those who are in care. Then for some reason or other hope begins to appear, and this means that the child, without being conscious of what is going on, begins to have the urge to get back behind the moment of deprivation and so to undo the fear of the unthinkable anxiety or confusion that resulted before the neutral state became organized. This is the very deceptive thing that those in care of antisocial children need to know if they are to see sense in what is going on around them. Whenever conditions give a child a certain degree of new hope, then the antisocial tendency becomes a clinical feature and the child becomes difficult.

At this point it is necessary to see that we are talking about two aspects of this one thing, the antisocial tendency. I would like to relate one of these to the relationship between the small child and the mother and the other to the later development which is the child's relation to the father. The first one has to do with all children and the second one is more especially the concern of boys. The first one has to do with the fact that the mother in her adaptation to the small child's needs enables the child creatively to find objects. She initiates the creative use of the world. When this fails the child has lost contact with objects, has lost the capacity creatively to find anything. At the moment of hope the child reaches out and steals an object. This is a compulsive act and the child does not know why he or she does it. Often the child feels mad because of having a compulsion to do something without knowing why. Naturally the fountain pen stolen from Woolworth's is not satisfactory; it is not the object that was being sought, and in any case *the child is looking for the capacity to find, not for an object.* Nevertheless there may be some satisfaction belonging to what is done in a moment of hope. The apple stolen from the orchard is more on the borderline. It can be ripe and can taste nice and it can be fun to be chased by the farmer. On the other hand the apple may be green and if eaten may give the boy a stomach-ache, and it may be that already the boy is not eating what he has stolen, but is giving the apples away, or perhaps he organizes the theft without running the risk of climbing the wall himself. In this sequence we see the transition from the normal prank to the antisocial act.

And so if we examine this first kind of expression of the antisocial tendency we can arrive at something so common as to be normal. Your own child claims the right to go into the larder and take a bun, or your little child of two years explores your wife's handbag and takes out a penny. If we examine all degrees we find at one extreme something hardening into a compulsive act without meaning and without producing direct satisfaction, but blossoming into a skill; while at the other extreme is something which happens over and over again in every family, a child reacting to some kind of relative deprivation by an antisocial act and the parents responding by a temporary period of indulgence which may very well see the child through a difficult phase.

Alongside this I want to examine deprivation in terms of the child and the father, but the principle is the same. The child, and this time I will say the boy, because if it is a girl I am still talking about the boy in the girl, finds that it is safe to have aggressive feelings and to be aggressive, because of the framework of the family representing society in a localized form. The mother's confidence in her husband or in the support that she will get, if she calls out, from local society, perhaps from the policeman, makes it possible for the child to explore crudely destructive activities which relate to movement in general, and also more specifically destruction that has to do with the fantasy that accumulates round the hate. In this way (because of the environmental security, mother supported by father, etc.) the child becomes able to do a very complex thing, that is to say, to integrate all his destructive impulses in with the loving ones, and the result when things go well is that the child recognizes the reality of the destructive ideas that are inherent in life and living and loving, and finds ways and means of protecting valued people and objects from himself. In fact he organizes his life contructively in order not to feel too bad about the very real destructiveness that goes on in his mind. In order to achieve this in his development, the child absolutely requires an environment that is indestructible in essential respects; certainly carpets get dirtied and the walls have to be repapered and an occasional window gets broken but somehow the home sticks together, and behind all this is the confidence that the child has in the relationship between the parents; the family is a going concern. When a deprivation occurs in terms of a breakup of the home, especially an estrangement between the parents, a very severe thing happens in the child's mental organization. Suddenly his aggressive ideas and impulses become unsafe. I think that what happens immediately is that the child takes over the control that has been lost and becomes identified with the framework, the result being that he loses his own impulsiveness and spontaneity. There is much too much anxiety now for experimentation which could result in his coming to terms with his own aggression. There follows a period which again (as in the first type of deprivation) can be fairly satisfactory from the point of view of those in charge, in which the boy is more identified with those in charge than with his own immature self.

The antisocial tendency in this kind of case leads the boy whenever he feels some sort of hope of a return of security to rediscover himself, and this means a rediscovery of his own aggressiveness. He does not know of course what is going on but he simply finds that he has hurt someone or has broken a window. In this case, therefore, instead of hope leading to an S.O.S. signal in terms of stealing, it leads to an S.O.S. signal in terms of an outburst of aggression. The aggression is liable to be senseless and quite divorced from logic and it is no good asking the child who is aggressive in this way why he has broken the window any more than it is useful to ask a child who has stolen why he took money.

These two clinical types of manifestation of the antisocial tendency are really related to each other. It is simply that on the whole the stealing relates to a deprivation that is *earlier* in terms of the child's emotional growth than is the aggressive outburst. There is something common to society's reaction to both types of antisocial behavior at this moment of hope. When the child steals or is aggressive, society is liable not only to fail to get the message, but (more than likely) it will feel stimulated to respond moralistically. The natural mass reaction is in the direction of the punishment for stealing and for the maniacal outburst, and every effort is made to force the young criminal to give an explanation in logical terms which in fact does not apply. At the end of a few hours of persistent questioning, fingerprint evidence, etc., antisocial children will come up with some kind of confession and explanation simply to bring to an end an interminable and intolerable inquiry. This confession has no value, however, because even though it may contain true facts it nevertheless cannot get to the true cause or to the etiology of the disturbance. In fact, time which is spent in extortion of confessions and on fact-finding commissions is wasted time.

Although what has been stated here, if correct, may have no bearing on the day-to-day management of a group of boys or girls, it is necessary to examine the situation to see whether under certain circumstances there might possibly be a practical application of theory. Would it be possible, for instance, for someone who is in charge of a group of delinquent boys to arrange for personal contact of a therapeutic kind? In a sense all communities are therapeutic insofar as they work. Children have nothing to gain from living in a chaotic group, and sooner or later, if there is no strong management, a dictator arises among the children. Nevertheless there is another meaning to the word therapeutic and this has to do with putting oneself in a position in which one can be communicated with from a deep level.

I think that it may be impossible, in most cases, for those who are in charge day and night to make the necessary adjustment in themselves which would enable them to allow a boy a period of psychotherapy or personal contact. I would certainly not lightly advise anyone to attempt to use the two methods. At the same time, however, I would think that these matters can be managed by some and that the boys (or girls) can make very good use of such specialized therapeutic sessions. What must be emphasized, however, is the absolute difference that there is in your attitude when you are responsible for general management and when you are in a personal relationship with a child. To start with, the attitude toward the antisocial manifestation is quite different in the two cases. For someone who is in charge of a group, the antisocial activity is just not acceptable. In the therapeutic session, by contrast, there is no question of morality except that which may turn up in the child. The therapeutic session is not a fact-finding commission and whoever is doing this therapeutic work is not concerned with objective truth but is very definitely concerned with what feels real to the patient.

There is something here that can be carried right over from psychoanalysis, since psychoanalysts know very well that in some of the sessions with their patients they are accused, for instance, of something of which they are innocent. Patients may accuse them of deliberately changing the place of an object in the room in order to trick them; or they may feel quite certain that the analyst has another patient as a favorite, etc. I am referring to what is called the "delusional transference." It would be very natural for an analyst who does not know to defend himself; to say, for instance, that the object is in the same place as it was yesterday or that a simple mistake has been made; or that he does his very best not to favor one person more than another. In doing so the analyst would fail to use the material that the patient presents. The patient is experiencing in the present something which has reality at some point in his past, and if the analyst will allow himself to be put in the role allotted there will be an outcome in the sense that the patient will recover from the delusion. Because of the therapist's need to accept the role allotted at the moment by the patient, it must be very difficult to switch over from the role of group management to one of individual acceptance, but if this can be done there can be rich rewards. Anyone who wishes to try this must be reminded, however, that this work cannot be lightly undertaken. If a boy is to be seen on Thursdays at three o'clock, then this is a sacred date and nothing must get in the way. Unless the appointment becomes predictable by being reliable, the individual boy will not be able to make use of it, and of course one of the first ways in which he will make use of it if he begins to feel that it is reliable is to waste it. These things have to be accepted and tolerated. There is no need for anyone in this role of psychotherapist to be clever. All that is necessary is to be willing in the specialized time set aside to become involved with whatever is there in the child at the time or with whatever turns up through the patient's unconscious cooperation which soon develops and which produces a powerful process. It is this process in the child that makes the sessions valuable.

Discussion

In the discussion a member asked the question how, among a lot of boys, would one recognize one that could be chosen out of all the rest for this kind of special treatment; and my answer, which had to be brief, was that probably one would choose a boy who has just boiled up into being especially difficult. This special clinical problem must either result in punishment and further hardening or else it can be used as a communication indicating a new hope.

The question is, what is this hope? What does the child hope to do? It is difficult to answer this question. The child, without knowing it, hopes to be able to take someone who will listen back to the moment of deprivation or to the phase in which deprivation became consolidated into an inescapable reality. The hope is that the boy or girl will be able to re-experience in relation to the person who is acting as psychotherapist the intense suffering that followed immediately the reaction to deprivation. The moment that the child has used the support that the therapist can give to reach back to the intense suffering of that fateful moment or period of time, there follows a memory of the time before the deprivation. In this way the child has reached back either to the lost capacity to find objects or to the lost security of the framework. The child has reached back to a creative relationship to external reality or to the period in which spontaneity was safe even if it involved aggressive impulses. This time the reaching back has been done without stealing and without aggression because it is something that happens automatically as a result of the child's arrival at what had previously been intolerable, the suffering reactive to the deprivation. By suffering I mean acute confusion, disintegration of the personality, falling forever, a loss of contact with the body, complete disorientation and other states of this nature. Once one has taken a child to this area and the child has come through to remember it and what went before, then one has no difficulty whatever in understanding why it is that antisocial children must spend their lives looking for help of this kind. They cannot get on with their own lives until someone has gone back with them and enabled them to remember by reliving the immediate result of the deprivation.

22] MUTATIVE CONFUSION

AT ADOLESCENCE

ROBERT W. SHIELDS

The interregnum between childhood and manhood, which we call adolescence, becomes increasingly prolonged with the sophistication and advanced development of a culture. Erikson (1950) talked of the "psycho-social moratorium of adolescence," by which I take it he meant that in our kind of culture there is a breathing space allowed for what, in favorable circumstances, permits the adolescent to experiment with life and with his own psychic processes; that the community to some extent accepts this and is willing to be lenient in judgment, and fairly patient and long-suffering; and it acknowledges that this experimental phase may be as confusing and even as painful for the adolescent as it is for those who have the care of him. The later capacity the adult shows for healthy adjustment to a complex society, and his ability to preserve the most positive elements of his personality intact, depend to a very large extent on the manner in which he used, and was permitted to use, this adolescent experimental period.

Adolescence, then, cannot be properly viewed simply as a hiatus between childhood and adulthood. It is a period during which vital dynamic processes are taking place, and must take place if the individual is to become free and creative and his personality consolidated and whole. It is a period of external friction and internal conflict, and it is the nature of this internal conflict that I wish to discuss.

Reprinted with permission from the Conference Report of the Twentieth Child Guidance Inter-Clinic Conference 1964—organized by the National Association for Mental Health, London. Also, used by permission of Robert W. Shields.

Conflictual Processes

Intrapsychic conflict exists throughout adolescence on several levels. First there is the obvious conflict between the secure and familiar past and the unknown, more uncertain future. The complexities that lie in facing the future may, from time to time, dismay the adolescent and drive him to take at least temporary relief in some form of regression. By regression in this context I mean that the individual may go briefly back to an earlier level of functioning or act, over a period, from an emotional standpoint that appears to be chronologically out of phase. Though necessary in order to avoid too intense pressure, regression of this kind activates considerable anxiety of its own, since the adolescent may then fear that if he regresses too much or over too long a period he will become dependent again on the adult world and thereby risk the loss of his own identity.

Most typically, therefore, the adolescent finds ways of thinking and behaving that have elements of both childhood and adulthood in them and will oscillate between these positions. Such a behavioral pattern serves to make the youth unacceptable in any society but his own peer group and misunderstood by child and adult equally. This ambiguity of mood and attitude is nicely illustrated by the mother who told how she felt a pang of nostalgia when her teenage daughter announced for the first time that she was going to put her hair up in curlers. Passing the bathroom as the youngster was engaged in this elaborate process, the mother was amused to see her daughter carefully wetting each curl with her water pistol.

The second conflict is that which is precipitated by resurgent instinctual drives, which, during adolescence, reach their climax just at a time when, in our society, there is the most urgent need for control.

The third area of conflict is that which is the result of sexual development in which there are three libidinal strands to contend with: (1) the final resolution of oedipal object choices, (2) homosexual fantasies and possibly acting out, and (3) the aim to reach, through fantasy and experimentation, a stage where the youngster may attain free choice in heterosexual love objects.

The fourth area of conflict is that between an evaluation of the self that has been primarily based on parental attitudes and ambition and an emergent self-image closely related to personal achievement and acceptance by peers. One sees this very typically in the adolescent today who echoes this kind of division very much in his clothing, which creates for him a uniform that is distinctive and wholly apart from those of child-hood and adulthood.

Conflict between the adolescent and his parents is inescapable at this point if the youngster is to achieve a soundly based narcissism which at first asserts independence of parental support but which will, in health, eventually lead to winning the approval of the parents, who are now compelled to view the child with a new eye—as an adult.

Without conflict there can be no real growth. On this point, as Anna Freud (1958) stated, clinical opinion is unanimous:

> The people in the child's family and school, who assess his state on the basis of behavior, may deplore the adolescent upset which, to them, spells the loss of valuable qualities, of character stability, and of social adaptation. As analysts, however, who assess personality from the structural point of view, we think otherwise. We know that the character structure of a child at the end of the latency period represents the outcome of long drawn-out conflicts between id and ego forces. The inner balance achieved, although characteristic for each individual and precious to him, is preliminary and precarious. It does not allow for the quantitive increase in drive activity, nor for the changes of drive quality which are both inseparable from the onset of puberty. Consequently, this stability of latency has to be abandoned in adolescence to allow adult sexuality to be integrated into the individual's personality. The so-called adolescent upheavals are no more than the external indications that such internal adjustments are in progress. . . .

From the adolescent's point of view there is a quality of discomfort in these confusional states that compels him to seek a solution. But a satisfactory solution can be arrived at only when the personal developmental aims have been achieved. If the external setting is a good and resilient one, the adolescent can withstand quite a prolonged period of inner confusion, during which time identity problems are under constant examination.

Tasks of Adolescence

When all goes well, the three major tasks of adolescence proper are carried forward. These tasks may perhaps be summarized in the following fashion.

1. The establishment of genital primacy. Much here depends on the individual's infantile experiences of sexuality and family attitudes. Severe suppression of infantile masturbatory experimentation, for example, may result in sexual development at adolescence being too heavily weighted with guilt and fear, and so lead to regression and pregenital

fixation points or else limit the free and creative use of preconscious fantasy. It can lead, as Winnicott (1963) suggested, to compulsive masturbation as a way of getting rid of sex rather than weaving it into a total integration of the personality, or else it can lead to pious, repressive forms of denial and antipleasure.

In attempting to deal with the pressures resulting from sexual development, the adolescent is in danger of accepting overrigid forms of control, often based on a primitive ethic. It was, no doubt, with this kind of conflict in mind that Samuel Butler wrote "We need an apologia for the devil. It must be remembered that we have heard only one side of the case: God has written all the books!"

2. The achievement of adult object love. The capacity for tenderness and mature experiences of love is not the inevitable consequence of sexual potency. It depends to a large extent on the final resolution of the oedipal situation which has to be worked through again during adolescence. It also depends on the psychic availability of the more primitive experiences of intimacy during the pregenital phases, as well as on the wholesome development of early narcissism and object relatedness.

3. Achievement of a firm sense of self, a sense of the self as free, creative, adventurous, and life loving. If the ego is successful here, the result is legitimate narcissistic gratification—wholesome pride, self-reliance, and self-regard.

Where these tasks are faced and mastered, adolescence becomes a period during which the individual grows to health in Freud's definition of health as "one who can love and work well." I am referring here to an occasion when Freud was asked what as a psychiatrist he felt the healthy man could do really well, and he answered in three words: "Lieben und Arbeiten." It should also lead to the capacity to use the mind productively and with flexibility, to become able to experiment with and interrelate abstract concepts, to respond subtly to changing stimuli, to combine fine perception with infinitely varied fantasy, to be free to use the mind as a mechanism for play, experimentation, and intrinsic pleasure and gratification (Murphy, 1963).

Second Edition of Childhood

My contention is, then, that these goals cannot be adequately achieved without the toleration on the part of the adolescent and of his environment of a fairly prolonged period of comparative disorganization and confusion. Adolescence has been called a second edition of childhood.

It is that, but much more. It involves the reexamination and resolution of many childhood patterns and experiences, and there is likely to be some regression in this. I am aware that the notion of regression at adolescence causes anxiety to many adults who fear the collapse of the adolescent personality, or else the emergence of behavioral patterns and moral attitudes that are felt to be deleterious.

Winnicott has pointed out that the small child has the right to make a mess on his mother, and it can be argued that most of the crucial experiences of love involve the mutual acceptance of the body products of the self and the loved object. There comes a moment in all high experiences of love when normal hygienic considerations and feelings of disgust are suspended, and complete intimacy and affection permit the tolerance of experiences that would be felt to be distasteful with any other object.

I am thinking here of the way in which in all really intimate and loving relationships there is some exchange of body products between the lover and the loved. The child actually feeds on the body products of the mother, and the mother tolerates the child's capacity to make a mess on her. In fact, the Welsh say that you can tell whether a baby loves you if he will urinate on your lap. (I have actually sat with a Welsh family where a baby was passed around to determine whom he loved most!) At later stages of development, too, in romantic attachments we do things that are really quite unhygienic, such as kissing, which most people can tolerate quite well. And, of course, in sexual intimacy this mutual exchange and toleration is again an integral part of the climactic experience.

Emotional Mess

In much the same way, but in a less physical form, the adolescent tests out his environment by making an emotional mess. If the environment can withstand this and still preserve respect and affection for him, the adolescent is able to preserve his narcissistic self-evaluation and at the same time establish a new and constructive dependence on the objects in his environment, a dependence that is now a relationship.

Adolescence and childhood have this in common: that during both periods "a relatively strong id confronts a relatively weak ego" (Freud, 1936). Not less significant is the fact that during both periods the individual is experimenting with self-consciousness and taking steps to arrive at personal identity. At the end of the second year of life, or thereabouts, the child is making a broad distinction between self and not-self, and this leads to friction between himself and the mother. The temper tantrums and disobedience so characteristic of this age are not a sign of failure in the nursing environment but a mark of its health. The child can only arrive at a definition of himself by being in opposition to his environment, and he can only dare this if the environment is reasonably healthy, loving, and resilient. In adolescence, this process is carried a stage further by much the same mechanisms but only if much the same qualities are to be found in the managing environment. For a time at least the youngster can bear the anxiety of a personally fragmented existence only because he knows that his environment is strong, flexible, and, even if not understanding, at least infrangibly affectionate. Blos (1962) states: "The oppositional, rebellious, and resistive strivings, the stages of experimentation, the testing of the self by going to extremes —all these have a positive usefulness in the process of self-definition. . . . Adolescent individuation is accompanied by feelings of isolation, loneliness and confusion."

Adult Reaction to Confusion and Messiness

The vehemence of id impulses at adolescence, as in infancy, tend to disturb and alarm the adult, especially if he himself was unable to satisfactorily resolve his own adolescent struggle with instinctuality and had to employ excessive denial and repression in order to adjust to adult life. Such an adult will find it particularly difficult to cope with the adolescent or else will adopt rescue and concern techniques, which run counter to the independent differentiation of the adolescent. Aware of the confusion and anxiety of the youngster, the adult may be tempted from an anxious sense of kindliness to offer emotional shortcuts to a resolution or, more damagingly, seek to end confusion by rigid disciplinary measures that impose external controls, which, in turn, prevent the development of internal paths to self-mastery. It is not to the advantage of the adolescent to have off the hook, readymade philosophies thrust at him in this way. Fortunately, most adolescents view dogmas and shortcuts with considerable suspicion, though the sense of inner stress and turmoil may tempt some to grasp at any easy way out of their confusion.

Where dogmatic or disciplinary methods succeed with the adolescent, any benefit is likely to prove temporary as well as damaging to the long-term development of the personality. As Winnicott (1958) said, though speaking here of the antisocial child, "While he is under strong management, a child may seem to be all right; but give him freedom and he soon feels the threat of madness. So he offends against society (without knowing what he is doing) in order to re-establish control from outside."

In those cases where the success of this technique is not temporary, control has only been achieved at the expense of loss of personal identity and the suppression of creative thinking and ability. Such a youth is likely to become a moralist out of desperation rather than conviction. Plato defined the bad citizen as "the man who does good by force of habit rather than from conviction." This view of acceptable behavior and the resolution of adolescent confusion by external force has immediate bearing on the treatment of maladjusted and delinquent children whose behavioral difficulties have led them into institutions. Unfortunately, a large number of our approved schools and even some of our schools for maladjusted children still work on the principle that the devil of delinquency will only be cast out by firm discipline and moral dragooning.

The adolescent who cooperates with this kind of handling may use a moral cloak to hide his unresolved violence and his acceptance of an external dogma to distract himself from the inner state of confusion. It has, moreover, one further unfortunate consequence in that it makes him unfit for any really free and abandoned experience of sex and love in later life.

Regressive processes in the adolescent, no less than confusional states, serve to create anxiety in the adult. My own feeling is, though, that the alarm is overdone. Much of the affective negativism of the adolescent that focuses itself around the parents is a means of avoiding regressive inclinations that parents, teachers, and even the adolescent himself may feel to be dangerous and frightening. This fear would seem to be based on the unproven supposition that to go back emotionally is to render one's self incapable of ever going forward again.

My experience of adolescence, as of adults in treatment, is that this is not so. I suspect that much of the hypochondriasis of adolescence, much of the physical illness and exaggerated passivity, really represents hidden regression to dependency states. It does, of course, suggest that superego development has to be delayed, but this may not be an irreparable disaster. Superego development does not properly fall within the scope of this chapter. Suffice it to say that emphasis on superego processes may inhibit the full development of the personality though it has much to commend it to busy or authoritative adults. This point is made by Martin James (1964):

378

Super-ego development relies upon suppression, prohibition and anticathexis, and is much less consuming of the adult's time and energy than displacement and sublimation. As such it has its appeal to over-busy adults . . . To use it in the wrong place is, however, dynamically a serious step in that it is much more limiting to the child, since it uses a threat—that of loss of love and loss of object.

Fear of Regression

As I see it, necessary regression or confusion in the service of revolutionary reorganization of emotional patterns is often feared by adults to be regressive disintegration or merely a general deterioration of the personality. Nevertheless, such regression and apparent deterioration may be the only possible way by which the child can deliver himself from developing a false self. Max Beerbohm says, "I was a modest, good-humored boy. It is Oxford that made me insufferable." It might well be argued in defense of Max Beerbohm that the insufferability of his later adolescent years did manage to preserve for him his creative abilities and rendered accessible to him a vast area of his own personality that would otherwise have been lost forever under the veneer of the modest, good-humored man he might have been.

It cannot be denied, of course, that the confusion and near delinquency of many adolescents puts severe stress on the managing environment. It is my opinion, however, that in the normal adolescent and, more especially, in the antisocial youngster, some actual experience of causing pain to the adult world is necessary if the capacity for making restitution is to come through. Without this capacity the adolescent will lack narcissistic esteem, lack the drive for genuine social integration, and have to endure the unresolved guilt of being an inert burden on his environment.

Though it may be true, as Winnicott (1963) suggested, that the adolescent does not want to be understood by the adult, it ought to be possible for adults to empathize with him: to sense the significance of his moods, to grant that his needs have validity, and to create and support an environment in which the adolescent can develop, regress, grow, withdraw, or fight as may be necessary. It should be stressed that empathy does not necessarily involve sympathy. To accept that the adolescent has deep-seated hostilities or areas of violence and confusion does not imply that the adult in any way sponsors these things.

The naïve observer, for instance, of the therapist working with adolescents is likely to be faintly horrified that the therapist does not reprove or blame the delinquent adolescent, nor seek to turn his mind to beautiful and pious thoughts. If, in treatment, the delinquent child cannot be prevented from acting out and stealing, magistrates are sometimes inclined to suggest that the therapist has granted the youth license to behave in an antisocial manner or even encouraged him to steal or run away from his school.

The Therapist's Role

Though empathizing with the adolescent and sponsoring the synthesis of id and ego functioning by his nonmoralizing attitude, the therapist is nevertheless himself a morally responsible adult who does not have a personal quarrel with his environment and is not using the adolescent to fulfill his own antisocial inclinations. What the therapist has in mind is to provide a firm, protective, sensitive, flexible management situation within which the adolescent may make experiments, mistakes, and inner discoveries.

J. Cotter Hirschberg, in his discussion of a paper by Masud Khan (1963), described the kind of environment within which the adolescent can work through the complex processes that stand between him and maturity. "Treating the adolescent patient," says Hirschberg, "requires an analyst who can offer a dependable relationship, one which provides direct and practical help without creating dependency; it requires an analyst who can offer protective control without sacrificing stimulus to growth; it requires an analyst who provides security while he concomitantly offers freedom." This is equally true of a school or of the home situation.

Hirschberg also speaks of the "fragile equilibrium" of the adolescent, and it is this fragility that may compel the ordinary healthy adolescent to use an adult as an auxiliary ego, but it is against exploiting this obtuse form of dependency that the adult has to be especially wary, otherwise the aim of personal growth may get overlaid with the less positive form of "growth along the lines the adult will accept." The kind of adult the adolescent needs is one who does not threaten to withdraw love, or make it conditional on conforming behavior, nor wish to inflict on the youngster his own solutions to this normative confusional period in development.

Much unnecessary difficulty has arisen from the tendency to equate regression with acting out. Because acting out may be a form of denial or a failure of nerve at some vital point, it has its own dynamic derived from the compulsion to repeat that which is not fully resolved. Thus, acting out is likely to persist unless and until interpretation can have its effect and the patient can deal with the predicament from which he had been fleeing into action. Regression, on the other hand, may involve exactly the opposite process by which the individual faces moods and intrapsychic situations that require courage to acknowledge, but the impact of which is so great as to be manageable only in a state of dependency once the environment has shown itself adequate to hold the individual over the critical period.

Case Report of an Adolescent Boy

Khan (1963) gave a vivid account of just such a process in the treatment of an adolescent boy who had broken down at school and become withdrawn and antisocial. As treatment progressed this youth lapsed into a state of abject passivity through which he had to be nursed at home almost as though he were a hospitalized patient. Only bit by bit did he find his way back to mobility and aliveness and become able to resume his studies. Khan reports a dream this patient had during the time when recovery was taking place. He dreamed that a pretty classmate came over to him, laid her head on his shoulder, and started to cry. The patient was able to comfort her. Khan says of this dream:

The patient was pleased that he had been able to dream in this way. To him it meant that he had begun to believe he could change another's mood and feelings . . . He felt now there could be mutual responsiveness and communication with another person . . . that he could recognise a depression outside himself in another person. He felt this gave him freedom and the ability to do something about it. He felt related to others. The dream was also an attempt to replace the incestuous object (mother) by a new, contemporary one. This, he felt, freed him to be friends with his mother once again.

Though Khan is here discussing the case of an adolescent boy in treatment who was forced to use the analyst in a special way, my contention is that this type of mechanism is typical of all adolescents in varying degrees. My own clinical experience in working with maladjusted and especially delinquent adolescents is that total awareness of others, of their moods and emotional predicaments, and the ability to act sensitively and constructively toward them, is achieved only when the adolescent has been able to inflict some measure of pain on the adult without destroying the relationship. This may take the form of defiance, withdrawal, hostility, or frequently, in the delinquent, violence,

381

and it involves running the risk of complete rejection. Once having dared this, however, the adolescent is able to get in touch with his own sense of responsibility and guilt and, at the same time, discover his capacity to make good and to restore the relationship. This is an altogether different experience from identification with the adult and his psychic predicament. It presupposes a certain psychic distance which permits the adolescent to view the adult as a real object, vulnerable and unidealized, who is in some measure himself dependent on the adolescent's capacity to restore the damaged relationship.

I never cease to be impressed with the new sense of personal responsibility and sensitive awareness of myself as a human being that the former delinquent would show toward the end of a successful period of treatment. One such youth told me that he had a new ambition to become a barrister so that, should I ever run foul of the law myself, he would be able to help me as I had helped him.

I do not wish to overstress the idea of regression at adolescence, for the fortunate youth in a healthy environment can use a few days of sickness at home or a moment of personal grief or distress within the family setting in order to experience very brief moments of dependence and in this way bring forward from infancy positive elements in relatedness to mother or father, work through the incestuous quality of these feelings, and so free himself for contemporary emotional attachments.

Neither do I wish to go into more detail concerning the use of pain and restitution. But these are two significant usages of the oscillating moods typical of adolescence which are far removed from the notion that adolescence is an ongoing, maturing, developing process.

Within adolescence there are many strands of experience that lead back to primary processes, to infantile attitudes, to the oedipal situation, and so on, and these have to run alongside the normal progressive and educational activities in which the youth is also caught up.

Much of the normal confusion of adolescence derives from the fact that the youth is working all the time on these two levels. At one moment one process is dominant; at another, the other; both have to be kept in play. Part of the duty of the managing environment is to permit the adolescent to know for himself which process must be allowed dominance at any given moment.

Positive Aspects of Confusion

Briefly then perhaps I can summarize the positive aspects of confusion in adolescence in the following manner:

1. Confusional states are not merely inner disorder; they are mutative. That is to say, they do not create anew but realign those positive processes that infancy set in motion but that may easily be lost under a rigid, ongoing, ambitious educational program or dogmatic moral ambition.

2. By slowing up the application of the individual to external pressures, parental ambition, working-seeking, and so on, confusion states may provide an opportunity for inward contemplation, reassessment, and passive withdrawal in which the healing of old traumata may take place and the adolescent may draw himself together into a consistent whole.

3. By enabling the adolescent to weld into his emergent self-image the long-repressed id satisfactions and applying these to the new instinctual development that sexual maturity brings, confusion states help him to resolve oedipal conflicts, to gain new freedom, and to welcome heterosexual object love.

4. Confusion states provide the adolescent with an opportunity to discover whether he is capable of an aliveness that is his own and not merely a false self-model of what others would expect of him. This may mean that he had to subject himself to an examination of the hurt he may have done in fantasy to his introjected parental figures and, perhaps, grieve for them, though this process can usually only be dealt with in analysis.

A patient of mine, for instance, who throughout her adolescence had been, in her own words, "a walking sepulcher" who had never experienced real aliveness of any kind, dreamed that she was walking in a high-walled garden. Outside the white wall there was activity going on. Inside, where she was, all was silence. She tried to speak but could not. As she walked on she came across white marble statues that, on closer examination, turned out to be people, all of them women, who had been suddenly frozen into salt, like Lot's wife, while still going about their normal duties. The air was filled with what she called the "heaviness of death." In the faces of the women she discovered the features of her mother. Following this dream she was seriously depressed for several weeks, weeping constantly, and sleeping most of the time that she was not actually at work. Only gradually did she emerge from this mood and, much later on, became able to dream again of finding a lake in the same walled garden. In the lake she saw her mother, drowning. In this second dream the patient was not overcome with the deadness of the place and was able to dive into the water and rescue her mother.

This dream marked the beginning of the patient's capacity to detach herself from her mother's depression and to seek life and love experiences on her own account.

5. Confusion at adolescence enables the individual to experiment with extremes of feeling: anger, romantic love, suicidal fantasies, hate, violence, and much else that can cause grave anxiety to the managing environment. In this the adolescent is testing the outward limits of human experience, knowing that he is relying on the solidity and affection of the adult world. It enables him not only to widen immeasurably his emotional repertoire by indulging in courageous experimentation with his own personality and affectivity but also takes some of the terror out of experiences that would always have been feared if they had not been daringly explored.

Recovery from Confusion

It could be an aphorism that no one can know order who has not experienced confusion. Or if he does know it, it is the order of cowardice that has never actually dared experiment with the enormously wide range of human emotionality and has clung defensively to the safe paths marked out by others.

Only through the tolerance of inner chaos over a comparatively brief period of development can the growing-up individual radically absorb unconscious fantasy by testing it out against real-life experience. Blos (1962) pertinently said:

Too little attention has been paid to the fact that adolescence, not only in spite of, but rather because of, its emotional turmoil, often affords spontaneous recovery from debilitating childhood influences, and offers the individual an opportunity to modify or rectify childhood exigencies which threatened to impede his progressive development. The regressive processes of adolescence permit the remodelling of defective earlier developments; new identifications and counteridentifications play an important part in this. The profound upheaval associated with the emotional reorganisation of adolescence harbours a beneficial potential.

On a very practical plane, then, those who administer or work in approved schools or schools for maladjusted children ought to be suspicious of their motives if they are inclined to advocate organizing these schools on ordered, disciplinarian, moralistic, or strictly educational lines, where moral rectitude and externally acceptable behavior are used as estimates of the therapeutic value of the institution.

The Conforming Adolescent

Anna Freud (1958) pointed out that the "good," conforming adolescent who is considerate of his parents, submissive and obedient, may be a very convenient child to have around the place. But this very convenience is a sign to be taken seriously:

These are children who have built up defences against their drive activities and are now crippled by the results, which act as barriers against the normal maturational processes . . . They are, perhaps more than any others, in need of therapeutic help to remove the inner restrictions and clear the path for normal development however "upsetting" the latter may prove to be.

Therefore, those individuals or organizations that manage schools for maladjusted children in which, by reason of one technique or another, the youngsters behave well and appear indistinguishable from the products of the best public schools, would be well advised to pay some heed to the positive mutative aspects of adolescent confusion and turmoil. I would not wish it to be thought that I am implying that confusion at adolescence and the infinite tolerance of emotional disorder and behavioral license are of themselves active therapeutic agents. I am, however, stating that there is now convincing clinical support for the contention that strict disciplinary measures, in home or in school, imposing moral attitudes and exemplary education organization can, and frequently do, militate against recovery from emotional illness and, even in the case of the comparatively normal child, may encourage the development of false attitudes and inadequate personalities.

REFERENCES

Blos, P. (1962). *On Adolescence: A Psychoanalytic Interpretation*. New York: The Free Press.

Eissler, K. R. (1958). Psychoanalysis of adolescents. *Psychoanalytic Study of the Child,* 13.

Erikson, E. H. (1950). *Childhood and Society*. New York: Norton.

Freud, A. (1958). Adolescence. *Psychoanalytic Study of the Child*, 13.

Geleerd, R. (1961). Some aspects of ego vicissitudes in adolescence. *Journal of the American Psychoanalytic Association*, 3.

Gitelson, M. (1948). Character synthesis: The psychotherapeutic problem of adolescence. *American Journal of Orthopsychiatry*, 18(3).

James, M. (1964). Interpretation and management in the psycho-analytic treatment of pre-adolescents. *International Journal of Psycho-analysis*, 45.

Khan, M. R. (1963). Silence as communication. *Bulletin of the Menninger Clinic*, 27(6).

Laufer, M. (1964). Ego-ideal and super-ego ideal in adolescence. *Psychoanalytic Study of the Child,* 19.

Murphy, L. B. (1963). *The Widening World of Childhood.* New York: Basic Books.

Spiegel, L. A. (1961). Disorder and consolidation in adolescence. *Journal of the American Psychoanalytic Association,* 9(3).

Winnicott, D. W. (1958). The capacity to be alone. In *The Maturational Processes and the Facilitating Environment.* London: Hogarth Press, 1965.

———. (1963). Adolescence: Struggling through the doldrums. *This Annual,* 1:40–50.

PART V

THE ADOLESCENT
IN THE WORLD

INTRODUCTION

Adolescence is not a phenomenon that is peculiar to the United States. There have always been rebellious activities among the young, especially among students. Centuries ago student unrest sometimes took the form of open warfare.

History, when focusing upon adolescent violence, generally restricts itself to the discussion of university students. One reads relatively little about the adolescent population in general. Furthermore, there is more than rebellion and violence that characterizes this age group.

To proceed further along an historical perspective leads to difficulties that are beyond the scope of the psychiatric profession. It is difficult enough to construct a composite characteristic picture of contemporary adolescence; consequently, we have to forgo any ambitions to construct a continuum from antiquity to the present, a continuum which would be desirable because it could shed some light on the confusing complexities of contemporary adolescent behavior. Until recently there seemed to be very little homogeneity in the attitude and behavior of adolescents throughout various parts of the world.

Our friendly and mutually instructive contacts with Latin American colleagues are making us dimly aware that perhaps their youth is not fundamentally different from ours, as we might have expected. The types of psychopathology encountered in Latin American countries also does not seem to be different either from a structural or a behavioral viewpoint.

At first, this seems surprising in view of their ostensibly patriarchal family organizations, where authority is well delineated and unquestioned. One would not have expected orientations in their children similar to ours since families in the United States have undergone numerous vicissitudes, at least since the Depression. With closer scrutiny, however, one soon recognizes that in Latin America, as well as in North

America, the so-called patriarchal family system, reminiscent of mid-Victorian times, has also disappeared. Their women are emancipated —at least in the middle and upper-middle classes—to a point that exceeds ours. Most of the wives of colleagues are professional persons themselves, not only in professions allied with those of their husbands', but in many instances quite unrelated, such as engineering, law, and architecture. What might at one time have been typical of the United States has infiltrated deeply South of the Border.

The adolescents of Israel are of great interest to behavioral scientists because of the dynamic growth of this youth-oriented country. The informality, openness, and present national purpose has led to great reliance and trust in their adolescents. Extensive child care experimentation such as the kibbutz system, widely used placement in youth villages and the like, and a rather permissive parental attitude has created a youth with interesting characteristics.

In view of wide-sweeping cultural changes, the study of the adolescent in the world becomes an increasingly important endeavor. The chapters in this section are the result of some of our international discussions. One can see that our concerns and interests cover a wide range of topics, from the consideration of intrapsychic structure and developmental vicissitudes to ideological problems as they impinge upon emotional development. Sharing ideas with colleagues from different countries will enrich our understanding of society, as well as of the individual.

23] INTRODUCTIONS FROM THE FIRST PANAMERICAN CONGRESS ON ADOLESCENT PSYCHIATRY

MAURICIO KNOBEL, BERTRAM SLAFF,
EDUARDO KALINA, AND SHERMAN C. FEINSTEIN

Mauricio Knobel

It is my honor and privilege to express our warm welcome to our colleagues from the American Society for Adolescent Psychiatry who, jointly with the Argentine Organizing Committee appointed by the Argentine Society for Psychiatry and Psychology of Childhood and Adolescence, have made this meeting possible. I also want to extend this welcome to our colleagues from different American countries who honor us with their presence and cooperation.

I believe that important things do not happen by chance. If this Panamerican Congress is taking place it is because of the joint effort of professionals who are interested in a problem of great significance. It is certainly not by chance either that all of us who are interested in the issues of psychopathology and normal psychology of youth are gathered here to consider the problems of adolescence. I want to emphasize the fact that we are interested in normal psychology of adolescence because without mastering it, it would be very difficult to know how to differentiate pathology in today's adolescent behavior.

As professionals, we are doubtless better acquainted with adolescent

First Panamerican Congress on Adolescent Psychiatry, Buenos Aires, Argentina, January 1971.

psychopathology, since those who come to us or are brought for consultation (as is usually the case) are those youngsters who have shown a greater or lesser incapacity to manage themselves in this convulsed and sometimes chaotic world.

In a suffering society, which is also termed "alienated" by some sociologists, the individual, in natural crisis because of the stage of his own developmental process, is unable to find easy ways to adjust his behavior to a task truly leading to a more stable and less conflicted adulthood. That is to say, it becomes difficult to establish an adult identity capable of actual enjoyment of life and to realize the opportunities of projecting oneself into a future of satisfactory realizations for the individual himself, and for his fellow men.

What kind of positive identification figures are offered to the adolescent by our adult society? Though different religions speak of peace, mercy, love, and concord, we show him a world of hatred, cruelty, and destruction. Though political leaders speak of harmony among peoples and countries, social and economic progress, and respect for human rights, we show him the dominance of arbitrariness, dictatorship, racial and religious persecution, and the supremacy of force over law. Though adults within their families and confronting society in different social groups speak of keeping the family together and of preserving moral, benevolent, and faithful work, we offer him images of robberies, violence, frauds, lies, compromising submissions, and conformist complicities.

Have there ever been such contradictory situations? I believe that this is what makes it so difficult to deal with the adolescent process today. The process itself has always existed in mankind, but now more than ever, it is we the adults who feel disoriented, misfit, and unable to find our way. If in the social and political field we can reconcile ourselves to wars, police persecution, and racial and religious discrimination, and encourage hatred in order to favor the political supremacy of certain groups, how can we demand that our adolescents behave in a more balanced and stable way? If in the international field mendacity has become a doctrine of law, what can we expect of our youngsters?

I would like to mention something that has moved us deeply and still brings uneasiness to our spirits. President Kennedy's assassination in the United States and the following investigation of the event gave us and our youth all over the world a feeling of hopelessness and frustration that will be very hard to overcome. The recent sentencings that took place in such apparently opposite political systems as those of Spain and the Soviet Union can only convey the image that violence is the driving force of man in today's world. What, then, is the effect of life patterns ruled by violent and prejudiced forces in the political, racial, and social areas?

If adults feel so certain about being the possessors of truth, have they renounced the old principle that states "Whoever is truthful does not have to fear"? I remember one adolescent brought to treatment for apparent psychopathic behavior, who said that whenever he would feel frightened, he could not do anything else but fight and brutally beat somebody up. He felt he was not right, but he needed to feel he was right. Is not this the same excuse used by the repressive forces all over the world when they want to impose certain behavioral patterns on the people?

If the boundary between normality and pathology in adult social behavior has faded away and settled where the most powerful and stronger adults want to put it, it becomes undoubtedly difficult to draw the line between "healthy," or "normal," and "pathological" in today's adolescents. The brutal or subtle use of force and violence by adults in the name of society, governments, certain "ideals," or within the limited context of family "authority," transforms all these institutions into something quite equivalent and can only bring about a conception of violence as a pattern of life.

It is not possible to fight violence with violence itself. We have created the generation gap. To understand our youth we must understand ourselves and our society.

Fortunately, the youngsters are showing us the way. They are doing so with courage, ingenuity, bravery, and sacrifice. Sometimes they are struggling between a relative normality and the threshold of psychopathology; at other times, in open pathological crisis; and many times in a meaningful and authentic revolutionary action that strikes our hearts crying out: "You are wrong! Change or we will have to make you change!"

All this vibrates in our adolescents who rebel at our attachment to obsolete frameworks. It seems as though one might speak of a linguistic generational difference rather than a mere idiomatic one.

If I have focused my attention on these political circumstances it is because social events are being intensively lived by today's youth. A breeze of change is agitating the world and involves all of us. If we cannot make ourselves aware of all these new events, we are bound to be led to old-fashioned paternalistic-like countertransference attitudes.

I hope that through our psychodynamic understanding we can get rid of old schematic and denigrative labels. Dynamic psychiatry is still a challenge that many psychiatrists are not able to accept. The psychiatric approach to adolescent problems requires knowledge and courage. Here is where the sociopolitical and the psychobiological lines come inexorably together. To attempt the separation of these elements means dissociating the adolescent personality.

There are too many "experts" in this field who are not here. They are in charge of bureaucratic assignments in different areas of this continent. From our discussions we hope to reach some conclusions that will be useful in giving some orientation to those who have the responsibility for the people's health. Our youth's mental health should have top priority.

Our duty as scientists is to point out the facts and evaluate them profoundly, without getting lost in a suicidal complicity with those who have power in different parts of the world by labeling as "sick" all those who are protesting. But we also must have the capacity to distinguish when the adolescent has fallen ill. Then his behavior stops being truly creative, genuinely revolutionary, and capable of meaningfully modifying his environment and manifests a psychiatric disorder that needs our professional assistance.

The ever-widening generation gap is the responsibility of the adult world. If we as scientists take up the challenge, studying what is taking place and offering possible solutions, we will then contribute to the establishment of a true generational communication. From the generation gap we can proceed to a generational encounter.

Only by fulfilling these requirements will we be helpful and fulfill our professional and civic duties.

I invite you to deliberate and to work on these arduous problems with scientific honesty and a citizen's passion. It is here where we can begin a true endeavor of human living together in order to overcome hatred, discrimination, and violence.

Bertram Slaff

It is a great privilege for me to be speaking to this First Panamerican Congress on Adolescent Psychiatry. I want to bring the greetings of all of us in the American Society for Adolescent Psychiatry to all of you in the Sociedad Argentina de Psiquiatria y Psicologia de la Infancia y de la Adolescencia. May I express our appreciation to you and to Professor Mauricio Knobel and Dr. Eduardo Kalina for your dedicated endeavors in bringing the congress plans to fruition and for your gracious hospitality. We are happy indeed to be here.

The issues we face in adolescent psychiatry fully transcend national barriers. Yet the teenagers will certainly be affected by the unique characteristics of their national culture. It is altogether fitting that this be an international meeting in which together we can seek to increase our knowledge of youth in general, our perceptions of youth in a particular culture, and our awareness of the individual young person.

Over the years it has become a tradition in discussions of adolescents for the speaker to read a complaint about the terrible qualities of contemporary youth, and then reveal that this was written several thousands of years ago. For example, the statement attributed to Socrates: "Children now love luxury. They have bad manners, contempt for authority. They show disrespect for elders, and love chatter in place of exercise. Children are now tyrants, not the servants of their household." "Plus ça change, plus c'est la même chose." It left the audience with the comfortable feeling that the problems of youth, though not easily solved, could still be lived with and survived.

This confidence can no longer be justified. In this atomic age the assumption that life will go on is quite subject to question. In an era when science has contributed greatly to extending the life span, overpopulation threatens to limit or reverse the benefits of this achievement. Oil spills on our oceans and industrial and radiation pollution of our atmosphere further challenge belief in the stability of our environment. In the United States the seemingly endless war in Vietnam has fostered a feeling of helplessness in the political sphere.

Today's youth have grown up in an age of instant communication by radio and television. The young have not liked what they have seen; this is not the age of heroes.

This troubled generation seems to have lost confidence in the traditional values and ways of life, but not to have discovered any alternative that justifies commitment. Anti-intellectual and antianalytic attitudes have become popular among young people; withdrawal, mysticism, and drug experiences have become an approved life style.

The professions are affected by this. The young lawyers, engineers, and physicians do not want to carry on the old ways. Youth has developed an extraordinary suspicion of success, accomplishment, power. The traditional paths of study to achieve credentials are becoming less attractive.

The relevance of these phenomena to those of us who deal with the psychiatric problems of children and youth is immediately apparent. We are all living in this world in which man's vulnerability as a species has rather suddenly become starkly apparent. For those of us in our middle years this is threatening enough, but at least we have had our opportunities to grow and learn in a world in which mere wars, revolutions, and economic depressions were the major dangers. The young fear that they may not even have this.

Under these circumstances we must avoid any suggestions to the young that in global matters their confusions derive principally from inexperience and that, with suitable attention to what their elders teach, these problems will be resolved.

What is needed is recognition by ourselves that life conditions have changed profoundly, and in the light of this awareness we must examine anew our assumptions about adolescent growth and development. We must be cautious indeed before declaring an adolescent's despair today to be the traditional *Weltschmerz* of sensitive, idealistic youth. Intense criticism of governmental response to social injustice must not glibly be seen as a transference of child-parent conflicts. "It's just a phase, and he'll outgrow it" may become increasingly difficult to support.

Since the traditional approaches to the problems of youth are no longer adequate to our times, we must learn to stretch ourselves, and to encourage the young to do similarly, so that we all can get through the generation-gap barrier.

We must acknowledge that there are new resistances to psychiatric approaches and must prepare ourselves to deal with them. Some of these are on the political level. In France the state mental health services provided for university students have been attacked by revolutionaries on the grounds that treating students was encouraging them to adjust to a rotten system and thus was counterrevolutionary. I have heard Dr. Daniel Douady, who heads the French program, respond wisely to this kind of charge with the comment that, under any political system, some people become ill and need medical care, and it is the responsibility of physicians to provide that care.

We must take note of the changing concepts of reality as conceived by the young. I am reminded here of Piaget's trenchant comment about children between two to three and seven to eight years of age: "Play is a reality which the child chooses to believe in by himself, just as reality is a game which the child chooses to believe in with grown-ups and with anyone else who believes in it." The conceiving of reality as of a higher order than play comes later in development.

Youth now seem to be reversing this. Some conceive of the drug "high" as a superior state. For others the quest for mystic experience has become dominant. The resurgence of interest in the literary works of Hermann Hesse gives expression to this.

So too is the growing interest in the studies of R. D. Laing (1967), who has written: "A revolution is currently going on in relation to sanity and madness, both inside and outside psychiatry. The clinical point of view is giving way before a point of view that is both existential and social."

These changes have become manifest in clinical symptoms. In consultations and in the psychiatric treatment of adolescent patients some familiar symptoms appear much less frequently; others are quite newly emphasized.

Many who work in this field agree that it is quite rare for a youth to seek therapy because of a sexual problem. Indeed sexuality seems not to be discussed often. When questioned about this, a youth may respond, "That's a psychiatrist's hangup, not mine." The unisex fad, with teen-age boys and girls wearing similar clothing and long hair, emphasizes these changing patterns of sexual behavior and identity. Occasional homosexual behavior in predominantly heterosexual youths and heterosexual behavior in predominant homosexuals is often thought not important enough to mention.

Therapists sometimes get the impression that sexuality is being used to gain closeness, body contact, reduction in feelings of alienation, companionship, and for diverse other purposes but not conspicuously genital pleasure.

One of the pioneers in the psychotherapy of adolescents has recently reported that the teenagers seen now seem to have significantly different qualities from those of a generation ago. There seems to be a greater tendency toward passivity and an unwillingness to invest the hard work necessary to convert fantasied achievements into realized ones. Egocentricity is conspicuous.

A review of these observations about contemporary youth suggests a profound anomie in the present and a pervasive doubt that there will be a future. It is hypothesized that character structure and psychiatric symptoms in teenagers are already reflecting these changes.

To be of help in this rather bleak world situation, I believe we must accept the validity of young people's pessimism today. If we acknowledge their loss of confidence in their own future, and if we show by our own concern a willingness to join with them in efforts to minimize these perils, I believe we can communicate that there still are possibilities for joy in the human experience.

Eduardo Kalina

My friends. I consider it a special honor to be co-president of this First Panamerican Congress on Adolescent Psychiatry and to have the opportunity to be with such esteemed colleagues as Sherman Feinstein, Bertram Slaff, and Mauricio Knobel as well as many other friends from different countries of the American continent. I lament only the absence of a great friend of all of us, Bill Schonfeld, with whom we initially planned these meetings. He was the force behind this movement toward Panamerican unity, which today has become a concrete reality.

As you have already seen during the last two days, these meetings have a different character than that usually encountered at scientific meetings. I am referring to the personal and friendly atmosphere. This is consistent with our interest in adolescence and is an expression of our positive identification with a characteristically youthful attitude. The adolescent carries the banner of change; we have also decided to change and have organized these meetings differently in that we have done everything possible to promote personal and informal dialogue among all. We have kept formal, hierarchically structured presentations to a minimum.

In other words, we have tried to officially incorporate into these meetings what we value most and hope to achieve from any meeting. I am referring to personal contacts and the interchange of ideas in hallways before, during, and after the scientific sessions.

We hope, moreover, that these hallway dialogues become officially extended to total participation, converting our program into an immense hallway.

We have also initiated an innovation, which we call supervisory clinics. These are small groups dealing with patients and leading to a discussion of different theoretical frames of reference that determine our clinical approach. To achieve such an exchange of ideas we have selected representatives of different schools as supervisors. We have given them, as well as the thirty members of each group, clinical material to study beforehand.

Finally, we will have five lectures delivered by such distinguished specialists as Roy Grinker and Peter Giovacchini from the United States, and Arminda Aberastury, Leon Grinberg, and Arnaldo Rascovsky from Argentina.

I believe that I have introduced you to the program we have prepared for this first Panamerican congress. Now I have only to express my thanks to the American Society for Adolescent Psychiatry and the Sociedad Argentina de Psiquiatria y Psicologia de la Infancia y de la Adolescencia, especially the organizing committee, which is composed of members from both groups, for their support, trust, and constant collaboration.

Sherman C. Feinstein

Dr. Knobel, Dr. Kalina, distinguished guests and colleagues, I bring you all personal greetings from your friends in the American Society for Adolescent Psychiatry. This First Panamerican Congress on Adolescent Psychiatry is more than a meeting. It is our attempt to bring friends and colleagues together to experience firsthand the milieu, the problems, and the people working to further healthy development of our youth.

The man who first conceived of this meeting is unfortunately not with us today. This gathering is in a way a testimonial to Dr. William Schonfeld's life and work. Dr. Malvina Kremer, in introducing the speaker at what is now called The William Schonfeld Annual Lectureship of the New York Society, pointed out that "History, according to Carlyle, is the record of the biographies of men. According to others, history is the sum of men's activities and the way in which these are organized. Still others regard history as the account of the ideas that move men and shape the events in which they are the actors." In a very real sense, Dr. Schonfeld exemplifies all these views. Interest in adolescence as a unique phase in maturation and as a specialized area in psychiatry is of relatively recent origin. This interest is a natural step in the evolution of psychiatric concerns. But this evolution did not take place spontaneously. There had to be some who could see the need, who had the energy and the imagination to take concrete steps to meet it. Dr. Schonfeld not only saw the need, but he had the vigor and the perseverance to create the organized form of activity to give it expression.

I believe that vast revolutionary changes are under way in our societies and that one can best study this phenomenon in the development of our youth. The industrialization of our cultures has had profound influence on our child-rearing techniques. It has allowed parents to pursue multifaceted lives in which their families are only one aspect of their responsibilities and gratifications. Women feel capable of being emancipated, and there is a striving for freedom and opportunities for self-expression outside of their typical child-rearing role. There is a demand for crèches and day-care centers to help mothers better prepare themselves and their children for the opportunities and demands of a complicated reality.

The time required for maturation has increased as a consequence of the lengthened life span and the need for more education and preparation for vocational choice. This growth delay has manifested itself essentially in adolescence, which now spans the years from twelve to al-

399

most twenty-five if Keniston's concept of youth as an interphase between adolescence and adulthood is considered a part of general adolescent resolution.

The sudden dilemma our youth are facing in their identity solutions seem to be an aspect of this revolutionary change. Educated, stimulated, and encouraged by their environment to be more expressive and self-searching, they look at corruption, war, hypocrisy, poverty, uncontrolled technology, ecological unbalancing, democratic process deterioration, and the commercialization of work and culture: They feel great stress and are unable to quickly resolve this crisis in their identity formation.

One of the most difficult aspects of dealing with adolescents is their aggressive ways of coping with growth. Dealing with aggression stirs up serious therapeutic problems and leads to strong transference and countertransference reactions with therapists, politicians, and policemen. Unfortunately, aggression in adolescents is frequently seen and dealt with as a regression to a drive level and therefore as spontaneous and destructive. If, however, the use of aggression in its sadistic and masochistic forms is seen as a defense against feelings of loss and a plea for help, it becomes clear that this behavior is at the service of ego mastery and not destruction.

The adolescent, in order to mature, must undergo a character synthesis resolving the basic problems inherent in first forming a human bond and then being able to tolerate his separateness and individuality. Through trust in human relations the developing individual develops empathy, learns to tolerate loss and mistrust, and eventually sees himself as taking a responsible role toward himself, toward others, and toward his environment.

If our children take our teachings seriously, they will refuse to compromise and will insist that human relationships continue along human lines. Charles A. Reich (1970) in his very popular *The Greening of America* sees youth eventually forcing the concrete and plastic world, which is developing, to turn back into a green, more natural state. He describes a state of consciousness in which there is a restoration of the nonmaterial elements of man's existence and where science and technology become tools of man rather than the determinants of man's existence. This allows for the further development of the aesthetic and spiritual aspects and a system of ecological and human ethics to replace the competitive, self-destructive defenses we are currently using.

Psychoanalysis has provided us with a dynamic theoretical system where the personality has been depicted in terms of conflicting inner forces. Developmental factors are also important, and the experiences of the first years of life, the first especially, have been assigned considerable significance in determining the eventual outcome of psychic integration. Thus, the interplay of constitutional endowment and the nurturing infantile environment, during which early object relations are established, leads to a sequence of developmental stages resulting in the structuring of the ego.

The longitudinal observational approach has confirmed the etiological importance of infancy on normal emotional development and the genesis of psychopathology. The oedipal period, during which the identificatory processes receive their greatest stimulation, continues to affect developmental growth. However, there is a growing conviction that adolescence as a developmental stage may be more important than has been recognized. It may achieve the same degree of significance as an etiological precursor of later development as has been assigned to the infantile period.

If adolescence has formative potential for future development, it represents a phase of life where there is a possibility of a second chance, one that might undo the harmful effects of a traumatic infancy. Possibly many of the disruptive and peculiar aspects of adolescence are examples of both successful and unsuccessful attempts to effect a reorientation that will rectify the distorted direction of previous development. Adolescent behavior, moratoriums, and other actions gain another perspective if they are seen as adaptations designed to achieve characterological stability.

Adolescence has only recently been seen as a specific phase of life with special technical problems. It can be thought of as a time for a major recapitulation of all the previous growth processes and should terminate with a synthesis of character structure that allows for continued growth, maturation, and creativity. If this synthesis is to be a healthy one it will eventually forge a more humanistic world with more efficient survival techniques.

REFERENCES

Laing, R. D. (1967). *The Politics of Experience and the Bird of Paradise.* New York: Pantheon.
Reich, C. A. (1970). *The Greening of America.* New York: Random House.

PETER L. GIOVACCHINI

The formation of organizations and congresses whose chief purpose is to understand the adolescent and the adolescent process is, in itself, a phenomenon worthy of study. Why should this period of life be singled out? Something of its importance is inherently felt by many therapists, and it exerts an attraction that should not be considered self-evident. Undoubtedly, our needs and ambitions to understand the adolescent process may be, in part, a reflection of the fundamental role it plays in determining adult character structure and psychopathology. There may also be other more personal reasons why this period of life is often held in awe. Still, even personal reasons, when understood, can add to our comprehension, and there may be some aspects of adolescence that have a tendency to stimulate rather common personal reactions in most of us. I believe that our reactions, idiosyncratic or otherwise, accentuate the unique importance of the adolescent process as a developmental phase. This theme will be explored in detail later.

In addition to viewing the personality from a psychoanalytic viewpoint, which emphasizes a cross-sectional, intrapsychic approach, studies of the development of the psyche, referred to as longitudinal, have also proven fruitful. The latter have occurred concurrently with shifts in our theoretical orientation.

Direct observations of the neonate have emphasized maturational biological factors. Though there have been many who have focused on mentational content, even during the first week of life, it is generally agreed that the direction of emotional development moves away from a preponderant biological orientation to areas where the chief elements

Presented to the plenary session of the First Panamerican Congress on Adolescent Psychiatry, Buenos Aires, Argentina, January 20, 1971.

are psychological. If one orients oneself around the axis of needs, the earliest needs refer to nourishment, warmth, sleep, and so on, those upon which survival depends, and later needs refer to more sophisticated requirements, which are a reflection of our cultural milieu and its aesthetic connotations.

From a theoretical perspective, the above progression can initially be explained best in terms of instinctual forces, a basic, biologically centered id-psychology. When the personality has reached high levels of integration and its needs have, so to speak, become more sophisticated and complex, in a sense, more highly individualized, it is best understood in terms of ego functions.

The change of focus from id-psychology to ego-psychology is not just a consequence of historical evolution and clinical necessity; it is also an outcome of our increasing interest in psychic development and the factors that lead to character structure. At certain points along the spectrum of emotional structuralization the viewpoint of the id has greater explanatory value and at other points, those where there is greater involvement with the external world, the personality is better understood in terms of ego-psychology. However, as should be clearly self-evident, these two viewpoints are not mutually exclusive; one supplements and complements the other. Each, the id and ego, is, after all, a significant part of the mental apparatus.

These two distinct theoretical focuses are also paralleled by the general movement from the biological and preoccupation with the self to involvement with the outer world and people, a movement away from a preponderant, if not exclusive, preoccupation with the self. Adolescence is a particularly fascinating period because it represents a point on the developmental spectrum where there is a tremendous involvement with the sociocultural milieu, especially when contrasted to earlier stages and yet, at the same time, there is an extreme upsurge of self-involvement which also has its biological concomitants (hormonal changes of puberty). This self-involvement is reminiscent of the neonatal stage where the main psychic activity is directed toward the self because of the pressure of instinctual needs. Thus, adolescence requires both an id and an ego orientation, although as one moves from puberty to adulthood, the ego perspective becomes increasingly important in defining an evolving character structure that can effect more varied and subtle interactions with the surrounding world.

Before limiting our discussion to the central theme of this chapter, that is, the study of the relationship between developing character structure and the adolescent process, it would be helpful to briefly view the various stages of development in terms of specific tasks required for both psychic survival and further development. As it is easy to comprehend that there is a hierarchy of needs ranging from purely biological pressures to complex, culturally related self-esteeming requirements, each period of life has specific tasks to perform, also arranged in an ascending order of complexity. The mastery, effected by the satisfactory performance of the phase-specific task, leads from a primal situation of vulnerability and total dependency to the assumption of independence, self-reliance, responsibility, and autonomy.

During neonatal phases it is difficult to think in terms of a task. At the most, one could say that the infant's task is to have his basic biological needs met. Presumably the outer world will respond to the physiological messages he transmits, which rather quickly acquire the qualities of primitive object relations.

During the ensuing period of childhood, the child's chief task is to acquire an education. He has an enormous amount to learn. The focus on learning how to communicate to others that he has instinctual requirements becomes less important, and the acquisition of techniques of how to deal with an ever-expanding external world becomes the central issue.

What the child learns is designed to help him deal with the outer world so he can be self-reliant. However, such a purpose is not particularly emphasized even though it is often made explicit. The fact of a child's dependence is generally accepted and what he learns seems to have very little relevance to his adult autonomy. The U.S. educational institutions seem to be concerned simply with preparing him for the next higher one. All that is changed is the location and complexity of the subject matter; his status is still one, as a rule, of total dependency on his parents. What he learns remains academic from several viewpoints, insofar as he does not apply his knowledge to specific tasks designed to gain independence.

There are, of course, many other childhood experiences that lead to the acquisition of adaptive techniques other than formal education. The child learns to be socialized and to fit into his culture. He acquires social graces, but again these are so constructed that his dependent status is maintained; indeed, sociocultural factors merely consolidate such a dependent status by formalizing it. There is before puberty and adolescence very little the child gains that helps him move out of the dependent frame of reference.

The adolescent faces a radically different situation. He is expected to relate to the surrounding world in a totally dissimilar manner than that of childhood. Even though he is still dependent upon his parents for money and nurture, he is supposed to be able to conduct himself as an adult, and, other than providing for his own livelihood, he is expected to assume responsibilities that approximate those of the adult. The latter applies mainly to social graces and the adoption of standards that are consonant with adult value systems. In spite of the fact that the adolescent may reject the Establishment, he is at least dealing in an adult framework and his concerns involve areas very remote from childhood orientations.

Within recent decades, there has been a tendency, especially in progressive education, to attempt to teach even the very young child concern about social problems and to involve him in areas of adult responsibility. He is supposedly given information and taught attitudes and opinions designed to prepare him to construct a better world for himself and society later in life. This humanistic approach, however, seems to have a minimal effect when practiced, and it is usually limited to a middle-class or upper-middle-class group.

Therefore, the adolescent seems to be precipitously cast into a role for which he has had very little actual preparation. Besides being expected to have the sociocultural concerns just mentioned and the skill and judgment to effectively react to such problems, he is expected to orient himself as if he *were* independent. This is an entirely new and sudden expectation.

The sociocultural demands made on the adolescent are not uniform throughout the whole adolescent period. There are different kinds of demands made on the early postpubertal adolescent in contrast to the middle or late adolescent. Nevertheless, when this period of life is compared with its predecessor, the demands of the environment are not only incomparably greater but rather than being the outcome of a gradual increase, they appear to be precipitous and sudden; they represent a *quantum jump* from one phase to another.

For example, during middle to late adolescence, the youth graduates from high school and moves away from home in order to go to college. This is a typical sequence in the United States, differing from other countries such as those of South America. It represents an abrupt change, and in the more unstable ego can result in serious breakdowns often characterized by identity crises. In many instances, the adolescent has had some preparation for living away from home, such as trips and summer camps, but these have been limited experiences and, as a rule, there were no particular expectations regarding independence and self-reliance. The adolescent knew he would return to his home and continue as before. When he goes to college, the atmosphere is different. It is implicit that circumstances will never quite be the same. He will return home on vacations, but now the context is different. He is supposed to relate at an adult level, and there has been little preparation for both this role and living only with one's peers the greater portion of the year. In many instances, he is expected to support himself when not in school. In spite of the fact that many adolescents have summertime jobs, they are often considered an extra bonus in addition to what the parents provide. The college students' parents often believe they have fulfilled their obligations by paying for their child's education; the student becomes responsible for his own support for the remainder of the year when he is not in school. Whatever the individual variations are, the change of status that accompanies beginning college is tremendous from both a material and emotional viewpoint.

Generally speaking, there is a lack of preparation in terms of a gradual continuum for the sociocultural demands imposed on youth. This lack of preparation is highlighted, indeed exaggerated, in psychopathological instances. For example, many of the clinical problems that confront us today can be explained in terms of a lack of adaptive techniques, a characterological focus rather than one primarily based on intrapsychic conflicts.

The following brief clinical vignette is an example of a young man who had extreme difficulties in coping with the exigencies of this demanding phase. His initial symptoms were similar to those classically described by Erikson (1956) as belonging to the identity diffusion syndrome. Shortly after beginning his work at a university in a city fairly distant from his home, he began experiencing a vague apprehension which in the course of several weeks continued mounting until it reached panic proportions. He could not relate it to anything in particular, but he was so paralyzed by overwhelming affect that he ceased to function in all areas. Of course, he could no longer attend to his studies, but, in addition, his personal habits deteriorated. He found himself unable to wash, brush his teeth, dress properly, or otherwise take care of his personal grooming. He felt confused, and even forgot who he was and the purpose and meaning of his existence. He was eventually hospitalized, and after two weeks on a psychiatric ward, where all of his physical needs were taken care of, he regained equilibrium, which he felt was precarious.

Psychoanalysis was recommended to him on discharge from the ward; the patient had already decided on his own to seek treatment. He dropped out of school, found employment driving a taxicab, and began therapy.

During analysis, he constantly emphasized his awkwardness and clumsiness in a variety of social situations, which included heterosexual activities. He complained about not knowing how to respond in certain settings, how to greet someone or make an introduction, how to make casual conversation, and how to conduct the usual social amenities. He also dwelled on his difficulties concerning his total inability to predict another person's responses. He did not know whether what he would say or do would cause the other person to be friendly or angry.

These problems were especially vexing regarding girls. He was aware of vague but distressing sexual feelings. Rarely he could relieve his tensions by masturbation but he had no idea of how to approach a girl for a date, and he had no concept as to how to make a sexual advance. In fact, he was not even able to conjure a sexual fantasy during masturbation.

The course of the analysis led me to conclude that this patient's social and sexual difficulties stemmed from his really not knowing how to act in mature social and sexual situations. Rather than repression of specific functions due to intrapsychic conflict, his behavior seemed best explained by the actual lack of adjustive techniques required to satisfy newly acquired sexual urges and to master problems more characteristic of the adult world. Instead of reporting inhibitions, he described literally not knowing how to react in these new "adult" settings, never having had previous experiences that would have taught him the elements of proper social conduct.

Consequently, a large part of his analysis consisted of efforts to cast me in the role of a teacher. He described himself as a helpless and vulnerable person who needed my omnipotent protection and wisdom. He regressed to early symbiotic stages of development and then he wanted to fuse with me and thereby achieve magical salvation from his feelings of inadequacy and self-hatred.

However, he also related in a fairly calm manner. During these occasions he continued attributing wisdom to me but without the idealized fervor that was characteristic of his symbiotic regression. He tried to make these interviews into discussion sessions, acting as a typical teenager might who is receiving wise counseling. During these moments, he often treated me as if I were a parent or a teacher, that is, with dignity and respect but devoid of magical omnipotence. He would, for example, ask me if the shoes he were wearing would be proper for a particular social event. Besides seeking advice as to how to dress properly for specific occasions, he inquired as to how to order at restaurants, the particular amenities to observe during a date, how to seek employment, and a variety of questions designed to further his adjustment in an age-appropriate fashion. I sometimes felt as if I were being treated as a columnist who features advice to teenagers.

When I questioned his reasons for casting me in such a role rather than attempting to answer his questions, he would often respond with anger and frustration. He might loudly protest that he did not know to whom he could turn; he had to know in order to survive. He emphasized that he felt as if he were an idiot in a world that demanded certain skills he never learned. He found the external world to be extremely complex, one he could not comprehend, and one in which he felt lost and confused. He stressed his helplessness and vulnerability and found it impossible to detach himself from dependent relationships, which, of course, prevented the development of autonomy.

When this patient stated that he literally did not know how to conduct himself in certain adult situations he was accurately stating his problem. Rather than repression due to intrapsychic conflict and thereby leading to inhibitions, he did not have the adaptive techniques appropriate to the task. His executive ego systems did not know how to respond.

This situation is similar to one where a certain type of knowledge is required to solve a problem but the person has never learned what he needs. Another patient often described himself as living in a world of calculus-like complexity but possessing only an arithmetic mentality. In ego-psychological terms, one can state that such patients do not have the *functional introjects* required to cope with the added complexities of adolescence when compared to childhood. Apparently childhood relationships, for a variety of reasons, did not add to the armentarium of the ego's executive system. These patients do not incorporate particularly helpful and adaptive experiences of memory traces and introjects. Since such introjects are not available, a further progression to being amalgamated in perceptual ego systems does not occur. Thus the ego remains constricted instead of reaching levels of higher integration as occurs as a result of the acquisition of an increased variety of techniques of mastery.

The identity system would, of course, reflect this lack of functional introjects. With simply an "arithmetic" mentality such patients feel frightened and inadequate when having to face problems that are found to be inordinately difficult. My patient's feelings of vulnerability and helplessness were further accentuated when he realized that others took such situations in their stride and considered them to be routine and pedestrian. He often compared himself to a bewildered stranger in a foreign country who does not know the language. His self-esteem was very low, and he reached special peaks of dejection when his helplessness became so intense that he lost practically all sense of personal identity.

The latter occurred because, to a large extent, the identity sense is functionally determined. A person often defines himself operationally.

He recognizes himself in terms of his main activities in life, for example, as a student or in terms of his occupation or profession. If a person lacks adaptive techniques, there is a corresponding lack of structure in the self-representation.

As stated, the process of acquiring such techniques begins with the acquisition of a functional introject. The child incorporates (learns from) experience. Useful introjects are the outcome of gratifying and integrative object relationships. Thus, the child introjects the person, the parent or the parental surrogate, and the adaptive technique associated with that person. An introjected object relationship includes the learning experience as well as the person. The adolescent draws from these introjects and *constructs his identity sense from what he has learned and by identification with the person who has been instrumental to his learning*.

The adolescent period acquires particular importance in the formation of the identity sense because the youth is suddenly required to use these earlier acquired adaptive experiences. As he, so to speak, exercises them, they lose more and more their character of discrete introjects and become more solidly entrenched in an egosyntonic fashion. They become part of the character structure and functional modalities and solidify the identity sense.

I believe this patient illustrates in an exaggerated form problems that all adolescents face. He indicated that during childhood he did not have experiences that would have prepared him for adolescence and adulthood. To look into the reasons for this developmental deficiency would involve us in specific aspects of psychopathology, which include an inability to utilize adaptive experiences when they were offered. Such a discussion would, however, be tangential here. I simply wish to emphasize that in addition to individual psychopathology, the sociocultural factor also plays a significant role.

Insofar as our culture provides only minimal opportunity for the acquisition of functional introjects to establish adult functioning and an identity, adolescence will, to some measure, *have* to be a problem period. The polarization of dependency during childhood and autonomy during adolescence with a discontinuity between these two phases leads to characterological problems, similar to those of this patient, but usually not so intense.

The study of the adolescent phase highlights the importance of the sociocultural variable as an explanatory adjunct. Comparative cultural studies indicate that there have been societies where adolescence as a unique phenomenon does not occur. Indeed, it is my impression that even in this century there have been noticeable changes in our society indicating that the adolescent period has only recently acquired its distinctive characteristics and that our concerns about this period are also relatively recent.

The study of the sociocultural factor is beyond our technical competence and would undoubtedly involve many complex issues. Furthermore, from the viewpoint of psychoanalytic treatment, it is not likely to be an important determinant. However, pedagogically and prophylactically, our understanding of this factor may prove to be highly valuable. It may well be the case that the troublesome and traumatic aspects of adolescence will stand in an inverse ratio to the smooth, rather than the quantum-jump discontinuous, transition from childhood to the post puberty period. The smoother the transition, the more likely that adolescence as a distinct period will cease to exist. If functional introjects are continuously acquired early in life, it is possible that a child will gradually, perhaps imperceptibly, blend into adulthood without the necessity of having upheavals during a specific intermediary stage. The advent of puberty will, of course, have its effects both from a physical and psychological viewpoint. The latter may still remain minimal.

Nevertheless, major personality changes occur during this period of life. The psyche acquires unique and individual features, and the character structure assumes a relatively permanent stability. Of course, this formation of character structure has far-reaching implications for adulthood in terms of both psychic health and psychopathology.

Many others have emphasized the redeeming features of adolescence insofar as it is a period of life when the harmful influences of infancy can, to some extent, be undone. Blos (1962) described a second chance aspect and Erikson (1956) thought along similar lines when he spoke of a psychosocial moratorium.

Here I wish to emphasize another aspect of the adolescent process besides its potentially corrective and restitutive elements. Insofar as the personality seems to erect its main characterological acquisitions during adolescence, the significance of this phase for future adjustment would be tremendous. It seems quite plausible to assume that this is a stage of life that has a similar etiological significance for adult psychic structure and equilibrium as has been assigned to the childhood period. From a theoretical viewpoint one can make the following qualifications.

Freud, in developing an essentially id-psychology, more so at the beginning of his clinical investigations, conceptualized emotional development primarily from the viewpoint of drives. Without dwelling on some of the drawbacks of the psychoeconomic hypothesis, a progressive structuralization of drives was a plausible and logical approach. The investigation of the first years of life led to many valuable insights about

410

the etiological significance of these years upon postpubertal life. With the biological maturation of the sexual organs, drive tensions increased, and the now familiar phenomenon of the return of the repressed led to defensive techniques, adjustive modalities, and a variety of mental mechanisms designed to achieve homeostasis in a physically mature organism.

Freud emphasized the sexual context of the drives, again a logical choice, insofar as what chiefly distinguishes a child from the adult is the operation of sexual organs and the acquisition of secondary sexual characteristics. Following these physiological changes, there is a tremendous revision in the postpubertal adjustment to the cultural milieu when compared to that of the child.

Freud also recognized in his later writings that characterological factors had to be added to his concepts of an hierarchical elaboration of drives if the developing personality is to be understood further. The ego and its subsystems were given far greater importance than previously, and the whole ego concept undertook new dimensions. Childhood is the period of maximum drive development; I believe that in a similar manner adolescence is a period when maximum characterological elaboration occurs.

Freud described psychopathology primarily from a psychodynamic viewpoint, that is, in terms of conflicts of drives. His clinical descriptions center around libidinal conflicts associated with a particular psychosexual stage of development. Ultimately, the central core of the neurosis revealed itself to be a basic oedipal conflict.

As emphasized at the beginning of this lecture, the evolution from id-drive concepts to ego characterological concepts was not simply a matter of theoretical comfort. Our clinical experience made such a shift of emphasis absolutely necessary. Cases such as the classic hysterics described by Freud are extremely rare as are all the other florid symptomatic neuroses he described. Instead, one sees patients similar to the one I describe where the problems are best conceptualized as defective adjustments, lack of self-esteem, and an amorphous, poorly developed self-representation rather than in terms of conflicting, discrete drives. These types of patients are common in all stages of life but especially so during adolescence.

These considerations will bring us back to the initial thought expressed at the beginning of this lecture, the reflection that so many of us find adolescence a particularly fascinating period of life. In spite of and in addition to personal and idiosyncratic motives, adolescence may be an especially intriguing topic because many of us, at one level or another, suspect that it is a phase that has profound significance for the

411

development of the future character in much the same fashion that the infantile period has for postpubertal drive status and the production of the psychoneuroses. Possibly, adolescence has the same etiological significance not for the formation of the psychoneuroses but for the development of psychopathology characterized by structural problems, such as character neuroses, borderline states, and psychoses (all of these being the bulk of our clinical experience), as well as for the construction of the relatively smooth functioning character.

These concepts go beyond the second-chance qualities of adolescence described by Blos (1962). It conceptualizes adolescence as a beginning developmental phase in a characterological frame of reference.

One may well question how one can speak of a beginning developmental phase occurring at a relatively advanced age. I believe here one has to emphasize that the concept of development is meaningful only if related to a specific conceptual frame. As stated, infancy as a beginning developmental phase is consistent with physical maturation, a predominantly biological frame of reference. It is an eminently logical approach since the body is visibly growing and the accompanying emotional changes are in context with such a physiological maturation.

Now, it behooves us to go beyond biological considerations as Freud, himself, led the way. Perhaps the external world is, to a large measure, responsible for the forms and manifestation of psychopathology. From a similar viewpoint, sociocultural factors acquire importance in shaping the characterological aspects of the personality, aspects that consist of adjustive modalities to the problems that the external world presents.

Drives, in contrast, have only a few manifest forms since they are basically organically determined. Once they are established, and it is this establishment that makes early infantile experiences so important, they have limited variability. Hunger and sexual feelings are felt in more or less the same fashion, regardless of the cultural setting. Of course, the techniques and objects that will satisfy these basic drives are quite varied and culturally based; these techniques are what we conceptualize as characterological modalities.

Thus, development can also be conceptualized in a sociocultural frame of reference as well as a biological one. As biological factors are the substrata of drive development, the socializing and educational aspects of the environment can be considered significant variables responsible for characterological development.

Formation of character begins mainly during adolescence. The combination of a relatively completed biological maturation and the new and unique demands of the environment create a situation that has profound importance for the final construction of personality, both in terms

412

of a comfortable adjustment and its psychopathological vicissitudes. The adolescent's culture contains many elements different from childhood, and most of them can be considered from the independence-dependence axis.

The adolescent environment's relatively new demands for independence constitute a stimulus, a problem that has to be mastered, and one that leads to psychological growth and structure. As the neonate has to construct techniques that lead to instinctual gratification and the subsequent refinement of biological needs to more varied gratifications, the adolescent also has to develop techniques, now known as characterological modalities, designed to achieve an adjustment within a relatively autonomous adult world.

To recapitulate, both infancy and adolescence are stages of life that have etiological significance for later developmental stages. The belief that the most significant experiences are those of early childhood has to be modified. Adolescence is now seen as having a similar meaningfulness as infancy, the latter in terms of achieving drive differentiation and the former in the final structure of the ego. This does not mean that infancy has nothing to do with character structure or that the adolescent experience does not contribute to further drive development. Each stage makes some contribution to later stages; this finding was especially elaborated when considering the contributions of pregenital factors to the oedipus complex. Still, when one focuses upon the etiological importance of a particular stage, one is making a quantitative distinction. Experiences during such a phase have a special impact. During infancy, Freud believed this was in part due to the special sensitivity of the immature organism; during adolescence there is a corresponding immaturity not in terms of biology, of course, but in terms of social immaturity within the context of adult autonomy. The infant has his physiological maturation in front of him and achieves it with the help and support of the surrounding world. Analogously, the adolescent has to find a new independence and here, too, the environmental contribution is crucial.

Summary

Adolescence is conceptualized as a developmental period where new demands toward independence arise, demands for which there has been relatively little preparation during infancy and childhood. A clinical vignette illustrates the psychopathological exaggeration of the lack of preparation for the independence and social maturity required of the

413

adolescent. Some of these adolescents, when patients, reveal that they literally do not know how to proceed in or respond to a variety of situations that others would consider pedestrian. This lack of adaptive techniques, virtually techniques of mastery, define the ego defect of many adolescent patients which is accompanied by extremely low self-esteem and a poorly constructed identity sense often manifesting itself in panicky feelings. These states of ego dissolution have been referred to as existential crises.

The chief task of the adolescent is the achievement of characterological consolidation and this has been discussed in conjunction with the analogous task of childhood, the achievement of drive differentiation in a supportive and gratifying environment. Both infancy and adolescence are conceptualized as stages that have etiological significance. Early neonatal experiences make profound contributions to emotional development, contributions that are preponderantly conceptualized in terms of drive differentiation. In a corresponding fashion the adolescent process is seen as crucial, that is, etiological, for the final development of adult character structure in all of its adjustive and psychopathological manifestations.

REFERENCES

Blos, P. (1962). *On Adolescence: A Psychoanalytic Interpretation.* New York: The Free Press.
Erikson, E. H. (1956). The problem of ego identity. *Journal of the American Psychoanalytic Association,* 4:56–121.

25] THE ADOLESCENT AND REALITY

ARMINDA ABERASTURY

Modern youth, in order to be better understood, has imposed on the conscience of the older generation the necessity of abandoning the complacent and comfortable designation of the "difficult age."

This change of viewpoint is also related to psychoanalysis and is reflected in the literature. Not only are there few articles about adolescence in comparison with those about infancy, but there is also very little focus on the involvement of the family and society with the adolescent. A general survey of the vital points that have been considered in the study of adolescence would reveal that at the outset great importance was attributed to genitality, later to the study of the ego and the mechanisms of defense, and finally to object relationships and, by extension, to the relationship of the adolescent to the external world in general.

The paucity of psychoanalytic literature on adolescence has been rationalized by pointing out the great technical difficulties that one encounters in the analysis of the adolescent, and among these, the most important are breaking off treatment entirely or frequently missing sessions.

On the other hand, the analyst of adults has difficulty making systematic formulations about adolescence insofar as his theoretical frame causes him to search for early memories and conflicts generated during the early stages of development. Anna Freud (1958) was the first to point out the necessity for pertinent formulations that go beyond those traditionally used for adult patients. Giovacchini (1973) points out that if the patient represses part of his adolescence and the therapist abandons his attempts to reconstruct it, this period of life continues to be an unknown and we lose a rich source of information concerning the relationship between infancy, adolescence, and adulthood.

Presented at the First Panamerican Congress on Adolescent Psychiatry, January 1971, in Buenos Aires, Argentina. Translated by Peter L. Giovacchini.

Recently, the understanding of the adolescent's relationship to his family and society have made it possible to delineate this period of life within a general cultural and contemporary frame of reference. Different techniques of treatment have been devised as a consequence of viewing the adolescent and his parents as an indissoluble core.

I believe that the refusal to treat adolescents is merely another aspect of the rejection of youth by the adult world. I wish to quote Margaret Mead (1970):

In the majority of debates that develop around the generation gap, one has to take a stand about the alienation of youth insofar as what tends to be omitted is the consideration of the alienation of adults. The discussants forget that true communication consists of a dialogue, but the problem is that the speakers lack a common vocabulary.

One can consider the adolescent's problems in terms of two phases: One phase consists of the conflicts that emerge when infantile ties are loosened so the adolescent can gain entry into the adult world, and the other relates to the adult's response to the adolescent's struggle for emancipation.

In a previous article (Aberastury and Knobel, 1970) I studied the mourning process consequent to loosening of ties, but I discussed it only from the point of view of the adolescent. The adolescent mourns the loss of his infantile body and infantile identity. I soon understood that this view was one-sided and then included the adult's grief experience in my formulations. These formulations are pertinent to the treatment situation because the adult therapist also experiences grief, and he is apt to be judgmental about the adolescent's struggle for change. Today, in a society punctuated with crises, this mourning process has become complex because society constantly interfered with its resolution.

One could debate which of the two worlds, the adults' or the adolescents', is primarily responsible for our chaos and confusion. Most likely there is a parallel relationship between the chaos of the adult world and the intolerable aspects of the adolescents'. The adult world's inflexibility and resistance to change complicate matters. The adult, in fact, lives in a world of whirlwind changes and as a consequence has had to fasten himself to the past in a defensive fashion. In contrast, the adolescent has always lived in a world characterized by such changes.

Owing to the efficiency of means of communication, youth has accumulated contradictory but very important information. In many instances he has been able to assimilate this information, which leads to change, better than his parents. The generation gap is intensified if the adult world remains as a mere spectator and tends to ignore these messages and changes. The world of the adolescent, however, is familiar with change since it has been born and raised in such an environment.

The modern adolescent could never understand the adolescence of his parents nor could he submit himself to the same rigors and renunciations. The adult in turn would not be able to live, except in fantasy, in the environment in which his children have lived during the major part of their development. According to Margaret Mead (1970):

True communication is possible only when both parties speak not one but two languages in which the same words have different meanings. But, if they are disposed to listen and question, they can start a long chat. There is a profound generation gap which is new and lacks precedence and its implications are world wide. Meanwhile, there are adults who believe that they can assume an introspective attitude based upon that of their parents and teachers. They feel that contemplating their own youth and experience will enable them to understand the modern adolescent. Such an adult will be lost.

Adults, in general, have not understood nor do they care to accept the deterioration of their culture and society. They have not accepted change and use the defense mechanism of negation, which leads to rigidity, fixation, and prejudice.

Youth in turn has had too many experiences in which it has faced the failure of the older generation. Youth cannot turn to the older generation for models. Youth has received contradictory information and dictums, insupportable ideals, and has been subjected to attacks and violence as well as snares and traps.

I believe, as does Margaret Mead, that we are at the threshold of the development of a new type of culture that will not be based upon past values and institutions. In this culture it will be the child, not the parents or grandparents, who will determine the future. The nonconforming adolescent understands the critical necessity for immediate action in order to solve the problems that affect the entire world.

To understand and study the profound changes of the adult world as imposed upon youth is the task of every conscientious investigator. The psychoanalyst, more than anyone else, faces this task, and he cannot and should not evade it.

The adolescent is aware of the chaos in which he lives, but he needs the adult to resolve it. To understand the adolescent, one has to turn to all areas of knowledge in order to deal with this chaos which leads to emotional inadequacy and psychic impotence.

The younger generation, by virtue of its numerical superiority (they constitute one-third of the world population), brings about revolutionary changes whose strength can only be assessed in the future. Insofar as the necessary conditions are created that permit this revolutionary force to emerge without violence, it will be possible to channelize it constructively, to lead to a reconstruction of the world in which the adolescent will play a role comparable to that of women after World War I.

In order to understand this we have to go back some years. Social changes due to the war caused women to abandon the home and occupy places that up until then were the private domain of men. Women had been an oppressed class. If they worked, their salaries were much less than men, and they seldom were promoted to positions of responsibility and leadership. I believe that today's youth is in a similar situation.

Women organized themselves in movements in order to fight oppression. To some extent they changed themselves physically; for example, they cut their hair. Attitudes varied as to the extent that women were accepted and allowed to work with men, but there were no violent reactions and society was, in general, accepting.

We may ask ourselves if the adolescent today is acting in a similar manner by letting his hair grow or by wearing bizarre clothes, a rebellion that, if expressed freely, leads to very severe sanctions. I believe youth's turbulent attitude has the same significance as the behavior of the feminists which eventually produced great social changes, leading to restructuring of the family.

We train youth to think but we place obstacles in his way when he attempts to act. Nevertheless, we have proof that if society gives the adolescent the opportunity to exercise his capacities and creative energy he is capable of attaining great success.

The changes effected by youth do not imply nor necessitate the exclusion of the previous generation in the same way that the working woman did not impugn man's confidence or lead to his exclusion. Only if the adult excludes himself will he be excluded. The battle between generations is a social problem. It is not unilateral, and the adolescent and the adult have to come to terms with each other. This could conceivably lead to a sharing of ideals and a harmonious working relationship. The young generation has a new view of the world, but it does not yet have sufficient access to action. Undoubtedly, the world of the future can be constructed only with the active participation of youth.

The question of why there is such a gap between the theoretical understanding and the technical treatment aspects of adolescents can always be pursued further. One especially important feature of the adolescent significant for both our theoretical and therapeutical understanding is that he uses the process of intellectualization more intensely than is usually seen in other phases of development. This is especially true of the late adolescent. It is also a relatively normal process in early adolescence insofar as it prepares him for action. If society later places obstacles in the way of action, youth will remain fixated with thoughts that will be expressed only in words rather than in motor behavior.

I believe the adolescent always had a lucid notion of what was happening to him within the adult world. This emerges clearly when we compare the words of a fifteen-year-old North American youth (quoted by Margaret Mead) with those of Anne Frank in her diary:

There is a general perplexity in the minds of those of my generation when we try to find solutions for ourselves and for the world which surrounds us. We see the world in terms of colossal chaos with a rapid sequence of wars, poverty, prejudices and a lack of understanding which exists between people and nations.

Thus, we have to stop and think; we have to have a better system and we must find it soon.

We see the immense confusion of exasperated individuals who struggle to beat their equals. All of this accumulates and provokes restlessness between nations and even in the home. My generation is used as if it were a machine. We must seek values and norms. We must watch after ourselves and acquire a refined education, one which will permit us to follow in the footsteps of our elders, but then, why? If we create a similar generation the situation will be worse. Still, how can we change? We need a large dose of love for all; we need universal understanding between people. We need to think of ourselves and to express our feelings, but this is not all. I still have to discover what we need the most, and then I have to apply such precepts to their very depth. But when I try to do this the disdain of my mentors falls upon me, they will either not listen to me or will consider the problem in an enclosed mind. Computers have taken the place of brains; electronics have taken over control and this serves to confound even more.

I recognize that we have to obey certain basic regulations and listen to the waves and the birds; I hear their clamor and eternal screams, and at times I pause. Still, each of us remains fixated to his small routines without daring to stop, and listen.

The answers will be found somewhere. We have to search for them.

We listen to this adolescent and also to Anne Frank who in 1944, shortly before her death, wrote:

What is the purpose of this war? Why can't men live in peace? Why all this destruction, this devastation? Why do they build bigger and bigger planes in England with heavier bombs and at the same time communal lodgings as part of their reconstruction? Why do they spend millions for war and have no money for medicine, artists, and the poor? Why are there men who suffer from hunger, while in other parts of the world food spoils because of its excessiveness? Why have men gone mad?

This diary was written during the period of the Jewish persecution and ended on the day that the Gestapo interrupted the life of the Frank family when they discovered them in their hiding place. Her diary was found embedded in the floor and was published by her father. It ended with these prophetic words: "I continue searching for a way of being what I would be capable of being if there were nobody in the world." I wonder how many young people in the world today could alter that sentence to read "I continue searching for a way of being what I would be capable of being if the adult world did not stop me."

I will now discuss how the external world complicates the normal mechanisms of adolescent mourning, a necessary process for the achievement of adulthood.

The loss of childhood status is the end of a process of detachment that began with birth. The adolescent process begins with bodily changes resulting from genital maturation. Not only does the adolescent experience the demands of his own body, but he is also subjugated to those of the external world, which tries to impose its standards on him. This is a double invasion, that of the body and that of society. Thus, the adolescent takes refuge by isolating himself, regression often reaching infantile levels. He would rather select his own ideals than those of the adult world.

He searches for these ideals in his immediate surroundings or he may attain them from famous musicians, authors, or from literature and politics depending on the social and cultural milieu to which he belongs.

Both internal and external changes lead to definite losses that require an elaboration of the mourning process. They mourn the loss of the infantile body and the dependent identity of childhood. The loss of the infantile body represents a double loss to the adolescent because it is a permanent loss and bisexual fantasies have to be abandoned when the procreative role is defined, which occurs in the girl with the appearance of menstruation and in the boy with the production of semen.

Defining the sexual role is fundamental. We could say that it is the most important task of adolescence and the form in which it is experienced will determine how the young adult will face paternity or maternity.

The mourning process is long and painful. There are many fluctuations, progression, and regressions. Because of these fluctuations, the adolescent presents a contradictory picture with fluctuating identities and confusion, and permanent changes, both physical and behavioral. His body and his clothes change not only during a period of days but during a few hours, and we can note that he is a child in the morning and a young adult in the afternoon. These fluctuations are disconcerting to the parents. Therefore, when we speak of mourning for the infantile body we have to keep in mind that not only does the adolescent experience grief but the parents do also when confronted with these changes.

These changes which are necessary for the achievement of maturity are often resisted by the parent who demands permanent infancy, or if the child has to change, that he change totally and immediately without accepting, understanding, or permitting the past to be included in the present as a preparation for the future.

Often parental rejection is disguised as excessive permissiveness, one given to the child in such a way that he experiences it as abandonment. In other cases, the attempt to control the adolescent's growth is more obvious. Instead of granting the child autonomy some parents reinforce their controls, especially when it comes to money matters.

To be sure, when biological development keeps pace with affective and intellectual development, the adolescent is capable of entering the adult world equipped with an identity, a system of values, and an ideology integrated with that of his milieu. He also elaborates political and social theories that conflict with those of the adult. At the time, this can lead to nothing but chaos.

The adolescent is able to translate ideas into actions only when he can find himself in his own body. When he can relate himself to the external world as well, he acquires a capacity to use his body and place in the world to convert ideas into action.

Rebellion, confrontation, and depreciation of adults are inherent aspects of the developmental process which involves loosening of infantile ties. However, parents are not prepared to face the manifestations of this process, and they react by becoming more authoritative or by affective withdrawal. During the beginning of adolescence the child may have to take refuge in the security of infantile dependency in order to establish a bridge to adult independence. On the other hand, the dissolution of parental idealization, an idealization that parents comfortably accept, is absolutely essential. Very few adults understand that the loss of idealization is just as painful for their child as it is for themselves. Moreover, if the adult has not resolved his problems, the acceptance of this nonidealized state is a shattering experience. Rivalry with the child increases. Parents feel inferior when they face youth's strength and creativity.

If the adult accepts the adolescent's strength, maturation, and growth, he also has to accept his deterioration, aging, and death. Conversely, the creative capacity and strength of the adolescent can be a source of identification for the adult, but this is possible only if envy is not prominent.

The adolescent process requires a special climate of stability in order to achieve optimal nonconflictual development. However, as we look at reality we have to accept that the climate that the adolescent is offering is the opposite of stability. The future is uncertain, the present confused, and the past can only be repudiated by the adolescent. He defends his values, depreciates those imposed upon him, and feels trapped. However, the suffering and contradictions he experiences and the confusion he feels are temporary, and they can be worked through if the external world, specifically the family, permits it.

As analysts, we are confronted with a group of adolescents who do not present us with the norms of all social classes and different cultures. In our South American culture this entrance into the adult world is painful for both the child and his parents. This is, however, not a pathological situation. Still, society can transform this normal developmental crisis into a pathological one, as we have frequently noted.

The adolescent cannot control bodily changes, but he plans his life on the basis of having the external world adapt to his needs rather than adapting to the exigencies of reality. But, is the adult world disposed to change? And what should be changed?

The adolescent feels a necessity for reform according to internal dictates, but it is also a response to real external injustices. At first, he limits his preoccupation with reform to merely thinking about it, since there is an increase in intellectualization during beginning adolescence. This period of intellectualization is similar to that which occurs in the first year of life when words are first acquired and assigned omnipotent meanings.

If the adolescent is deprived of the freedom to act, he feels impotent. He regresses to the stage of omnipotence of thought. One frequently remarks that the adolescent speaks and does not act. Nevertheless, it has been frequently demonstrated that the process of intellectualization, a tendency to theorize, can precipitously give way to action when the external milieu permits it. The adolescent seeks external solutions to his problems but he also feels the necessity to resolve them through action. He has abandoned the "as-if" of play and apprenticeship. He has to distance himself from the present, project himself into the future, and proceed independently.

What does the adolescent want? He wants the freedom to defend his ideology. He wants to love and work. He cannot be enclosed by the canons of previous generations of adolescents. No longer can we say that he seeks refuge in apathy and flees from reality. Everything in the world interests him, at first in a theoretical fashion and later the necessity for action and change awakens. He has to participate fully, sexually, socially, and culturally.

The normal attitude of the adult world would be to accept and favor the adolescent's participation in the troubled, social atmosphere. This will lead to emancipation and the acquisition of rights and freedom, permitting the adolescent to maintain himself with stability within the adult society.

REFERENCES

Aberastury, A., and Knobel, M. (1970). *Adolescencia Normal.* Buenos Aires: Paidos.
Freud, A. (1958). Adolescence. *Psychoanalytic Study of the Child,* 13:255.
Giovacchini, P. L. (1973). Character development and the adolescent process. *This Annual,* 2:402–414.
Mead, M. (1970). *Cultura y Compromiso: Estudio Sobre la Ruptiora Generacional.* Buenos Aires: Granica.

26] IDENTITY AND IDEOLOGY

LEON GRINBERG

Identity problems are accentuated during adolescence. Young people ask themselves who they are, as well as question their relationships with others and their surrounding society, assiduously seeking the true meaning of life. One is dealing with a period shaken by the difficult processes of maturation and growth. Many works describe the distinct nuances of the adolescent process with its alternative and diverse forms of expression. The changeable state of the psyche, its oscillating outbursts of rebellion and dependence, the struggle for integration and consolidation of the identity sense, the search for solitude or its opposite, participation in the group which guarantees protection, the need to find definition and a precise place in the world, the imperious desire to find a solution for sexual needs are some of the conflicts that overwhelm the adolescent. Nevertheless, I will not consider these elements in detail, because the purpose of this communication is more specifically involved with those aspects of adolescence that refer to identity and a search for an ideology.

To begin, I will briefly mention ideas that I have developed in other works, concepts about the acquisition of the sense of identity, which has been viewed as being due to the interrelationships of three bonds: the bonds of spatial, temporal, and social integration. The first refers to the relationship between different parts of the self and includes the soma. This spatial bond maintains cohesion leading to differentiation between the self and the nonself as the psyche composes and contrasts various objects. The second, the bond of temporal integration, refers to relationships between discrete self-representations in a temporal context, thereby establishing continuity between parts of the self and erecting a base for the identity sense. The third bond refers to the social aspects of

Presented at the First Panamerican Congress on Adolescent Psychiatry, Buenos Aires, Argentina, January 1971. Translated by Peter L. Giovacchini.

identity and is based on the relationship between parts of the self and external objects, a relationship mediated by the psychic mechanisms of projective and introjective identification.

From a practical viewpoint, it is impossible to study adolescence without considering the social milieu. Spiegel (1964) emphasized that the family and society are responsible for the development of the super-ego and the ego ideal of the adolescent. He added that a large part of the frustrations that augment the pubertal neurosis are imposed upon the adolescent by society and his particular social class.

In fact, the adolescent world should be viewed as a real social structure containing many elements which vacillate between two poles: (1) instability caused by psychobiological changes and the insecurity created by the social milieu and (2) the search for a stable structure that confers solidity and security to a tottering identity.

Moments of confusion, owing to an accentuation of the uncertainties regarding the differentiation of internal and external, adult and infantile, good and bad, and masculine and feminine (dichotomies characteristic of pregenital development) aggravate this emotional instability. The differentiation of erogenous zones merely adds to this confusion. Among the extreme defenses the adolescent uses to counterbalance the anxiety resulting from his confusion are dissociation and projective identification, defenses that, for the moment, allow him to externalize his conflicts.

The disequilibrium and dissolution of stable relationships between psychic systems and the increasing disturbance in ties with external objects which inevitably occurs during emotional development significantly contribute to pathology of the identity sense. Confusional crises, provoked by the vicissitudes of psychobiological development and augmented by the failure of the group upon which he is dependent to provide solutions, create moments of true depersonalization.

The adolescent, because of his particular problems, has been designated as a spokesman of a society consisting of the family and the remainder of his contemporary environment, a society that is considered to be in a state of crisis. From this general group the adolescent becomes the spokesman for social marginal groups because he is in a transition state and considered marginal in our society. The puberty rites of primitive societies are a clear example of severe external limitations and the prohibitions of the superego determined by society, which do not allow the transgressing of certain norms of the privileged adult group. These norms are threatened by the impulsive tendencies of the young adolescent which are determined by psychobiological turbulence. This would explain the suspicion and mistrust that usually characterize the relationship between the adolescent and his parents, and which lead him to constantly search for parental surrogates with whom he can feel free of conflict and thus find more capable of satisfying his aspirations. These surrogates can also serve as models of identification and thereby contribute to the formation of a longed-for ideology, which serves as a substitute for identity.

Aberastury (1969) described the frictional elements of the world of the adolescent. Frequently these elements consist of confrontations similar to those seen in class struggles in which economic factors play an important role. The parents use economic dependence as their authoritative power over their children, which, in turn, augments the resentment between the two generations.

Often the parents do not realize the complex conflict that is created for their children when they reach adolescence and can no longer idealize them. In exchange for idealization, the adolescent seeks new ideologies and value systems, new perspectives from which he can contemplate the world. The parents' loss of their omnipotent, admired, idealized status contributes to a series of depressions which the adolescent has to pass through during the course of his development; depressions that the parents also help elaborate. I have repeatedly insisted in previous works on the importance of considering depression (in terms of the lost parts of the self) a fundamental part of the developmental process. This helps us better understand the vicissitudes encountered in the consolidation of the sense of identity (Grinberg, 1963).

Throughout the course of development, there are diverse situations (painful experiences) that threaten both the identity sense and the integrity of the ego, resulting in damage and partial object losses, which, in turn, produce both depressive reactions and anxiety. Living implies an inevitable succession of sorrows. Growth, the passage from one stage to another, is accompanied by losses of certain types of behavior modalities and object relationships that, even though they are replaced by better differentiated ones belonging to higher stages of integration, still cause the ego to experience insufficiently elaborated reactions of sorrow. It leads to the familiar but paradoxical phenomenon in which the same mechanisms of defense used by the ego against anxiety are converted into offensive factors, threatening the ego's structure and integrity and leading to its debilitation. In its struggle against persecutory anxieties the ego dissociates and becomes fragmented, the separated parts being projected into external objects. More or less, the ego of the adolescent fears that these disjointed parts will never return. This is experienced as an irremediable loss, which develops into a depressive reaction creating true grief that leads to vicissitudes of the identity sense.

426

All in all, I have emphasized that the sense of identity implies that the ego is essentially dependent upon the continuity and similarities of unconscious fantasies, whose antecedents are the outcome of somatic sensations and of primitive affects and anxieties experienced by the ego in relation to internal and external objects. This identity sense has similar functions, both from a qualitative and quantitative viewpoint, as the defense mechanisms. The interactions of unconscious fantasies will lead to a cohesive ego state which is able to sustain a definitive identity sense that can tolerate environmental threats and losses within certain limits. This inevitably occurs during adolescent development, but in a form that gives the ego time to deal with internal changes and losses and to recuperate from the transitory disturbances of the identity sense. However, in pathological cases, owing to a failure to work through these depressive moments, grave disturbances of the identity sense result.

Still, an external object is always required to achieve and establish the identity sense. Laing (1969) emphasized the concept of complementarity as a function of interpersonal relationships in which the external object complements the self. For example, a woman cannot be a mother if she does not have a child. Similarly, the adolescent, at times, feels compelled to play certain roles which are imposed upon him by the family or social group. Though they are complementary roles, they may lead to an undesired identity.

The identity sense also depends on being separate and distinct from others. When a child succeeds in integrating his multiple impressions, which were previously dissociated, in the concept of one person, he finds that his reality consists of two factors, the mother and the father, and the relationship between them. This leads to the triangular configuration of the oedipal object relationship in which the child discovers that he is neither the father nor the mother. The tie between the members of the father-mother pair also has decisive importance for the establishment of the ultimate identity sense.

I have already indicated that the adolescent tries to establish a determined ideology as a point of departure for the consolidation of his identity. This attempt also presupposes a type of mourning because it also involves a breakdown in previous structures and identities in order to achieve a later reintegration based on different modalities. This constitutes a revolutionary change because he has to undergo a chaotic experience with periods of disorganization and dissolution of psychic systems and established value and specific object ties in order to reintegrate an organization that will lead to a new identity. On the other hand, such experiences also include creative moments associated with rebirth fantasies. Certain cases are characterized by especially intense regressions which remind us of Erikson's (1963) abysmal attitudes, described as the ultimate limits of regression, a touching bottom that occurs with unconscious rebirth fantasies, which ultimately lead to a new identity.

Now, we can raise the question of what we mean when we speak of ideology. According to Erikson (1963) an ideological system is a shared coherent system of images, ideas, and ideals providing orientation, total coherence, and a systematic simplification of space and time as well as means and goals. Althusser (1967) said,

ideology is a system (that processes its own logic and discipline) of representations (images, myths, ideas or concepts) . . . in the context of a given society. Without entering upon the problem of the relationship of science with its ideological past we can say that ideology has a system of representations distinguished from science in that the practical, social function is more important than the theoretical function (or that of knowledge).

Ideological systems, whatever their objectives, nature, or specific content, are destined to satisfy the various needs of the individual and society. Among these needs one especially finds in youth the need to affirm the sense of identity. A specific group identity can serve the function of both encompassing and limiting and, at the same time, discriminating and consolidating the various identities of the group members. Such a group also guarantees the survival of identity in regard to a plan of life and determines social and temporal ties assuring the group of the maintenance of the identity sense and its continuity into the future. Though the members of the group change or develop individual and distinct characteristics, the ideology nevertheless maintains itself at the same basic level. Though it may undergo certain modifications, the individual still finds himself better integrated and more complete. He will relate to the parts of himself he has projected into the group and feel controlled and secure. He will know where they stand in the present and where they will go in the future.

Regardless of the nature or the authentic value of the ideological system, it still has an inherent force that tends to reinforce the individual's transient fantasy of immortality, one that in turn is projected into the ideological system and thereby gains permanence. The future becomes a receptacle that protects what has been put into the ideological system, and the ideological system acts as a defense against persecutory anxiety.

As we have just seen, continuity with its transcendental qualities is intrinsically bound to the identity sense and manifests itself in ego terms by such statements as "I am the same as I was yesterday and will be tomorrow." Thus, one can observe that an ideology can become necessary to secure one's identity and at the same time one's identity can also ensure the preservation of the ideology.

One of the important elements involved in the consolidation of the identity sense is the dynamic equilibrium between similarities and differences in regard to time as it involves another person or a group. In a group relationship with a shared ideology we note that the adolescent still has to differentiate himself from others. Even though they share a common ideology, he cannot allow himself to be submerged by the group though belonging to the group achieves differentiation from the outside community. The group offers a solution for the dilemma of being diluted in the larger group of society in general, which leads to anonymity. On the other hand, the burden of achieving an individual identity, one that cannot be shared, is also obviated by the group. Excessive individualism leads to isolation, rigidity, lack of communication, and the loss of objects that the group offers.

The content of the chosen ideology should be carefully studied. The social, political, and economic environment surrounding the adolescent can influence his choice. Other factors, such as sensitivity and education, as well as significant external objects also exercise a decisive influence regarding his choice of an ideology. One has to add deeper motivations and specific unconscious fantasies that are outcomes of early infantile object relationships as relevant to later identifications and general orientations that are instrumental for the adolescent's selection of value systems.

Can one assume, then, that persons who share a common ideology also have similar identity structures that are instrumental in the selection of the ideology? Would this mean that one has the ideology he "deserves"? Even if this were the case, all psychological phenomena are multidetermined. Ideologies stem from different parts of the personality, which can be considered as sane or insane. In the former case, one would achieve an ideology that permits clear and meditative decisions and implies rational knowledge not based on defensive motivations. In the latter case, psychic conflict determines the choice of ideological systems based upon compulsive qualities necessitated by peremptory internal demands. For example, there are persons who choose ideologies based upon submission. They are afraid of being excluded from the group. On other occasions, such a submissive attitude is due to a lack of sufficiently strong convictions that would defend one against the intrusions of foreign ideologies. In such cases an ideology by imposition acts like a parasitic superego to control and dominate the internal life of the individual, a superego that is similar to the psychopath who vic-

429

timizes and dominates his victims. Persons embracing such ideologies have weak personalities characterized by a deficient identity sense.

In other instances, identification with the aggressor can be the dominant motivation that leads to the adoption of a specific ideology. The individual projects his inner self-affliction and transforms himself into a person persecuted by the external world.

Certain ideologies are characterized by a lack of authenticity, their purpose being mainly defensive. The essential characteristic of these ideologies can be labeled "as-if" or "pseudo as-if." They tend to utilize a body of coherent ideas belonging to an established ideology, but this is merely superficial and self-protective. Ideologies often provide avenues of escape for their adherents who are trying to avoid their inner conflict and needs; rigid political systems often serve such a purpose.

Erikson's (1963) classification based upon Freud's (1923) distinction between ideologies stemming primarily from the superego and the ego ideal provides us with a useful means for determining whether an ideology is selected because of neurotic or sane reasons. The superego is the most archaic representative of a blind morality that perpetuates the past and demands obedience and submission to rigid traditions. On the other hand, the ego ideal involves social aspects to a greater extent. As Freud (1923) indicated, "the ego ideal is very important for our understanding of group psychology. Besides its individual aspect, it has a social aspect. It is also an ideal common to the family, to the clan and to the nation."

Besides discussing the relationship of the oedipus complex to the superego, Freud also described other related aspects of the superego, such as the role of identification with the father in its formation, as well as differentiations within it, for example, "You must be like your father, but in other aspects you must not be like him." This not only implies the incest prohibition but also indicates an imperative which acts as a stimulus for differentiation and discrimination. Thus, differentiation and discrimination become two important factors for the establishment and consolidation of the identity sense. As the identity sense becomes better established, the superego begins to behave according to aspirations of the ego ideal. Ideology enables the sane part of the individual to transform the superego into the ego ideal, and the ego tends to identify with the latter.

Here, I have referred to group or collective ideologies, but now I wish to emphasize individual or private ideologies, which correspond to personal "philosophies of life" that are also able to contribute sane parts as well as sick ones to various levels of the personality. It is an applied philosophy of daily life. At times it expresses neurotic conflicts. For example, a patient's private ideology may consist of a belief that

430

since he had no choice in being brought into the world, his parents and, through generalization, the entire society should take care of him all of his life. His difficulties in working and in being independent are rationalized away by such ideological principles. Another patient has a similar but more extended ideology, one shared by various groups and dominated by the belief that since she is a woman her husband had to take complete care of her without any reciprocity on her part. The first, as well as the second patient, adopts an exclusive, rigidly delineated role that does not allow the acquisition of other roles, and from this restricted role, the various directions of the totality of his life is determined. The state of "child-baby" or "woman-dependent" refers not only to a particular ideology but to a circumscribed identity as well.

Identity and ideology appear to be, in effect, two aspects of the same process. Both provide the necessary conditions for the individual's maturity and the solidarity that leads to the consolidation of a common identity.

An unshared ideology can undermine harmonious and tolerant object relationships. It can destroy long friendships and reconcile stubborn enemies.

Ideological differences determine whether people form partial bonds disturbed by tensions and suspicions. By contrast, those individuals who share an ideology have a common language, full of implicit understanding, and a particular code by which the world and daily events can be understood.

An ideology can attain greater importance (have a higher place in the hierarchy) than nationality or language in establishing affective bonds between individuals. The partisans of a specific ideology tighten their bonds with those who support the same ideology far beyond the barriers of language and religion and, if necessary, they may oppose even their own countrymen and intimate acquaintances. We are reminded of an eloquent sentence from a person with strong ideological convictions who in referring to his own family wrote to one of his comrades: "If I refer to them as brothers, what should I call you?" Each ideology is rooted in the foundation of identity. All the members of an ideological community feel themselves to be brothers, not only because they struggle for shared aspirations but because they also have a common idealized object that represents a primitive love object. Thus, all ideologies are emotionally charged insofar as they symbolize the most cherished aspects of the mother and father of the early stages of life. In other words, the ideology represents internal objects incorporated in the ego nucleus "through whose eye the person views the world" (an expression used by Wisdom, 1962).

431

If we try to focus upon identity from other viewpoints we encounter such characteristics as hate, aggression, and resentment. The rebellion of youth against adults, the conflict of generations, is now well known. There is a compelling search for radical changes in social structures as well as for a new social identity.

The phenomenon of adolescent rebellion has emerged almost simultaneously in different parts of the world, and has significantly reached its peak in those countries that have achieved the most social, cultural, and industrial development. It has expressed itself with the greatest intensity and cohesion in universities; the common characteristic of adolescent violence consists of a rejection of adult society and a struggle against conformity and despotism, which, according to youth, characterize the bourgeois.

Some authors interpret such a rebellious attitude as a new expression of parricidal feelings, a re-edition of the battle of generations that originally occurred between the primitive horde against the totem. However, such an interpretation is unilateral. More significantly, one encounters latent and disguised filiacidal impulses in adults. A. and M. Rascovsky (1968) thoroughly studied filicide, and postulate that it is of major importance for the understanding of war. One fact is undeniable: Adults make the decisions to conduct war, but youth is sent to fight and die. The young are cathected with persecutory guilt through the projections of adults. Youth, in turn, experiences an increase in his inner destructiveness, which leads to killing but, more significantly, exposes him to death. I believe that an autodestructive tendency also exists in filicide. Aspects of the self that one wishes to destroy are projected onto one's children, who then are exposed to death.

The adolescent attempts to liberate himself from guilt and anxiety by attacking social systems identified with oppression and submission. On many occasions, society acts as a constraining mother, who rejects violence but does not know how to restrain or resolve the mounting anxiety which is the basis for destructive adolescent protest. This protest is also an alarm signal, an appeal for help. On the other hand, there is a reparatory tendency in this rebellion which is expressed by the desire to destroy the old and infirm in order to construct the new and healthy.

Marcuse (1968) defined juvenile rebellion as a moral, political, and sexual rebellion. Revolutionary violence is a response to institutionalized violence. According to him, the young are violent because they are in a state of despair. At times, rebellion takes an apparently nonviolent, passive form, as seen in hippies. They oppose war and protest against Puritanism and hypocrisy. However, in various ways, they turn their destructiveness toward themselves as evidenced by the use of

432

drugs, rationalized by such arguments that they achieve profound sensations that can lead to a true identity.

World surveys of ideologies and politicosocial economics and even scientific areas demonstrate a highly complex, confused, and confusing panorama. Technological development has created a tempo that has never previously existed, and the human mind cannot absorb its rhythm. In addition, the terrible swiftness of communication exposes youth to a large quantity of all types of messages from various parts of the world which he can neither assimilate nor synthesize. On the contrary, they become contradictory. His environment has become vast compared to that of childhood. Massive communication, the bombardment of advertisement, the narcotic use of television are among the many factors responsible for ideological confusion. The adolescent, through reaction formation or desperate defenses, compulsively seeks a structured ideology in order to escape chaos and the danger of a confused and alienated identity.

From a developmental viewpoint one could describe different categories of ideologies, beginning with primitive and rudimentary ones, which finally attain higher levels of abstraction containing complex systems of ideas. Perhaps, it would not be too bold to speak of protoideologies such as those that correspond to primitive, unconscious fantasies about the idealized breast. Thus, an ideology would include systems of ideas or fantasies that are highly valued because they satisfy basic needs. Naturally, the characteristics of these primitive ideologies coincide with the mechanisms of the schizoid-paranoid position described by Melanie Klein (1957), specifically those dealing with idealization, dissociation, and projective identification.

Certain ideologies remain fixed to primitive levels corresponding to the schizoid-paranoid position, and they make use of mechanisms such as idealization and dissociation to an extreme degree. In other cases the ideology embodies all virtues for itself and projects negative aspects onto other ideologies. We are dealing with saturated ideologies, because they are closed to all possibility of change and development. They are rigid and dogmatic, and the individual attaches himself fanatically to them.

Others, in contrast, use better developed ideologies, which contain less schizoid-paranoid mechanisms such as idealization and omnipotence; when dissociation is used it later develops into discrimination. They seek to establish order in the external and internal world through the use of obsessive mechanisms. These ideological systems are not saturated. They can develop further, and tend to make reparation. Naturally, identities imbued with such integrative qualities produce solid, mature, and flexible identities that permit development and change instead of rigidity and submission.

Erikson (1969) indicated that each generation of youth has to find an identity in harmony with its own childhood and a corresponding ideology in order to find its place in historical perspective. However, during adolescence the code of infantile dependency slowly begins to reverse. Not only can the elderly teach the young about life in either its individual or collective aspects, but youth, by response and actions, tells the elderly whether life has meaning. Adolescents have the power to confirm those who confirm them and by consolidating their problems they also have the power to renovate and regenerate or to reform and rebel.

REFERENCES

Aberastury, A. (1969). El adolescente y la libertad. *Revista Uruguaya de Psicoanalisis,* 11(2):151–166.
Althusser, L. (1967). La revolucion téorica de Marx. Mexico: Siglo Veintiuno.
Erikson, E. H. (1963). The problem of ego identity. *Revista Uruguaya de Psicoanalisis,* 5(2–3):267–338.
———. (1969). La juventud: Fidelidad y diversidad. In: *La Juventud en el Mundo Moderno,* E. H. Erikson *et al.* Buenos Aires: Horme.
Freud, S. (1923). The ego and the id. Standard Edition, 19. London: Hogarth, 1961.
———. (1933). New introductory lectures on psychoanalysis. Standard Edition, 22. London: Hogarth, 1964.
Garcia Reinoso, D. (1970). *Adolescencia, Familia y Sociedad.* Paper presented at the Association Psiconalitica Argentina.
Grinberg, L. (1961). El individuo frente a su identidad. *Revista de Psicoanalisis,* 18(4).
———. (1963). *Culpa y Depresión.* Buenos Aires: Paidos.
———, and Grinberg, R. (1966). L'adquisición del sentimiento de identidad en proceso analítico. *Revista Uruguaya de Psicoanalisis,* 8(3).
Klein, M. (1957). Notes upon some schizoid mechanisms. *Revista de Psicoanalisis,* 14(2).
Laing, R. D. (1969). *Self and Others.* London: Tavistock.
Marcuse, H. (1968). *Declaraciones: En Marcuse Polemico.* Buenos Aires: Jorge Alvarez.
Rascovsky, A., and Rascovsky, M. (1968). Sobre el filicidio y su significado en la genesis del acting out y la conducta psicopatica en Edipo. *Revista de Psicoanalisis,* 24:717–740.
Spiegel, L. A. (1964). Identity and adolescence. In: *Adolescents: A Psychoanalytic Approach to Problems and Therapy,* ed. S. Lorand and H. I. Schner. New York: Harper & Row.
Wisdom, J. O. (1962). Comparative study of psychoanalytic theories of melancholia. *International Journal of Psycho-analysis,* 43:113–133.

27] ADOLESCENCE IN ISRAEL: THOUGHTS ON THE MIDDLE-CLASS URBAN ADOLESCENT

EMANUEL CHIGIER

In Israel as elsewhere more attention has been paid recently to the phenomenon of adolescence and its psychopathology. However, owing to the varied nature of the Israeli society, it is difficult to talk of a typical Israeli adolescent. Varieties of the species would include urban middle-class and lower-class adolescents, those in orthodox and ultraorthodox religious settings, in development towns, and, of course, on the kibbutz (collective settlement). This discussion is limited to the urban middle-class adolescent and is based on the author's personal experiences with teenagers at the high schools in the Tel Aviv area over the past eleven years.

There are certain features about contemporary Israeli society that need to be taken into account when dealing with any psychosocial aspect of life in the country. These include the following:

1. Israel is a young state. Having been founded only in 1948 and now only twenty-five years old, the country's emphasis has been strong on the young. Until recently the public was hardly aware of the presence of aged people as a community problem and responsibility. The atmosphere is still imbued with the feeling of novelty about the existence of an independent state and of looking forward to further growth, expansion, and development.

2. Israel is a mosaic. A tourist need but spend five minutes on the main boulevard of Tel Aviv's Dizengoff Street in order to be aware of the varied shapes, sizes, and color pigmentation of the Israeli society. From a population of 600,000 Jews in 1948, the country's population has grown to include 2.5 million Jews, the majority of whom are fairly

435

recent immigrants, coming from at least seventy countries of the world. In addition, Israel has 500,000 citizens from the Arab, Druze, and other minority groups. Tel Aviv has restaurants that cater to West European, East European, Balkans, Yemenite, Middle East, and North African tastes. Apart from the Hebrew theater, theater groups perform in Yiddish and Rumanian, while one of the most veteran dance groups in the country is Inbal, presenting Yemenite traditional dances. Foreign language daily newspapers published include those in English, French, Rumanian, German, Yiddish, Hungarian, and Polish. Ethnic differences as well as prejudices exist to a noticeable degree, though acculturation is proceeding, and the percentage of cross-ethnic marriages in 1970 reached 17 percent.

3. Israel is an open society. Despite the distance from Europe and America the country is not isolated from the mainstream of Western thoughts. There are 0.65 million tourists every year. Six thousand overseas students study at universities in Israel. Hundreds of African and Asiatics come each year for short-term or long-term courses. Twenty thousand teenagers spend summer vacation here and thousands of young adult volunteers spend one to two years working in the country. The Israeli adolescent gets quite an exposure to the winds of change blowing across the United States and Western Europe.

4. Israel is a threatened state. The small country of Israel is surrounded by vast Arab territories with 100 million inhabitants who regard Israel as a thorn in their flesh. Three wars have been fought in less than twenty years. Thousands of adults in the country have personally gone through a dangerous existence in Europe during the Nazi regime, or as refugees from Muslim countries. Children and adolescents grow up with perpetual awareness that physical security and continued existence as a state is not something that can be taken for granted but rather something that has been hard won and hard kept and requires further vigilance and effort to maintain.

5. Israel is a dynamic technological society. Despite the many shortcomings, progress in the country can literally be seen and felt. National production and exports keep rising. Immigration runs at 50,000 a year, while tourism is a rapidly expanding industry which is expected to double in size during the next five years. New universities have been set up in the last four years, with rapid escalation in the number of university students. Last year, 3,518 new book titles were published in the country. Despite its small size, Israel ranks sixth in the world in the annual number of scientific papers published in accredited journals. The general mood is one of confidence, optimism, of striding upwards.

Social Features

Against this background some of the factors that play a part in shaping the outlook of the middle-class urban adolescent can be delineated.

INFORMALITY

Casual style of dress has always been permissible both for teenagers and adults, even at symphony concerts in the Tel Aviv main auditorium. Because of the natural informality, flamboyant forms of dress as a symbol of protest are little in evidence simply because it would be regarded as a silly form of protest. Long hair may cause friction between some parents and their teenage sons, but the minister of education has gone on record as having no objection (provided it is clean). Some high schools permit twelfth graders to grow beards. Miniskirts are to be found at most high schools. The noise at schools, especially during intermissions, is impressive in its amount. Many urban high schools have their own discotheques at the school.

Many adults in professional and authoritarian roles, for example, teachers, head nurses, psychologists, are known to the young by their first names. Many high-ranking officers in the defense forces have nicknames that are used in newspaper reports. It would seem that generally speaking the atmosphere of informality takes a lot of the sting out of the need for protest on the part of the younger generation.

SPONTANEITY

Visitors to the country comment on the phenomenon of young people singing loudly on bus rides. Outward expression is the norm from politicians to young children, whether it be the wiping away of tears by the prime minister when she took on the job or the singing of young children on television in the Children's Song Festival. Being "bottled up," "keeping a stiff upper lip," or being "up tight" is not common among Israeli teenagers. It would seem that the persistence of spontaneity of expression into adolescence and to a certain extent into adulthood probably contributes to a better state of mental health.

TOLERANCE

Despite fierce verbal fights on political and religious issues, especially the latter, Israel is a tolerant country. Foreigners are treated with curiosity and interest. The policy is live and let live. Though the law against homosexuality is still in the statute, it is left over from the period of

British mandatory government and has not been enforced. Similarly, despite the law against abortion except for compelling medical reasons, abortion is carried out quite extensively in a quasi-legal sort of way.

Divorce has always been easy to come by in Israel and has very little stigma. The sexual behavior of prominent politicians has never been regarded as a reflection on their political capabilities, nor has it stood in the way of advancement. Israel is one of the few countries in the world with extensive legislation to protect the rights of the common-law wife. The musical "Hair" ran for over eight months in Israel, barely causing a ripple. A poor imitation of "Hair" did not succeed simply because it was a bad production. Many movies are classified as not for people under the age of sixteen years, but few attempts are made to enforce this ruling.

Though begging, peddling without a license, or building without a permit are all illegal, on the rare occasions where the hand of the law intervenes public sympathy is usually for the individual. With such an atmosphere, youth find it difficult to muster up protest. A few high school underground newspapers appeared but soon died through lack of interest. The New Left has made inroads among the urban high school student population, but to a small extent. Hippies in Israel are rare. It would seem that the tolerant attitude in the country usually permits exposure to outside elements to occur with a certain amount of jolting but without a severe rocking of the boat.

A SENSE OF NATIONAL PURPOSE

The Israeli adolescent grows up with a heavy exposure to national feeling. From childhood onwards, national religious festivals, such as New Year, Passover, Chanukah, are celebrated in the school, street, and home, imbuing the child with an awareness of the past heritage of the Jewish people. Current history is reflected in national observances on Holocaust Day, Soldier's Memorial Day, and Independence Day. Grade school children go on organized school outings all over the country. High school students are organized into the Gadna premilitary program, which includes short periods of national service, preliminary military training, work camps, annual marches, and outings. The youth movements, though not so strong as in the past, involve many adolescents in social, scouting, and national activities. Youth are active in protests against the treatment of Jews in Russia and in the Arab countries. In a small, tightly knit country, young people are inevitably involved in national issues, with a correspondingly high level of national identification.

POSITIVE ATTITUDE TOWARD THE YOUNG

In many cases, the older generation in this country is regarded as the generation of the wilderness, and the younger generation as the generation of the future. The American style of humor about adolescents, for example, "Beware, a teenager lives here!" does not go down well in Israel, mainly because of its irrelevance. The young are taken seriously. When a group of twelfth graders wrote a letter to the prime minister stating that they were concerned because they felt that the government was not doing enough to promote peace, television, radio, newspapers, and cabinet ministers paid attention to them and discussed the problem with them comprehensively. Though, paradoxically, in practice political power remains to a surprising extent in the hands of the old guard, the mood is one of promotion of the young toward responsibility and toward taking over the reins.

SOCIALIZATION

More than in other countries, the Israeli child and adolescent is a social being and is exposed to a strong socialization process. Most toddlers in the cities start going to nursery school from the age of three, whether the mother is at home or at work, because it is regarded as a good thing that children should learn as soon as possible to get on with other children. From then on parents, teachers, and psychologists pay attention to the sociability of the young child and adolescent, and efforts are made to provide as many suitable social settings as possible. Being able to socialize is regarded as more desirable than being able to compete; being an accepted member of a group is regarded with more satisfaction than being a loner, both for male and female adolescents. Some parents will be prepared to allow their adolescent son or daughter to have the family apartment for a party on Friday evenings and will absent themselves until it is all over, so as to ensure the social success of the evening. Living in fairly crowded conditions in apartments in the cities allows young people to meet easily and be out and about with the blessing of their parents, except when overactivity in the social sphere seems to be acting as a threat to progress in school studies. Despite the fact that the kibbutz population in the country is a small one (3 percent), the strong peer-group emphasis that is characteristic of the kibbutz way of life has some conscious or unconscious influence on the life style of many young people even in urban communities. Finally the vast majority of eighteen-year-olds go into the army for twenty months (females) or up to three years (males), which has an important socioeducational impact.

The outcome seems to be twofold: (1) Social independence and maturity seem to come fairly early. (2) Conflicts between family and peer-group loyalty are usually not too severe, since many parents accept with equanimity that the adolescent is too busy with his social group to spend leisure time with the family and they assume that adolescent group activities are innocent until proved otherwise.

Mental Health Status

Probably as a result of these factors, the Israeli middle-class urban adolescent, in general, seems to be in fairly good mental health.

Adolescence does not seem to create a state of acute crisis or confusion for most adolescents. In a 1966 survey of 960 adolescents from the tenth to twelfth grade (579 females and 381 males), the adolescents replied to the question, "Based on your own experience, do you think there is a crisis in adolescence?" in the following manner: decidedly so, 5 percent; yes, 42 percent; perhaps, 33 percent; personally, no, 10 percent; no reply, 10 percent. Those who answered in the affirmative went on to describe the dominant feature of the adolescent crisis, as they saw it. The following categories were listed: emotional problems, 41 percent; social problems, 25 percent; problems with parents, 22 percent; sexual arousal, 11 percent; learning difficulties, 9 percent; miscellaneous, 1 percent.

Runaways do occur among adolescents, mostly female from the Eastern urban families with a low socioeconomic status. However it is very rare among middle-class urban adolescents, male or female. (One practical reason may be that with the country so small, the resourceful middle-class parent probably can track down a runaway adolescent without too much difficulty.)

In the area of sexual behavior, sexual mores are generally not extreme. Communes do not exist, and promiscuous sexual acting-out behavior is rare among middle-class adolescents.

In the survey of adolescents in high schools in the greater Tel Aviv area, the following replies were received to the question, "What is your attitude toward sexual relationships before marriage?": in favor, 29 percent; permissible for men, 2 percent; depending on the situation, 6 percent; against, 47 percent; no reply, 16 percent. Of eighty detailed replies in favor, the reasons given were as follows: it is natural, 45 percent; one should get experience, 34 percent; a modern outlook, 10 percent; a sign of love, 6 percent. Reasons against, among 260 replies, were as follows:

risk of pregnancy, 31 percent; loss of honor or purity, 18 percent; can cause emotional complications, 14 percent; a disturbing factor in my life, 14 percent; social norms, 14 percent.

The attitude toward sexual behavior is generally forthright and pragmatic without marked neurotic overtones. (It is of interest that Portnoy finally became impotent when confronted with the down-to-earth sexual outlook of an Israeli young woman.) Unwed mothers are as rare as rain in the desert, the overall rate in the country being less than 0.5 percent of all births. This is probably due to a number of factors: less promiscuity, less demonstrative sex, less opportunities in obtaining contraceptive devices and pills, and the availability of abortion for an undesired pregnancy.

Despite the relative ease in obtaining drugs and the wide publicity given to the subject, drug abuse has not become a major problem with urban middle-class adolescents in high school. No exact figures are available, but the general impression is that where drug use occurs (usually hashish, sometimes LSD) it does so among marginal adolescents who have emotional problems or among the small group of bohemian types. A preliminary survey of attitudes among eleventh and twelfth grade students at a Tel Aviv high school, regarded as more liberal in outlook than most, indicated the following trends among 174 male students: 91 percent agreed that the police should be more active in apprehending drug sellers; 58 percent agreed that the police should be more active in apprehending drug users; 27 percent agreed that the law should be changed so as to permit the smoking of hashish; 23 percent agreed that there is an assumption that drugs help a person to understand himself; 22 percent agreed that they would smoke hashish if it were offered to them. As things stand at present, it would seem that drug use is not regarded as normative behavior by most urban middle-class adolescents but as a peripheral phenomenon even though drugs have been easily available for the past three years and can be used with consequences that are not so punitive as in the United States.

COMPARISON WITH THE UNITED STATES

Five extended visits to the United States over the past seven years, with an opportunity to observe many areas of the subcontinent, have led me to derive two general conclusions about the American scene with regard to adolescent mental health problems, as compared to Israel. (As with all generalizations, there are probably many exceptions.)

1. American adults attempt to delay acquisition of independence by adolescents. In Israel the youth is the future of the country. In America, today, the present adolescent generation is expendable as far as popula-

tion and the economy are concerned. In Israel, on reaching the age of eighteen, legal adulthood is achieved with the right to vote, carry a gun, drive a car, carry out independent sexual behavior, use contraceptives, get married, and go to your own doctor. In America, progress in this direction is still slow. Only very recently have eighteen-year-olds been given the vote, and then not in all state elections. The paraphernalia of classification of adolescents into age categories that can see a certain kind of movie, grow long hair, drink beer, enter a liquor store, go to a doctor independently, be able to buy contraceptives, tends to blur the impact of adulthood, causes unnecessary frustration, and creates inevitable problems. An acceptance by society, including legislators, that adolescence is a period of diminishing adult responsibility and increasing adolescent responsibility, culminating in recognition of eighteen years as a time of full responsibility (rather than twenty-one years) would undoubtedly help in diminishing the generation gap and the ferocity of the adolescent crisis in many families.

2. Increasing affluence has led to increasing social isolation. The Israeli middle-class adolescent generally lives in an urban milieu; his American counterpart is usually in a suburban environment. The nature of Israeli urban living is such that opportunities for spontaneous socialization exist all the time, with reinforcement through parental attitudes and encouragement. The American child and preadolescent in the suburbs cannot drop in and out of the homes of peers nor meet them casually at the corner. Children may have to arrange with their mothers for transportation to and from other homes and may have to arrange for times to play with other children. The loose, unstructured, fluid, spontaneous form of interaction, which is the basis of the socialization process, and its attendant importance in promoting maturity becomes lost as a result of the need for making topographical arrangements.

For convenience and comfort the growing adolescent in a comfortable suburban environment is successively provided with his own bedroom, play area, television set, bathroom, telephone, and in some families his own refrigerator and automobile. The absence of social traffic and interaction with members of the family around sharing of bathroom, telephone, television, car, and so on, may minimize friction but helps to create a situation of social isolation by providing the comforts of withdrawal. Some adolescents react by going onto drugs, which accentuates the process of inwardness, others may react by moving away and by seeking to make up the socialization deficiency through joining groups, living in pads, or becoming members of a commune.

The adolescent socializing problem becomes augmented by the American adult's fear of adolescent groups. Most Israeli adults in thinking of adolescent groupings will regard them favorably or neutrally. My impression is that in mentioning adolescent groups in the United States, most adults will have an initial association with the concept of a gang, that is, a negative, threatening kind of group.

As a result of the two above mentioned factors, whose problems exist between generations in the United States, a confrontation situation arises rather quickly, with acute polarization making it difficult to find compromise and reach accommodation.

Conclusions

It is uncertain that the present, relatively better situation with adolescents in Israel will be maintained, and many consider that it is just a matter of time before Israel catches up with other Western communities in relation to drug use, unwed pregnancies, and so on. Others feel that with increasing affluence and emphasis on materialism, the ideological basis that has helped maintain the positive approach by adolescents will soften and disintegrate. Another commonly held viewpoint is that the basic threat to society and the state of tension induced by it is what holds society together and that with the onset of peace, friction, social tension, and disorganization will become apparent.

My own feeling is that as long as the Israeli society looks favorably upon its young and promotes their socialization through operation of the peer-group principle, most Israeli urban middle-class adolescents will reach maturity with relatively moderate storms and stresses. An opportunity to carry out a research project on the rehabilitation of severely retarded institutionalized adolescents in Israel through the use of a group technique (Chigier, 1970) has reinforced this conviction and has demonstrated the gainful impact toward social maturity that exists with the operation of small-group dynamics.

It seems that adolescent psychiatrists working in the United States may have overlooked the therapeutic potential that lies with the acceptance of the need to belong to a peer group as a basic principle in mental health, more emphasis being placed on the value of individual therapy and shoring up the family when the mental health problems of the adolescent members become acute.

Perhaps it would be more useful for psychiatrists to view the phenomenon of adolescent psychopathology within the framework of the social environment or social ecological system, with fewer assumptions about intrinsic weaknesses in parents and/or adolescent. Perhaps it

443

would be more valuable to work on the assumption that various environmental factors allow all of us—therapist, parent, and patient—to play up or play down weaknesses that exist in our personality make-up.

With the rapid tempo of change in the adolescent scene in Israel, the United States, and elsewhere, it will be of interest to follow the trends in adolescent psychiatry in the coming years.

REFERENCE

Chigier, E. (1970). *The Use of a Group Approach in the Rehabilitation of Severely Retarded Adolescents in Agriculture in Israel.* Israel: Akim.

CONTRIBUTIONS IN VOLUME I

446

INDEX

Aberastury, A., and Knobel, M., 416
Aberastury, Arminda, 398, 426
abreactive therapy, 82
Abroms, G. M., 344
abysmal attitudes, 428
academic or work failure: sudden, 58, 59, 64, 65
acting out, 15, 16, 40, 93, 94, 206, 242, 248, 252, 258, 275, 280, 281, 289, 290, 342, 380, 381
addiction: definition, 71
adolescence and adolescents: abandonment depression in, 197, 248, 249, 251, 252; academic failure ("sudden"), 58, 59, 64, 65; adaption failure, 275; and adaptive reality, 295; and adaptive techniques, 279, 406, 414; and adult framework, 405; and adulthood, 96; and adults, 93, 377, 416; and affection, 3, 31; and affirmation, 35; and affluence, 117, 118, 121, 442; and aggression and aggressive drives, 51, 76, 294, 305, 400; alienation of, 35, 279; and ambiguity, 32, 42; and anger, 35, 36; and angry affect, 327–328; and anorexia nervosa, 311, 330, 336; antisocial, 90, 379; anxiety, 35; and armies, 54–55; asking for help, 90, 254; and autonomy, 275, 276, 277, 295, 327, 421; and authority, 42, 120; as a beginning developmental phase, 412; behavioral disorders, 44, 46; and behavior modification, 309; being needed as well as wanted, 31, 32; and belief, 33; bitterness, 35; black, 41; and bodily competence, 96; and body image, 201, 293, 295; borderline syndrome and states, 25, 197, 240–265, 269–284, 412; breakdown related to a task, 59, 60; and career choice and preparation, 34, 38, 39; and centrifugal family forces, 223–224, 234, 236; and centripetal family forces, 215–216, 235; and change, 32, 416, 417, 418; and chaos in adult world, 416, 417; and character, 44, 200, 269, 279, 281, 411, 412; and characterological modalities, 413; characterological problems, 278; and characterological stability, 401; and childhood deprivation, 275; climate for, 31, 421; cognitive development, 141, 201; "collective" traumatic neuroses, 4, 46; college education, 34, 38, 42, 405, 406; and commitment to the common good, 35; common types of patients, 411; comparative cultural studies, 409; and conflicts from earlier developmental phases, 44–45; and confrontation, 35, 421, 426; confusion, 35, 374, 377, 379, 382–383, 384, 420, 421, 422, 425; and consistency, 31; and continuity, 33; and contradictory information, 416, 417, 433; and conviction, 33; and cooperative living, 35; and courts, 54–55; creative capacity of, 421; crisis of, 7; criteria for resolution, 116; critical spirit of, 35; dating behavior, 166–168, 169; and death of fetus or infant, 285–298; death of parent, 285; death as a reality, 61; and decathexis of childhood object representations, 203; decompensations, 274; defensive stabilizations, 274; defiance, 35; delayed, 3; and depreciation of adults, 421; depression, 35, 118, 121, 426; description of, 7; and destructive symbiotic fusion, 277; developmental arrest, 197; developmental conflicts of, 4, 45; developmental processes, 277; as developmental stage, 4, 57, 58, 401, 402, 412, 413; and differentiation, 211; difficulty of treating, 303; dis-

448